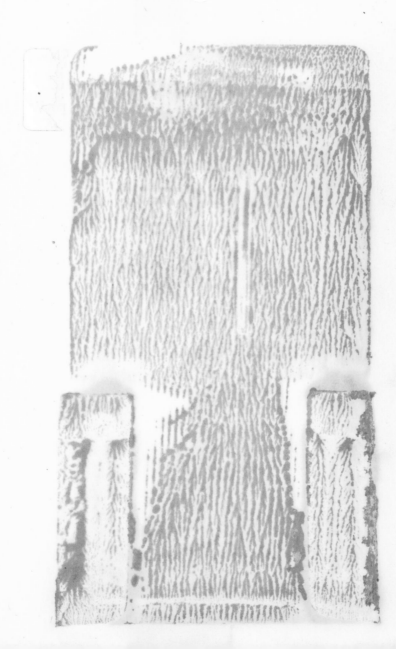

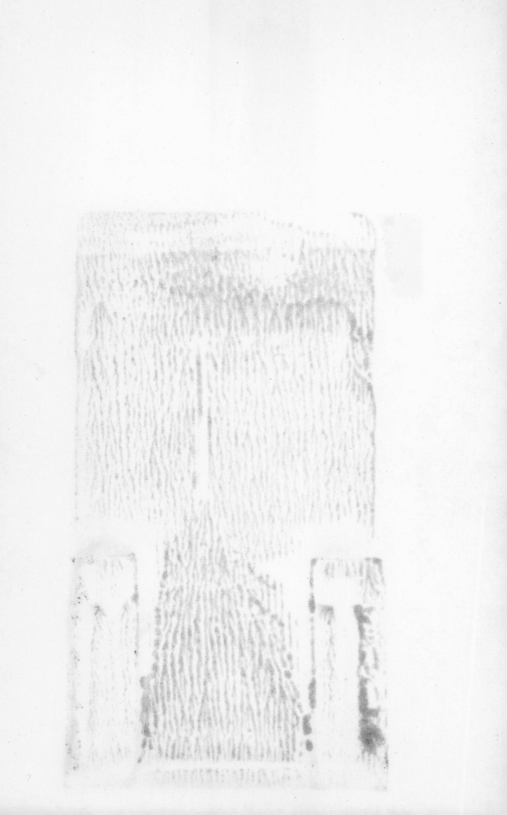

THEORY OF NUMBERS

THEORY OF NUMBERS

SECOND EDITION

B. M. Stewart

PROFESSOR OF MATHEMATICS
MICHIGAN STATE UNIVERSITY

The Macmillan Company, New York
Collier-Macmillan Limited, London

Library of Congress catalog card number: 64–10964

THE MACMILLAN COMPANY, NEW YORK
COLLIER-MACMILLAN CANADA, LTD., TORONTO, ONTARIO

Printed in the United States of America

PREFACE to the Second Edition

For emphasis on the fact that this text on the theory of numbers contains not only the traditional elementary material but also an introduction to modern algebra, this new edition exhibits a separation into Part I, an intuitive approach, and Part II, an axiomatic approach. For those who desire just a standard course or for those who wish a two-term sequence of related materials, this new arrangement should provide a sufficient number of interesting and challenging topics. Many chapters of the original text have been completely rewritten and new chapters have been added.

In Part I there are twenty-eight chapters of moderate length. The material on mathematical induction has been expanded. The "theory" and "practice" in solving linear congruences has been rewritten and applied directly to the solution of linear Diophantine equations in a way that is easily mastered by students. New chapters have been added on homogeneous quadratic Diophantine equations and Egyptian fractions.

In Part II there are sixteen chapters of somewhat greater length. The object is one of introducing the maturing student to abstract algebra by means of examples based upon number theory. After a development of the concepts of mappings, groups, rings, domains, and fields, including algebraic and transcendental extensions, the work comes back to two abstract characterizations of the rational domain of number theory—first, as the only well-ordered domain and, second, as a built-up structure *à la* Peano and Landau. Although the subject of matric theory is developed only for the 2-by-2 case, there is a surprising richness in the algebraic varieties which can be so described and used to illuminate the concepts of unique factorization and commutativity, or the lack thereof.

Acknowledgment is due a host of students, colleagues, and correspondents who have kindly supplied the author with lists of errata, obscurities, and omissions in the several printings of the first edition.

From the Preface to the First Edition

The quotations with which the chapters begin are meant only for pleasant meditation, but in places they are almost in context and reflect, in part, the attitude which the author would hope to implant in his student readers.

Acknowledgments and references are to be found at various places in the text, but two of more personal nature demand relating here.

It was Professor A. J. Kempner of the University of Colorado who first showed me that mathematics could be a delightful, creative, challenging pursuit. "Just for the fun of it," he said as he set me to reading Carmichael's monograph. I still recall the kindly way he sent me off to read for myself in Dickson's *History* how Descartes had anticipated me by several hundred years in devising some multipli-perfect numbers.

It was the late Professor C. C. MacDuffee of the University of Wisconsin whose forbearance and encouragement made life as a graduate student brighter. In retrospect, this book seems little more than an elaboration of his explanations; yet it is my hope that these lessons will in some way attract new minds to mathematics and number theory and thus extend the chain of indebtedness.

B. M. STEWART

Lansing, Michigan

CONTENTS

Contents

PART I

An intuitive approach

to number theory

CHAPTER 1

Preliminary considerations

1.1. Prerequisites

In this textbook on the theory of numbers we shall assume that the student has completed the usual work in college algebra, so that he is well acquainted with such topics as symbols of grouping, exponents, and factoring. We want to make use of inequalities and absolute value and we include below a brief review of these essential notions. Although we shall make occasional use of ideas from analytic geometry, beginning calculus, and the theory of equations, we shall try to make the exposition of such topics self-contained. The whole point of these preliminary remarks is to encourage the reader of modest background and to point out that our real subject matter is more directly related to grade-school arithmetic than it is to advanced courses.

For over 2000 years both amateur and professional mathematicians have been attracted to the theory of numbers. One reason is that while some of our problems can be stated so that anyone can understand what is wanted, generations of workers have failed to find solutions. Naturally, in an introductory textbook we shall present topics that have been well worked out and problems for which definite methods of attack can be suggested. Nevertheless, even in our somewhat elementary situations mastery of the

3

topics will require a mature attitude of study and critical thinking, and solution of some of the exercises will require considerable ingenuity.

In each set of exercises we try to provide some problems which are rather routine mechanical applications of theory to numerical cases. The student should use these to help test his understanding of the theory and should invent other similar problems for himself. However, there will usually be included some exercises which are more general and theoretical. The analysis of these problems and the invention of special methods for their solution will provide a real challenge to interested and serious students.

1.2. Integers

Our purpose is to study some of the properties of the ordinary *integers*, i.e., the positive and negative whole numbers and zero:

$$\ldots, -3, -2, -1, 0, 1, 2, 3, \ldots.$$

We shall assume that the arithmetic of these numbers is well known to each student; that the *addition* and *multiplication tables* and the *rules of exponents* are perfectly understood; and that the *representation* of these numbers *using the base* 10 is completely mastered, so that a symbol like 7203 is immediately recognized as an abbreviation for

$$7(10)^3 + 2(10)^2 + 0(10) + 3.$$

We shall assume that the algebraic symbolism in postulates like the following is readily interpreted and that the laws here expressed are willingly granted (but in a later lesson we shall indicate how these laws may be proved as theorems on the basis, of course, of other still simpler postulates):

The *associative* laws for addition and multiplication:

$$(a + b) + c = a + (b + c), \quad (ab)c = a(bc).$$

The *commutative* laws for addition and multiplication:

$$a + b = b + a, \quad ab = ba.$$

The *distributive* law relating addition and multiplication:

$$(a + b)c = ac + bc.$$

The law that *subtraction* is always *possible*:

$$\text{if} \quad a + x = b, \quad \text{then} \quad x = b - a.$$

For all these laws it is understood that a, b, c are *any* integers, *not necessarily different* and that the equation $a + x = b$ is always solvable for x, an integer, without inventing any new numbers.

The *identity* integer is denoted by 1 and is assumed to have the multiplication property $1a = a$ for every integer a.

The *zero* integer is denoted by 0 and is defined as the solution of the equation $1 + x = 1$.

The *negative* of a given integer a is denoted by $-a$ and is defined as the solution of the equation $a + x = 0$.

In order that all the above laws may hold, the following properties *must* also hold, but there is no harm for the present in thinking of them as assumptions about the integers.

The law that *zero* is an *identity of addition*:

$$a + 0 = a.$$

The law that *zero* is an *annihilator for multiplication*:

$$a0 = 0.$$

The *double negative* law:

$$-(-a) = a.$$

The *rules of sign* for multiplication:

$$a(-b) = -(ab), \quad (-a)(-b) = ab.$$

We assume the law that there are *no proper divisors of zero*:

$$\text{if} \quad ab = 0 \quad \text{and} \quad a \neq 0, \quad \text{then} \quad b = 0.$$

We shall assume that the student has sufficient maturity to appreciate statements like the following: "If a and b are given integers, the equation $ax = b$ is, in general, impossible of solution in integers." For example, simple possible and impossible cases are $2x = 4$ and $2x = 3$, respectively. Of course the student will be expected at times to deal with numbers like $3/2$, but the point is that he must not admit their use in problems where only the integers are under consideration. The student must learn to appreciate the warning: "The statement that a given equation is possible, or impossible, of solution is meaningless until the system in which solutions are sought has been specified." From such warnings the student must learn to state theorems, problems, and solutions with precision.

1.3. Inequality

Preliminary to the discussion of inequality it is helpful to describe the separation of the integers into three exhaustive and mutually exclusive sets—namely, P, the positive integers; the zero; and N, the negative integers —by listing three properties of the set P:

P.1: If $a \neq 0$ and a is not in P, then $-a$ is in P.
P.2: If a and b are in P, then $a + b$ is in P.
P.3: If a and b are in P, then ab is in P.

Inequality is a relation between a pair of integers a and b, which we write $a < b$ and read that "a is less than b," which holds if and only if

$$b - a = p, \quad \text{where } p \text{ is positive.}$$

(Equivalently we write $b > a$ and read that "b is greater than a.")

For example, $-3 < 5$ because $5 - (-3) = 8$, a positive number. However, $-5 < -3$ because $-3 - (-5) = 2$, a positive number.

If it seems to the reader that the listing $\ldots, -3, -2, -1, 0, 1, 2, 3, \ldots$ is a natural way in which to order the integers, then he already has a good intuitive idea of the meaning of $a < b$, realizing that it is equivalent to saying that in the above listing, a occurs "to the left" of b. The symbol $a \leqslant b$ will indicate that a is *either* equal to b *or* less than b. For example, $x > 0$ is a convenient way to say that "x is positive," $x < 0$ a way to say that "x is negative," while $x \geqslant 0$ is a way of saying that "x is nonnegative" meaning that x is either positive or zero. Again, if x is an integer and is either $-2, -1, 0, 1, 2$, or 3, then an easy way to indicate this last restriction is to write that $-3 < x < 4$, for this is understood to mean that x must satisfy *both* the conditions of being less than 4 and greater than -3; an equivalent statement would be $-2 \leqslant x \leqslant 3$.

A preliminary observation is the law of *trichotomy*: for any two given integers a and b one and only one of the following relations must hold

$$a < b, \quad a = b, \quad a > b.$$

Proof: The integer $b - a$ is uniquely determined and is positive, zero, or negative.

Important rules about inequalities are as follows:

R.1: If $a < b$, then $a + c < b + c$ for any integer c.

Proof: The hypothesis $b - a = p > 0$ implies $(b + c) - (a + c) = p > 0$.

R.2: If $a < b$ and c is positive, then $ac < bc$.

Proof: The hypotheses $b - a = p > 0$ and $c > 0$ imply $bc - ac = (b - a)c = pc > 0$ by **P.3**.

R.3: If $a < b$ and c is negative, then $ac > bc$.

Proof: The hypotheses $b - a = p > 0$ and $c < 0$ imply $-c > 0$ by **P.1** and $ac - bc = (b - a)(-c) = p(-c) > 0$ by **P.3.**

R.4: If $a < b$ and $b < c$, then $a < c$.

Proof: The hypotheses $b - a = p_1 > 0$ and $c - b = p_2 > 0$ imply $c - a = (c - b) + (b - a) = p_1 + p_2 > 0$ by **P.2.**

The exercises include several other rules about inequalities.

1.4.   Absolute value

At times we find it convenient to speak of the *absolute value* (or numerical value) of a number, using the symbol $|a|$ whose definition is as follows:

$$|0| = 0; \quad \text{if } a > 0, \text{ then } |a| = a; \quad \text{if } a < 0, \text{ then } |a| = -a.$$

For example, $|6| = 6$ and $|-10| = 10$.

Two important rules about absolute value are as follows:

V.1: $$|ab| = |a|\,|b|.$$

V.2: $$|a + b| \leqslant |a| + |b|.$$

The reader can establish these rules by considering the various cases that arise if one of a or b is zero, if a and b have like or unlike signs, and if $|a|$ or $|b|$ is the greater, or if $|a| = |b|$.

EXERCISES

1.1.   For any integer x prove that $x^2 \geqslant 0$.   (Hint: Use **R.2** and **R.3**.)

1.2.   Supposing x to be an integer, interpret the following statements (i.e., find all solutions in integers): (a) $0 < x < 9$; (b) $x^2 < 9$; (c) $x^2 \leqslant 9$; (d) $|2x + 3| < 9$.

1.3.   Show that $|x| < b$ is equivalent to $-b < x < b$.

1.4.   If $a < b$ and $r < s$, prove that $a + r < b + s$. (Hint: Use **R.1** and **R.4**.)

1.5.   If $a < b$ and $r < s$, prove that ar need not be less than bs.

1.6.   By the method suggested in the text prove **V.1** and **V.2**.

1.7.   If a, b, c are integers with $ac > bc$ and $c > 0$, does it follow that $a > b$? (Hint: Try a proof by contradiction.)

1.8.   If $a \geqslant b$ and $b > c$, prove that $a > c$.

1.9.   If x is any integer, show that $f(x) = x^2 - 4x + 5$ satisfies $f(x) > 0$. [Hint: $f(x) = (x - 2)^2 + 1$; apply EX. **1.1**, **R.1**, and **R.4**.]

1.10. Use the rules of sign and properties of P to show that if a and b are in N, then ab is in P.

1.11. If x is any integer, show that $g(x) = x^2 - 5x + 6$ satisfies $g(x) \geqslant 0$. [Hint: Factor $g(x)$ and apply **P.3** and EX. **1.10**.]

CHAPTER 2

Mathematical induction

2.1. The axiom of mathematical induction

One of the most useful and most powerful tools of mathematics is the principle or axiom of mathematical induction which is intimately related to the theory of numbers. Here is a proposition so basic that no proof is expected, but a proposition that we are willing to grant as an essential characteristic of the positive integers.

It will be assumed in the statement of the axiom and in the examples and exercises which follow that the student is familiar with the use of the symbol . . ., called the *ellipsis*, which when interposed between two numbers, either in a list of numbers or in an expression involving operations on the numbers, stands for *all numbers of the same type which intervene* between the two given numbers. Often it is necessary to give more than the end numbers, or to insert some formula, or to give a description in words so that it will be absolutely clear just what type of number is intended in the unwritten ellipsis.

One precise statement of the axiom of mathematical induction is as follows:

L.1:   If a set M of positive integers is such that

(I) M contains the integer 1; and

(II) on the assumption that M contains all the integers 1, $2, \ldots, n$, it can be proved that M contains the integer $n + 1$;

then the set M contains all positive integers.

It certainly seems that anyone who has considered the process of counting should be willing to grant that the set M described in the axiom is such that no positive integer is omitted from the set.

The uses of this axiom are manifold in all branches of mathematics. In a later chapter we shall indicate how the basic laws of addition and multiplication may be established with little more than mathematical induction as background; and in later problems we will become increasingly aware of the possibilities of using this scheme of proof. For the present, then, perhaps one simple example, discussed in detail, will suffice.

2.2.   An example using mathematical induction

Consider the meaning of, and some way of establishing, the following formula:

$$1 + 3 + 5 + \cdots + (2n - 1) = n^2$$

where it is evident that the formula has meaning only for positive integral values of n. By substituting special values of n, say $n = 1, 2, 3$, we find that the formula states that

$$1 = 1^2, \quad 1 + 3 = 4 = 2^2, \quad 1 + 3 + 5 = 9 = 3^2,$$

in these respective cases. We begin to see that this formula is not like the usual function notation, at least on the left side, for the left side continually changes form as n changes. In words, the proposition seems to be as follows: "The sum of the first n odd numbers is equal to the square of the integer n." But the formula is apparently an infinity of formulas, changing as n changes, and it is evidently hopeless to prove such a proposition, in the way that laboratory sciences "prove laws," by checking the first thousand cases. What we need is the definite procedure of mathematical induction by which the complete proof for the infinity of cases is made to depend upon just *two* steps, namely: (I) the usually very easy task of checking the formula in the case $n = 1$ (or sometimes the first positive integer for which the formula has meaning is the integer that is tested here); this may be called the *basis* for the induction; and (II) the making of the *hypothesis H* that the formula is correct in all the cases $1, 2, \ldots, n$, and then the *proving* that, as a consequence of the hypothesis H and previously known theorems, the formula is correct in the case $n + 1$; this step may be called the *core of the induction proof*. Finally, if (I) *and* (II) have been established, we can apply the axiom of mathematical induction and make the *conclusion* that the formula under consideration is true for *all* positive integers [or for all positive integers beginning with the smallest integer than can be used in step (I)].

In the example proposed above the complete proof by induction should read somewhat as follows:

Problem: Prove that $1 + 3 + 5 + \cdots + (2n - 1) = n^2$.

Proof: We shall use an induction proof on n.

(I) When $n = 1$, the formula is true because $1 = 1^2$.

(II) We make the hypothesis H that the formula is correct in each of the cases $1, 2, \ldots, n$; in particular, this includes the case n so that we are assuming that $1 + 3 + 5 + \cdots + (2n - 1) = n^2$. Let us then consider the next case where n is replaced by $n + 1$. On the left side of the formula *one more summand* will appear, and since $2(n + 1) - 1 = 2n + 1$ is the next odd number following $2n - 1$, we find that we have to consider the following sum:

$$1 + 3 + 5 + \cdots + (2n - 1) + (2n + 1) = n^2 + (2n + 1) = (n + 1)^2.$$

The first equality is justified by the hypothesis H, the second equality is justified by a well-known factoring formula, and reading from first to last we find that we have established the truth of the formula in the case $n + 1$.

From (I), (II), and the principle of mathematical induction, the given formula is correct for *all* positive integers n.

2.3.   Words of caution

In the application of the principle of mathematical induction the student must be careful to establish *both* (I) and (II). The situation has been likened to that which arises in the children's game of lining up toy soldiers (or cards or dominoes) so that if one falls he will knock over the next. If either no soldier is pushed over [so that (I) fails] or if some soldier is A.W.O.L. [so that (II) fails], then the complete line will not fall.

For example, (I) can be established for the *false* formula

$$1 + 3 + 5 + \cdots + (2n - 1) = n^3 - 5n^2 + 11n - 6$$

using either $n = 1, 2,$ or 3; but (II) *cannot* be established for this formula. In fact, a *false* formula, correct for the first thousand cases (!), but not correct thereafter, is easily given, as follows:

$$1 + 3 + \cdots + (2n - 1) = n^2 + (n - 1)(n - 2)\cdots(n - 999)(n - 1000).$$

As another example, we can establish (II) for the *false* formula

$$1 + 3 + \cdots + (2n - 1) = n^2 + 5,$$

i.e., *if* the formula were true in the cases 1, 2, ..., n, we could prove it true in the case $n + 1$, yet this formula is not correct for any value of n, so (I) fails to be true in a "big" way.

In carrying out the step (II), which is the core of the proof and sometimes difficult, the student should be on the alert for some way of rewriting the formula in the case $n + 1$ so as to involve one, or even several, of the formulas for the cases 1, 2, ..., n, so that the hypothesis H can be actively employed, for surely one will have to use the hypothesis H in some way before being able to complete step (II).

Finally, we should note that this principle of induction is primarily a method of proof for a known or suspected formula, and it is not in itself a tool for discovering such formulas. Thus in the problems that close this lesson, some of the fun of mathematical investigation is lost because the formulas are stated without asking the student to uncover them for himself. But until the principle of mathematical induction is completely mastered there is not much point in guessing at formulas that one cannot rigorously establish.

2.4. Other forms of the mathematical induction principle

In the example of **2.2**† and in many of the exercises which conclude this chapter, it is the hypothesis that M contains n which is all that is needed in proving that M contains $n + 1$. However, in many cases (see, for example, **5.1**) it is convenient to have the full power of the hypothesis that M contains all integers x for which $1 \leqslant x \leqslant n$ to use in proving that M contains $n + 1$.

With a fairly straightforward argument we can show that the following version **L.2** of mathematical induction is equivalent to the form **L.1**.

    L.2: If M is a set of positive integers such that
           (I.2) M contains the integer 1; and
           (II.2) on the assumption that M contains n, it can be proved that
                M contains $n + 1$;
then the set M contains all positive integers.

† A boldface reference; e.g., **2.2**, is to the second section of Chapter 2.

At the same time we can introduce a third principle **L.3** which at first glance seems quite different and yet is equivalent to both **L.1** and **L.2**. For a set S of integers we say that x is a *least element* if x belongs to S and if for every y which belongs to S it is true that $x \leqslant y$. Then we may state **L.3**, which is called the *well-ordering* principle, as follows:

L.3: Every nonempty set S (finite or infinite) of positive integers has a least element.

In particular, from this point of view, the integer 1 is characterized as the least element of the set of all positive integers.

The proof of the equivalence of these three principles is in three parts. We shall show

    (A) **L.2** implies **L.3**,   (B) **L.3** implies **L.1**,   (C) **L.1** implies **L.2**.

Consequently, in cyclical combination, each principle implies each of the others.

(A) Assume **L.2**.   Suppose that **L.3** is false so that there exists a nonempty set S of positive integers without a least element. Let M be the set of all positive integers x such that for every y in S we have $x < y$.

(I.2) M contains 1; for if 1 is in S, then 1 is a least element of S (see EX. **2.8**).

(II.2) If M contains n (so that for every y in S we have $n < y$), then M contains $n + 1$; for $n < y$ implies $n + 1 \leqslant y$ (see EX. **2.9**) and if $n + 1$ is in S, then $n + 1$ is a least element of S; hence $n + 1 < y$ for every y in S, so $n + 1$ is in M. By (I.2), (II.2), and **L.2**, M contains all positive integers. Hence S is empty, a contradiction. In other words, **L.2** implies **L.3**.

(B) Assume **L.3**.   Let M be a set of positive integers satisfying (I) and (II). Let S be the set of all positive integers not in M. Suppose S is not empty, then by **L.3** there is a least element x in S. We know from the remark following **L.3** that $1 < x$ because by (I) M contains 1. Hence $n = x - 1$ is a positive integer such that all of the integers y satisfying $1 \leqslant y \leqslant n$ belong to M, for $y \leqslant n$ and $n < x$ imply $y < x$. By (II) it follows that M contains $n + 1$. But $n + 1 = x$ is in S. This contradiction shows that S must be empty. Hence M contains all positive integers. In other words, **L.3** implies **L.1**.

(C) Assume **L.1**.   Let M be a set of positive integers satisfying (I.2) and (II.2). Evidently M satisfies (I) which is the same as (I.2). Also M satisfies (II) for if M contains all integers y such that $1 \leqslant y \leqslant n$, then in particular M contains n, and by (II.2) M contains $n + 1$. By (I), (II), and **L.1** it follows that M contains all positive integers. In other words, **L.1** implies **L.2**.

EXERCISES

By mathematical induction establish the following formulas:

2.1. $1 + 2 + 3 + \cdots + n = n(n + 1)/2$.

2.2. $1^2 + 2^2 + 3^2 + \cdots + n^2 = n(n + 1)(2n + 1)/6$.

2.3. $1^2 + 3^2 + 5^2 + \cdots + (2n - 1)^2 = (4n^3 - n)/3$.

2.4. $(x - 1)(1 + x + x^2 + \cdots + x^n) = x^{n+1} - 1$.

2.5. $1^3 + 2^3 + 3^3 + \cdots + n^3 = n^2(n + 1)^2/4 = f(n)$.
Compare with the result in EX. **2.1**.

2.6. Use EX. **2.5** to complete the following formulas:
$$1^3 + 2^3 + 3^3 + \cdots + (2k)^3 \quad = f(2k) \qquad =$$
$$2^3 + 4^3 + 6^3 + \cdots + (2k)^3 \quad = 8f(k) \qquad =$$
$$1^3 + 3^3 + 5^3 + \cdots + (2k - 1)^3 = f(2k) - 8f(k) =$$

2.7. Assume that for all positive integers n there may be a formula of the type
$$1^2 + 4^2 + 7^2 + \cdots + (3n - 2)^2 = An^3 + Bn^2 + Cn + D,$$
where A, B, C, D are constants independent of n. Use (II.2) to determine the only suitable values of A, B, C. Use (I) to find D. Without further proof you should be sure the formula is valid for all positive integers n. Why?

2.8. Use **L.2** to prove that every positive integer n satisfies the inequality $1 \leqslant n$.

2.9. Use EX. **2.8** and **R.1** to show that if x and y are integers such that $x < y$, then $x + 1 \leqslant y$.

2.10. For any integer a and any positive integer n define *exponentiation* as follows: (I) $a^1 = a$, (II) $a^{n+1} = a^n a$. Why can such a definition be regarded as complete? For a fixed positive integer b prove by induction on n that (a) $a^n a^b = a^{n+b}$; (b) $(a^b)^n = a^{bn}$.

2.11. Restate the principle **L.2** so that it may be applied to prove propositions which concern the following sets: all integers y such that (a) $5 \leqslant y$, (b) $-10 \leqslant y$, (c) $y < 0$.

2.12. Use the abbreviation $r!$, read "r-factorial," to mean $r! = 1 \cdot 2 \cdot 3 \cdots r$ when $r > 0$; and define $0! = 1$. Define $\binom{n}{r} = n!/r!(n - r)!$ for $0 \leqslant r \leqslant n$. Use mathematical induction on n to establish the "binomial theorem" which follows:
$$(x + y)^n = \binom{n}{n} x^n y^0 + \binom{n}{n - 1} x^{n-1} y^1 + \cdots$$
$$+ \binom{n}{r} x^r y^{n-r} + \cdots + \binom{n}{0} x^0 y^n.$$

2.13. Define $S(k, n) = 1^k + 2^k + 3^k + \cdots + n^k$. For a fixed positive integer k, use mathematical induction on n to prove that
$$\binom{k + 1}{k} S(k, n) + \cdots + \binom{k + 1}{2} S(2, n)$$
$$+ \binom{k + 1}{1} S(1, n) = (n + 1)^{k+1} - (n + 1).$$

(Hint: Make good use of EX. **2.12** with special values of x and y.)

2.14. Use the recursion formula developed in EX. **2.13** to compute, successively, formulas for $S(1, n)$, $S(2, n)$, $S(3, n)$ and $S(4, n)$.

2.15. It is said that at the time of the creation, there were placed in one of those incredible temples at Hanoi in Indo-China some 64 golden washers or disks, no two the same in size, all set on one of three golden needles; and the priesthood of the temple were set busy moving the disks, one at a time, to *any one* of the needles, subject always to the condition, which held also at the outset, that no disk be placed above a smaller disk. The needles were farther apart than the outer diameter of the largest disk. The priests were to aim at arranging all the disks on *another one* of the needles and they were pledged both to move one disk every minute and to make their moves so that the goal would be achieved in the least number of moves. When the appointed task was completed, there would come the day of doom for many, but of reward for the faithful. Naturally, some of the unfaithful, as they watched the ceaseless activity at the temple, the shifts by night and day, and the sage noddings of the wise men who directed the laborers, were much concerned as to just how soon to expect the judgment day. We could have aided them considerably, for by assuming that there are n disks in the problem, we can show by mathematical induction that the minimum number of moves is given by $2^n - 1$. And a few minutes of translating $2^{64} - 1$ minutes into years will bring considerable comfort to the most unfaithful. (E. Lucas.)

2.16. One worshipper at the temple of Hanoi (see EX. **2.15**) suggested that it would be easier for the priests if they arranged the three needles in a row and limited themselves to moving each disk to an *adjacent* needle. But it was discovered that the suggestion was influenced by a mundane sect of mathematical inductors who had discovered that to move n disks *from one end needle to the other end needle*, under this new restriction, would require $3^n - 1$ moves.

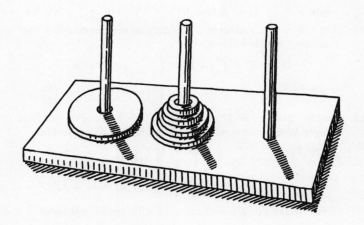

Arithmetic has a very great and
compelling effect, elevating the soul to
reason about abstract number, and
if visible or tangible objects are obtruding
upon the argument, refusing to
be satisfied.—PLATO

CHAPTER 3

The division algorithm

3.1. Long division

An algorithm is a step-by-step process, complete in a finite number of
steps, for solving a given problem. By the division algorithm we mean
that process with which the student became familiar in arithmetic, where
he was given, say, the dividend 712, the divisor 13, and was asked to find
the quotient and the remainder. By a long division he found

$$
\begin{array}{r}
54 = q \\
b = 13 \overline{\smash{\big)}\, 712 = a} \\
650 \\
\hline
62 \\
52 \\
\hline
10 = r
\end{array}
$$

and concluded that the quotient is $q = 54$ and the remainder is $r = 10$,
with the process ending at this point because $10 < 13$. Certain steps of the
long division work are tentative; for example, to find that the first part
of the quotient is 50, not 40 or 60, may require a student who does not
know the multiples of 13 to make several trials, but not more than nine
(fewer, we hope!). Also there is a certain agreement that the answers

15

$Q = 50$ and $R = 62$, although not incorrect, are considered incomplete and represent merely the first stage of the algorithm.

3.2. The division algorithm

We formalize what is desired in the long division process in the following theorem:

The division algorithm: (A) For any given integer a (the dividend) and any given *nonzero* integer b (the divisor) there *exist* integers q (the quotient) and r (the remainder) such that

(*D.1*) $$a = qb + r, \quad \text{and}$$
(*D.2*) $$0 \leqslant r < |b|;$$

    (B) q and r are *unique*; and

    (C) q and r can be found in a *finite* number of steps.

(A) *Proof: Case 1:* Suppose a and b are both positive numbers. If $b = 1$, everything is trivial, since for each a we can take $q = a$ and $r = 0 < b$, and write $a = a \cdot 1 + 0$. We assume that $b > 1$ and make an induction proof on a. Let M be the set of all positive integers a for which (*D.1*) and (*D.2*) can be satisfied. Since $b > 1$, (*D.2*) will have the form $0 \leqslant r < b$, with no need for absolute value bars.

(I) M contains 1, for since $1 < b$ we can take $q = 0$ and $r = 1 < b$ and write $a = 1 = 0 \cdot 1 + 1$.

(II) We assume that M contains all integers y such that $1 \leqslant y \leqslant a$ and prove that M contains $a + 1$. In particular, M contains a for which Q and R are assumed to exist so that $a = Qb + R$, $0 \leqslant R < b$. We note that the last conditions may be written $0 \leqslant R \leqslant b - 1$ (see EX. **2.9**) and that two cases may be distinguished if $0 \leqslant R < b - 1$ or if $R = b - 1$.

When $0 \leqslant R < b - 1$, we have $a + 1 = Qb + R + 1 = qb + r$, where we set $q = Q$ and $r = R + 1$. Since $1 \leqslant r < b$, we see that both (*D.1*) and (*D.2*) are satisfied.

When $R = b - 1$, we have $a + 1 = Qb + b = (Q + 1)b = qb + r$, where we set $q = Q + 1$ and $r = 0$ and see that both (*D.1*) and (*D.2*) are satisfied. This completes the proof of (II).

By (I), (II), and **L.1** we know M contains all positive integers. So (A) is established for Case 1.

Case 2:   If a' is negative and b is positive, we may proceed as follows. Consider $a = -a'$ and note that $a > 0$. Then from Case 1 we may assume that we have found Q and R so that $a = Qb + R, 0 \leqslant R < b$. If $R = 0$, then $-a = (-Q)b + 0$, so we may take $q = -Q$ and $r = 0$ to write $a' = qb + r$, satisfying $(D.1)$ and $(D.2)$. But if $0 < R < b$, we note that $-a = -Qb - R = -(Q + 1)b + (b - R)$, so we may set $q = -(Q + 1)$ and $r = b - R$ and write $a' = qb + r$ which will satisfy both $(D.1)$ and $(D.2)$ since $0 < R < b$ implies $0 < b - R < b$.

For example, if $a = -712$ and $b = 13$, we can use our introductory example in **3.1** to write $a = -54b - 10$. Then to avoid the negative remainder we can do exactly as in the proof above and by subtracting and adding $b = 13$ we find $a = -55b + 3$. Thus with $q = -55$ and $r = 3$ we satisfy both $(D.1)$ and $(D.2)$.

Case 3:   If $a = 0$, we take $q = 0$ and $r = 0$ to satisfy both $(D.1)$ and $(D.2)$.

Case 4:   Finally, if b is negative, then $|b|$ is positive. Hence we may use the previous cases to find Q and r so that $a = Q|b| + r, 0 \leqslant r < |b|$. Since $|b| = -b$ we take $q = -Q$ and have $a = qb + r, 0 \leqslant r < |b|$.

This completes the proof of (A).

From (A) there exists at least one pair of integers q and r such that both $(D.1)$ and $(D.2)$ are satisfied. From the example in **3.1** we see that the condition $(D.1)$ by itself is not enough to require unique answers for q and r, since for $a = 712$ and $b = 13$ we have $a = 50b + 62$ and $a = 54b + 10$, as well as $a = 55b + (-3)$. But we can show that q and r satisfying both $(D.1)$ and $(D.2)$ are uniquely determined.

(B) *Proof:*   Suppose there are two sets of solutions, say, $a = qb + r$, $0 \leqslant r < |b|$, and $a = q_1b + r_1, 0 \leqslant r_1 < |b|$. When we equate the two expressions for a and rearrange the result we have $(q - q_1)b = r_1 - r$. The relation $0 \leqslant r < |b|$ implies $-|b| < -r \leqslant 0$ which may be combined with $0 \leqslant r_1 < |b|$ to show that $-|b| < r_1 - r < |b|$ which is equivalent to $|r_1 - r| < |b|$. But $|r_1 - r| = |q - q_1| \, |b| < |b|$ implies, since $b \neq 0$, that $|q - q_1| < 1$. Consequently, $q - q_1 = 0$ and $q = q_1$; hence $r_1 - r = 0$ and $r_1 = r$. Thus the quotient and remainder in the division algorithm are unique.

(C) *Proof:*   Reviewing the proof of (A), we see that it suffices to consider the case where a and b are positive. Then the assumptions $1 \leqslant b$ and $0 < a$ imply $a \leqslant ab$. Hence $a = qb + r$ with $0 \leqslant r < b$ shows $0 \leqslant q \leqslant a$. These restrictions indicate a finite number of possibilities for both q and r.

3.3. Critique

Influenced by the introductory example, the reader of the previous sections probably always carried in mind the long division process with integers expressed in the base ten. However, the importance of the proof in **3.2** is its completely theoretical approach—quite independent of any particular way of representing the integers. But we should note that the mathematical induction method in Case 1 of (A) does not give a very practical algorithm for finding q and r unless a is rather small. For the present, as a practical matter, we can resort in exercises to representing the integers in the familiar way with the base ten and to using our carefully learned tables of multiplication, addition, and subtraction for a quick determination of q and r.

To repeat, from the induction argument we know that q and r exist. So we are not wasting our time to search for them, but we do not have to use induction to find them. We may use any tool we choose, and if we have learned our arithmetic tables well, we can see that these give us a practical algorithm. Since the solutions are unique, an easy algorithm is to be preferred.

We shall devote Chapter 5 to the question of representing the integers and designing helpful addition and multiplication tables. Meanwhile, we pause in Chapter 4 for diversion; we shall apply the division algorithm to the case $b = 2$, where the remainder r can have just one of the two values 0 and 1, and make good use of the consequences.

EXERCISES

3.1. In each of the following cases find integers q and r to satisfy $(D.1)$ and $(D.2)$: (a) $a = 7153$, $b = 17$; (b) $a = -2044$, $b = 130$; (c) $a = -6080$, $b = -42$.

3.2. If a certain integer a has the remainder 11 when divided by $b = 16$, determine the remainder r with $0 \leqslant r < b$ when $a + k$ is divided by b for each of the cases $k = 1, 3, 5, 7, 9, 105, -17$.

3.3. (a) Determine r with $0 \leqslant r < b$ when $a = 2^{45} - 1$ is divided by $b = 31$. (Hint: Use EX. **2.4.**)

(b) The same problem with $a = 2^{35} + 13$. (Hint: $a = 2^{35} - 1 + 14$.)

3.4. With respect to divisibility by 6 show that the set of all integers is divided (exhaustively) into six (mutually exclusive) classes, where members of the same class have the same remainder.

3.5. Review **R.1** to **R.4** and EXS. **1.3** to **1.8** and justify in detail the implications in the proof of (B).

3.6. Justify in detail the implications in the proof of (C).

3.7. If $b = 2B + 1 > 0$, prove that for any integer a there *exist* integers Q and R such that $a = Qb + R$, with $|R| \leqslant B$. Also show that Q and R

are *unique*. (For example, if $b = 5$, the division can be arranged so that R has one of the values -2, -1, 0, 1, 2.)

3.8. Reconsider EX. **3.7** when $b = 2B > 0$. Show that the difficulty is not with the existence of Q and R but with their uniqueness. Can you modify the statement of the results to achieve uniqueness?

CHAPTER 4

Number theory in the game of Solitaire

4.1. Parity

Almost every textbook in the theory of numbers leads off with a few
interesting problems and games whose solution depends in some way on the
properties of integers. In line with this tradition, but desiring not to
duplicate the usual examples, we present here a description of the game of
Solitaire. But first we shall give the bit of number theory required in the
mathematical theory associated with the game.

By the division algorithm when $b = 2$ and a is an integer, the possible
remainders are $r = 0$ and $r = 1$; when $r = 0$, the integer a is called *even*
and has the form $a = 2q$; when $r = 1$, the integer a is called *odd* and has
the form $a = 2q + 1$. If two given integers s and t are both even, or
both odd, then s and t are said to be of the *same parity*; but if one of s
and t is even, and the other odd, then s and t are said to be of *different
parity*.

We need the following observation which we shall call a *lemma*,
meaning a tool, or a subordinate, theorem, useful in proving other more
interesting or more important theorems.

20

Lemma: The difference $s - t$ of two given integers s and t is even if and only if s and t are of the same parity.

Proof: The four possible cases are as follows:

$$2S - 2T = 2(S - T),$$
$$(2S + 1) - 2T = 2(S - T) + 1,$$
$$(2S + 1) - (2T + 1) = 2(S - T),$$
$$2S - (2T + 1) = 2(S - T - 1) + 1.$$

4.2.   The game of Solitaire

Of ancient origin is the game we are about to describe, although the first mathematical mention of it seems to be by Leibnitz. The game of Solitaire is played upon a field, of arbitrary but fixed shape, consisting of squares arranged in rows and columns. On certain of these squares appear playing pieces, at most one piece to a square. A move, or jump, is possible when on three adjacent squares A, B, C of a row or column (but *not* a diagonal) there are pieces on A and B, but none on C. The jump consists in moving the piece on A to C and removing the piece on B from play. The object of the game is by a succession of jumps (of course at least one square must be empty initially so that the game can begin) to leave the remaining pieces in some stated configuration upon the field (usually to leave only one piece on the field).

The object of a mathematical study of Solitaire is to show that some proposed games of Solitaire are impossible of solution or that the final outcome is limited in some way. Since we anticipate using the theory of integers, it is natural to write down equations which describe the progress of the game and which have as variables the number of pieces and the number of jumps, for neither fractional pieces nor fractional jumps are allowed, and this procedure will surely lead to a Diophantine problem. Such an analysis is possible if we first label the squares along one set of diagonals, say those running from upper left to lower right, in a systematic manner: first, say, a diagonal colored green, the next colored purple, the next tan, and the next green, and then all the rest in cyclic manner: purple, tan, green, purple, tan, green, etc. For example, in Figure 1 such a labeling has been carried out for a rectangular 7-by-5 field with the obvious abbreviations: G for green, P for purple, and T for tan.

With such a labeling it becomes possible to assert that every jump ending on a square of one color increases by one the number of pieces on squares of that color and decreases by one the number of pieces on each of the other two colors. Let G, P, T be given the new meaning of indicating, respectively, the number of pieces initially present on squares of green, purple, or tan color. Let g, p, t indicate, respectively, the number of jumps ending on squares of green, purple, or tan color. Let G', P', T' indicate, respectively, the number of pieces finally present on squares of green, purple, or tan color.

G	P	T	G	P
T	G	P	T	G
P	T	G	P	T
G	P	T	G	P
T	G	P	T	G
P	T	G	P	T
G	P	T	G	P

B	R	Y	B	R
R	Y	B	R	Y
Y	B	R	Y	B
B	R	Y	B	R
R	Y	B	R	Y
Y	B	R	Y	B
B	R	Y	B	R

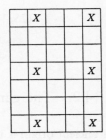

FIGURE 1.   FIGURE 2.   FIGURE 3.

Then using our previous observation about the effect of each jump, we find that these *integers* must satisfy the following system of equations:

$$(4.1) \qquad G + g - p - t = G', \quad P - g + p - t = P',$$
$$T - g - p + t = T'.$$

By any of the usual methods, such as adding the equations in pairs, we can show the system (4.1) to be equivalent to the following system of equations:

$$(4.2) \quad 2g = (P + T) - (P' + T'), \quad 2p = (T + G) - (T' + G'),$$
$$2t = (G + P) - (G' + P').$$

Inasmuch as all the variables are integers, we are in a position to apply the lemma given in **4.1** and to conclude that *one set* of *necessary* conditions for the game of Solitaire to be possible is that the initial and final distribution of the pieces are such that

$$(4.3) \qquad \left. \begin{array}{l} P + T \text{ and } P' + T' \text{ are of the same parity,} \\ T + G \text{ and } T' + G' \text{ are of the same parity,} \\ G + P \text{ and } G' + P' \text{ are of the same parity.} \end{array} \right\}$$

This set of conditions (4.3) is sometimes powerful enough in itself to decide that a proposed game of Solitaire is impossible of solution. Another set of necessary conditions is obtained by labeling with colors the diagonals that run from upper right to lower left. If either set of conditions fails to be satisfied, then the game is impossible. That these two sets of conditions are necessary, but not sufficient, to guarantee a solution may be shown by the reader by studying a very small playing field or one with widely separated pieces. When the two sets of conditions are satisfied, one can sometimes show the existence of a solution to the game by the perhaps nonmathematical, but amusing, process of carrying out a suitable sequence of jumps.

Let us apply this theory to the 7-by-5 field shown in Figure 1, supposing that initially all squares except the top left one are occupied, so that $G = 11$, $P = 12$, $T = 11$. Suppose that only one piece is to be left at the end of the game, so that (G', P', T') is either $(1, 0, 0)$ or $(0, 1, 0)$ or $(0, 0, 1)$. Both the first and last of these suggested endings violate (4.3), so to attempt to leave the final piece on the lower left square, for example, is to attack an impossible game. However, the ending $(0, 1, 0)$ is compatible with the conditions (4.3).

Now let us employ a set of labels on the other diagonals, say red, blue, and yellow, indicated by R, B, and Y, respectively, as in Figure 2. Then using the same type of symbolism as before, we find that the proposed game has $R = 12$, $B = 11$, $Y = 11$. Conditions analogous to (4.3) then require $(R', B', Y') = (1, 0, 0)$, or otherwise, the game will be impossible.

Combining these two sets of conditions we see that if the proposed game is possible, beginning with only the upper left square empty and closing with but one piece on the field, then the final piece *must* be on one of the squares marked X in Figure 3, for these are the only squares carrying *both* a purple and a red label.

To the uninitiated there must surely be something of black magic in such assertions, and we feel the fascinating lure of number theory when we see that the whole matter depends essentially on setting the problem in such a way that we can apply the trivial lemma of **4.1**.

4.3. "Red Cross" Solitaire

To illustrate a somewhat more difficult variation of Solitaire, let us consider the 7-by-5 field and study the possibility of having but one square initially empty and the final five pieces in the position shown in Figure 4. Since we first proposed this game as a means of attracting attention to a charity drive, we have taken the liberty of calling it "Red Cross" Solitaire.

The complete field has $P = 12$, $G = 12$, $T = 11$. In the "Red Cross" ending, $P' = 2$, $G' = 1$, $T' = 2$. Hence if but one square is empty initially, the parity conditions (4.3) can be satisfied only if the empty square is a P-square. Similarly, with reference to the other set of diagonals, the empty square must be a B-square. Thus a necessary condition is that the initial configuration be as in Case 1 or Case 2 of Figure 5. That either of these

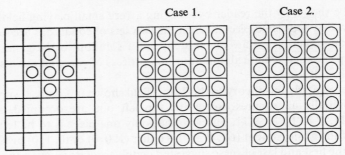

FIGURE 4.   FIGURE 5.

conditions is also sufficient we show by producing the play-by-play solution.

The reader should, of course, not deny himself the fun of trying this game, but if he tires from failures to reach the desired ending, he can trace through the plays indicated in Figure 6. In that figure the first two rows show how both cases can be brought into the same form, so that the remainder of the solution, in the other rows of the figure, is the same for the two cases. In each diagram a "plus" circle shows the piece which is to make the jump and a "minus" circle shows the piece which is to be removed from the field. The arrows connecting the diagrams show the sequence in which the jumps are to be performed.

EXERCISES

4.1. For the Solitaire game described in **4.2** show that at least some of the endings suggested in Figure 3 are possible by actually carrying out the game. (In fact, two well-planned attacks can be found, leaving the last three moves variable, to prove that all six endings are possible.)

4.2. On the 7-by-5 field, as shown in Figures 1 and 2, prove that if the upper middle square is the only one which is initially empty, it is then impossible to end the game with just one piece on the field.

4.3. In the lemma of **4.1** is it correct to replace the word "difference" by the word "sum"?

4.4. Show that if Solitaire on any field is to end with just one piece on the field, then G, P, T must not all be of the same parity; and if one of these three is *exceptional*, by being of opposite parity to the other two, then the final piece must be on a square of exceptional color.

4.5. (F. Gozreh) (a) If a Solitaire field is 1-by-n where $n = 2k$ and the only square initially empty is the second one, show that the game can end with just one piece on the field. (Hint: Describe the method of play using induction on $k \geqslant 1$.)

(b) The same problem if $k \geqslant 3$ and the only square initially empty is the fifth one.

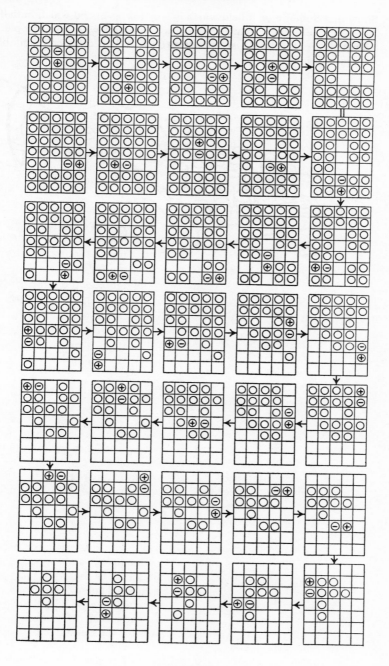

FIGURE 6.

4.6. Show that Solitaire on a field which is 3-by-$(3k - 2)$ and which initially has only one corner square empty has a solution with just one piece left on the field. (Hint: Use induction on $k \geqslant 1$ to describe a suitable sequence of jumps.)

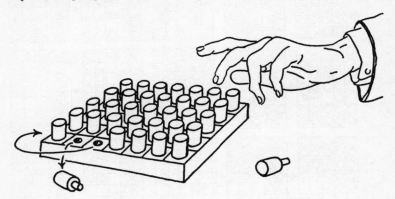

> To explore a misty region we need
> the lantern of mathematics, so what is
> dimly visible will loom up in firm, bold
> outline. Let the old phantasmagoria
> disappear. We need to see better,
> and farther.—IRVING FISHER

CHAPTER 5

Representation of the integers

5.1. Representation with the base b

It is clear that if we can find some convenient way of representing any positive integer a, then the symbol $-a$ can be used for the companion negative integer, and the symbol 0 can be used for the zero, and we will then have a way of representing all the integers—positive, negative, and zero.

Our scheme of representation requires us to use exponents, so it would be well for the student to review the basic definitions and rules for exponents (for example, see EX. **2.10**). In particular, recall that it is convenient to define $b^0 = 1$ when $b \neq 0$.

Representation theorem: If b is a fixed positive integer with $1 < b$, then for any given positive integer a, a nonnegative integer n can be found and a set of $n + 1$ integers: $a_0, a_1, \ldots, a_n$, such that a may be represented uniquely in the following form:

$$a = a_0 + a_1 b + a_2 b^2 + \cdots + a_n b^n$$

with $0 \leqslant a_i < b$ for $i \neq n$ and $0 < a_n < b$.

Proof: (A) We show that at least one representation is possible by using mathematical induction on a. Let M be the set of all positive integers a for which the representation theorem holds.

(I) M contains 1, for we may take $n = 0$ and $a_0 = 1$ which will satisfy $0 < a_n < b$, since a major premise of the theorem is that $1 < b$.

(II) If we assume that M contains all the integers $1, 2, \ldots, a - 1$ (for $a > 1$), we can prove that M contains a. For from the division algorithm we have $a = qb + r$, $0 \leqslant r < b$. If $q = 0$, we have $1 < a = r < b$, so we take $n = 0$ and $a_0 = r$ to satisfy $0 < a_n < b$. If $q > 0$, we note, since $1 < b$, that $q < qb = a - r \leqslant a$. Consequently, q belongs to the set $1, 2, \ldots, a - 1$ to which the induction hypothesis applies. Suppose

$$q = q_0 + q_1 b + \cdots + q_k b^k, \quad 0 < q_k < b; \quad 0 \leqslant q_i < b, \ i \neq k.$$

Then for $a = qb + r$ we may take $n = k + 1$, $a_0 = r$, $a_n = q_k$, and $a_{i+1} = q_i$ for $i = 0, 1, \ldots, k - 1$, to obtain the representation

$$a = r + (q_0 + q_1 b + \cdots + q_k b^k)b = a_0 + a_1 b + a_2 b^2 + \cdots + a_{k+1} b^{k+1}$$

with the required conditions $0 < a_{k+1} < b$, $0 \leqslant a_i < b$, $i \neq k + 1$.

By (I), (II), and the principle of mathematical induction in the form **L.1**, we draw the conclusion that M contains all positive integers and the proof of part (A) is complete.

(B) The steps in the induction proof above suggest that the representation of a with the base b must be unique. For we have already noticed that the quotient and remainder in the division algorithm are unique. Consequently from

$$a = a_0 + a_1 b + \cdots + a_n b^n = a_0 + (a_1 + a_2 b + \cdots + a_n b^{n-1})b$$

we see that the unique r and q of $a = r + qb$, $0 \leqslant r < b$, must be $r = a_0$ and either $q = 0$ if $n = 0$, or if $n \geqslant 1$, then $q = a_1 + a_2 b + \cdots + a_n b^{n-1}$. By the same argument the unique r_1 and q_1 of $q = r_1 + q_1 b$, $0 \leqslant r_1 < b$, must be $r_1 = a_1$, and either $q_1 = 0$, or if $n \geqslant 2$, then $q_1 = a_2 + \cdots + a_n b^{n-2}$. Then $q_1 = r_2 + q_2 b$ with $0 \leqslant r_2 < b$ yields a unique $r_2 = a_2$, etc. Of course, the "etc." conceals a "limited induction" on the subscripts $i = 0, 1, \ldots, n$.

A direct argument can be presented showing how two different representations will lead to a contradiction. Suppose that $a = a_0 + a_1 b + \cdots + a_n b^n = c_0 + c_1 b + \cdots + c_t b^t$ with $0 \leqslant a_i < b$ when $i \neq n$ and $0 < a_n < b$, and $0 \leqslant c_i < b$ when $i \neq t$ and $0 < c_t < b$. Unless $n = t$ and $a_i = c_i$ for $i = 0, 1, \ldots, n$, it follows by subtraction that $0 = d_0 + d_1 b + \cdots + d_k b^k$ with $k > 0$ and with $d_i = a_i - c_i$ and $-b < d_i < b$ for

$i = 0, 1, \ldots, k$, and $d_k \neq 0$. Since $d_k \neq 0$, there is a smallest subscript $i < k$, such that $d_i \neq 0$. Then from

$$0 = d_i b^i + d_{i+1} b^{i+1} + \cdots + d_k b^k$$

we find that

$$d_i = -b(d_{i+1} + \cdots + d_k b^{k-i-1})$$

so that d_i is a multiple of b. But $|d_i| < b$, hence $d_i = 0$. This contradiction establishes the uniqueness of the representation.

This completes the proof of the theorem.

5.2.   The choice of a base b

The important implication of the theorem presented in the preceding section is that in addition to the symbol 0 only $b - 1$ other symbols are required (allowing repetitions, of course) to represent *any* integer a, a total of b symbols! Anthropologically and geographically and historically speaking, by far the most important choice of the base b is the choice which we call "ten," motivated, it is sure, by the usual supply of fingers among the primates. Here, modified from Hindu-Arabic sources, the set of b symbols is as follows:

$$0, \quad 1, \quad 1 + 1 = 2, \quad 2 + 1 = 3, \quad 3 + 1 = 4, \quad 4 + 1 = 5,$$
$$5 + 1 = 6, \quad 6 + 1 = 7, \quad 7 + 1 = 8, \quad 8 + 1 = 9.$$

The next following integer is $9 + 1 = b = 0 + (1)b$ with $n = 1$.

But our theorem shows that this customary choice of the base b is by no means necessary, and indeed the history of number representation among various peoples in various parts of the world at various times in history reveals uses of the bases "five," "twenty," "sixty," and several others.

Any departure from the usual representation cannot result in any really different theorems about the integers. However, it is still true that for certain problems the choice of some other base than "ten" may make the proof of a theorem shorter or more easily understood.

For example, using the notation of the preceding section, we may desire to reduce the value of n, and this may be accomplished by increasing b; of course, this would require additional symbols. Quite widely advocated is the adoption of the "dozen" or "twelve" system, wherein we might write $9 + 1 = x$, $x + 1 = L$, and $L + 1 = b$.

On the other hand, we may desire to reduce the number of symbols needed, even at the sacrifice of using larger values of n. The extreme case, in this direction, is the "binary" or "two" system, which has been especially useful to mathematicians and designers of some types of computing machines; in this system the only symbols required are 0 and 1, since $1 + 1 = b$.

To avoid writing the powers of b and the $+$ signs we shall agree to adopt the following *positional notation*:

$$a = a_0 + a_1 b + \cdots + a_n b^n = (a_n \cdots a_1 a_0)_b$$

where a_i occurs in the $i + 1$ position, counting from the *right*. The only danger is that this symbol may be interpreted as the product of the coefficients, so be wary! Of course the b-subscript specifying the base may be dropped if the context indicates the value of b.

5.3. Representation with the base "six"

Had we been born in a certain mountain village on the border between France and Spain where, so the anthropologists tell us, inbreeding has resulted in a whole community of people with six fingers on each hand, it is conceivable that in kindergarten we might have learned to count in terms of "sixes," i.e., 0, 1, 2, 3, 4, 5, then "six" which in the positional notation would be written 10, followed by 11, 12, 13, 14, 15, then 20, 21, etc. We would have learned "addition" and "multiplication" tables like the following:

+	0	1	2	3	4	5
0	0	1	2	3	4	5
1	1	2	3	4	5	10
2	2	3	4	5	10	11
3	3	4	5	10	11	12
4	4	5	10	11	12	13
5	5	10	11	12	13	14

×	0	1	2	3	4	5
0	0	0	0	0	0	0
1	0	1	2	3	4	5
2	0	2	4	10	12	14
3	0	3	10	13	20	23
4	0	4	12	20	24	32
5	0	5	14	23	32	41

Having once learned these tables we could have progressed easily to more complicated arithmetic—speaking of unit digits, b-digits, b^2-digits, etc., carrying, borrowing, and arranging our harder multiplications, for example, by virtue of the associative and distributive laws, in rows and columns. For example, to multiply 3204 by 513 we would write

$$
\begin{array}{r}
3204 \\
513 \\
\hline
14020 \\
3204 \\
24432 \\
\hline
2533300.
\end{array}
$$

But, having learned as we did, we will probably find the last example more convincing, or at least feel that it has been properly checked, if we first convert the multiplicand and multiplier to the base "ten" as follows:

$$(3204)_6 = 4 + 0 \cdot 6 + 2 \cdot 6^2 + 3 \cdot 6^3 = (724)_{10};$$
$$(513)_6 = 3 + 6 + 5 \cdot 6^2 = (189)_{10};$$

and then carry out the problem as follows:

$$
\begin{array}{r}
724 \\
189 \\
\hline
6516 \\
5792 \\
724 \\
\hline
136836.
\end{array}
$$

Our answer of $(136836)_{10}$ we convert to a representation in terms of the base 6 by repeated applications of the division algorithm with the divisor always 6, as follows:

$$
\begin{array}{c}
136836 \\
\text{quotients} \left\{
\begin{array}{rr}
22806 & 0 \\
3801 & 0 \\
633 & 3 \\
105 & 3 \\
17 & 3 \\
2 & 5 \\
0 & 2 \\
\end{array}
\right\} \text{ remainders.}
\end{array}
$$

Hence we find $(136836)_{10} = (2533300)_6$ and this checks our previous work in the "six" system.

To justify the last procedure for taking a number given in a known system, say with the base 10, and converting it, by repeated divisions in the *known* system, to a representation with a different base b, perhaps b equal to 6, we observe that if $a = a_0 + a_1 b + \cdots + a_n b^n$, then $a = (a_1 + a_2 b + \cdots + a_n b^{n-1})b + a_0$; and since $0 \leqslant a_0 < b$, we see that the division algorithm $a = qb + r$, $0 \leqslant r < b$ must yield $r = a_0$ and $q = a_1 + a_2 b + \cdots + a_n b^{n-1}$. Similarly, $q = q_1 b + r_1$ yields $r_1 = a_1$; $q_1 = q_2 b + r_2$ yields $r_2 = a_2$; etc. The argument is very similar to that in the first paragraph of (B) in **5.2**, except that now thorough familiarity with the arithmetic of some known system of representation is being assumed.

EXERCISES

In the following five exercises (1) carry out the indicated operations, using the tables given in **5.3**, entirely within the "six" system; then (2) convert the given numbers to the base "ten" and carry out the operations in the familiar ten system; (3) convert the answers obtained in step (2) to the base "six"; and (4) check the results obtained in step (3) with those obtained in (1).

5.1.   Add $(3542)_6$ to $(1135)_6$.

5.2.   Subtract $(3025)_6$ from $(11111)_6$.

5.3.   Multiply $(234)_6$ by $(531)_6$.

5.4.   Divide $a = (3014)_6$ by $c = (12)_6$ to find q and r so that $a = qc + r$, $0 \leqslant r < c$.

5.5.   Use the square root extraction process to find the square root of $(24041)_6$.

5.6.   Use the representation of integers in the "binary" or "two" system to show that a properly chosen set of n weights will suffice to weigh objects of weights $1, 2, 3, \ldots, 2^n - 1$, if the weights are put in one pan of a balance and the object to be weighed in the other pan.

5.7.   If the base $b = 2K + 1$ with $K > 0$, discuss the possibility of representing any positive integer a in the form $a = a_0 + a_1 b + \cdots + a_n b^n$ with $-K \leqslant a_i \leqslant K$, $i \neq n$, and $0 < a_n \leqslant K$. (See EX. **3.7**.)

5.8.   Use EX. **2.4** and the representation of EX. **5.7** for $b = 3$ to show that a properly chosen set of n weights will suffice to weigh objects of weights $1, 2, 3, \ldots, (3^n - 1)/2$, if the weights may be placed some in one pan and some (if desired) in the other pan along with the object to be weighed.

5.9.   Establish part (A) of the representation theorem another way. Note from EX. **2.4** that $(b - 1)(1 + b + \cdots + b^k) + 1 = b^{k+1}$. Make an induction argument from $a = a_0 + a_1 b + \cdots + a_k b^k + \cdots + a_n b^n$ to $a + 1$ depending on (1) $a_0 < b - 1$; (2) for $k < n$, $a_0 = a_1 = \cdots = a_k = b - 1$, but $a_{k+1} < b - 1$; or (3) $a_0 = a_1 = \cdots = a_n = b - 1$.

CHAPTER 6

The Euclid algorithm

6.1. Classification of the integers by divisibility properties

If a, b, c are integers and $c = ab$, then c is called a *multiple* of b, and b is called a *divisor* or *factor* of c.

The *zero* is exceptional from this point of view since $0a = 0$ shows that 0 is a multiple of every integer.

If a and b are integers and $ab = 1$, then b is a *unit*. The only units among the ordinary integers are $+1$ and -1.

If p is an integer which is not a unit and if $p = ab$, where a and b are integers, implies that either a or b must be a unit, then p is a *prime*. The first five positive prime integers are 2, 3, 5, 7, and 11.

An integer which is neither zero, a unit, nor a prime is said to be *composite*. The first five positive composite integers are 4, 6, 8, 9, and 10.

Thus on the basis of rather simple divisibility properties the integers are separated into four mutually exclusive categories. It is the purpose of this and the following chapter to show that the primes are fundamental building blocks in terms of which all the composite integers may be conveniently and uniquely represented. This program will be initiated by studying two ideas that are very useful in themselves and which provide

33

the key ideas for the next chapter, where our program will be finally achieved.

6.2.   Definition of a greatest common divisor

If $a = Ad$ and $b = Bd$, then d is called a *common divisor* of a and b.

Given the integers a and b, if there exists an integer d such that

(*1*) d is a common divisor of a and b;

(*2*) every common divisor of a and b is a divisor of d;

then d is called a *greatest common divisor* of a and b, and is designated by $d = (a, b)$.

The student reader will probably consider himself already acquainted with this idea, since without much effort he can recognize that $(15, 21) = 3$. Upon greater consideration he can see that his success depends on factoring the numbers into prime factors: $15 = 3 \cdot 5$ and $21 = 3 \cdot 7$ and then selecting the correct powers of common prime factors. In this simple case the selection is easy and (as we shall show later) the factorizations are unique and 3 is indeed a correct greatest common divisor. The remarkable thing about the argument of the next section is that it in no way depends upon factoring a and b into prime factors (a task which may be formidable for large numbers), and yet it proves the existence of, and provides a direct construction for, a greatest common divisor.

6.3.   The Euclid algorithm for finding a greatest common divisor

If we are given a pair of positive integers a and b, it is merely a matter of notation to assume $0 < b \leqslant a$. By the division algorithm we may write $a = qb + r$ with $0 \leqslant r < b$. If $r = 0$, we stop with the one equation $a = qb$. In the more important case where $r \neq 0$, we apply the division algorithm repeatedly, say $k + 2$ times, to obtain the following sequence of equations which is universally known as the *Euclid algorithm*:

$$a = qb + r, \quad b = q_1 r + r_1, \quad r = q_2 r_1 + r_2, \quad \ldots,$$
$$r_{k-2} = q_k r_{k-1} + r_k, \quad r_{k-1} = q_{k+1} r_k + 0,$$
$$b > r > r_1 > r_2 > \cdots > r_k > r_{k+1} = 0.$$

Since the remainders form a decreasing sequence of positive integers, it follows that in a finite number of steps the process will terminate, say as indicated with $r_{k+1} = 0$. It is understood, of course, that k will vary depending on a and b.

We are now in a position to discuss in a constructive way the problem of the existence of a greatest common divisor.

Theorem: For any given pair of positive integers a and b, a greatest common divisor $d = (a, b)$

(A) exists,

(B) is unique except for a unit factor,

(C) is such that there exist integers x and y for which $d = ax + by$,

(D) is such that the integers d, x, y can be found in a finite number of steps by the Euclid algorithm.

Proof: (A) We consider the Euclid algorithm described above. If $r = 0$, so that the algorithm consists of the one equation $a = qb$, it is clear that b satisfies both requirements (*1*) and (*2*) of the definition of a greatest common divisor, so we take $d = b$. If $r \neq 0$, we shall show that r_k, the last nonzero remainder in the Euclid algorithm, is a greatest common divisor of a and b (in case $r_1 = 0$, we agree to define $r_0 = r$). We must show that r_k possesses properties (*1*) and (*2*) of the definition given in the preceding section.

Proof of (1): From $r_{k-1} = q_{k+1}r_k$ it follows that r_k divides r_{k-1}. From $r_{k-2} = q_k r_{k-1} + r_k = (q_k q_{k+1} + 1)r_k$ it follows that r_k divides r_{k-2}. In similar fashion, tracing *back* equation by equation in the algorithm, we find eventually that r_k divides b and finally that r_k divides a. Thus r_k is a common divisor of a and b.

Proof of (2): Let D be any common divisor of a and b, so that, say, $a = PD$ and $b = QD$. We rearrange the first equation of the Euclid algorithm to see from $r = a - qb = (P - qQ)D$ that D divides r. Then the rearranged second equation $r_1 = b - q_1 r$ shows that D divides r_1. And moving *forward* equation by equation in the algorithm, we find finally from $r_k = r_{k-2} - q_k r_{k-1}$ that D divides r_k. Thus every common divisor of a and b divides r_k.

Since we have shown that r_k possesses properties (*1*) and (*2*), it follows from the definition of d that $r_k = d$. Hence at least one integer $d = (a, b)$ exists.

(B) Let d and d' be two greatest common divisors of a and b. By property (*2*) it follows on the one hand that $d = kd'$ and on the other hand that $d' = md$. Then $d = kmd$ and since $d \neq 0$, it follows that $km = 1$, hence k and m are units. Conversely, if m is a unit and d is a greatest common divisor of a and b, then $d' = md$ is also a greatest common divisor of a and b (see EX. **6.1**).

Thus the greatest common divisor is unique only up to a unit factor, and $-d$ has to be considered as equally acceptable an answer as d. In number systems which we shall investigate later, where still more units are available, even greater freedom in the selection of $d = (a, b)$ is to be expected. The use of the adjective "greatest" is merely a hangover from the simplest case where one considers only positive integers.

(C) and (D) Furthermore, if $r \neq 0$, by straightforward (even if lengthy) successive eliminations of $r_{k-1}, r_{k-2}, \ldots, r_1$, and r from the system of equations of the algorithm, beginning with

$$r_k = r_{k-2} - q_k r_{k-1} = (r_{k-4} - q_{k-2} r_{k-3}) - q_k(r_{k-3} - q_{k-1} r_{k-2}),$$

etc., etc., we discover, in a finite number of steps, suitable integers x and y such that $r_k = ax + by$. (In the next chapter we shall show a mechanical scheme for performing this elimination.) In case $r = 0$, then $d = b$, so we can take $x = 0$ and $y = 1$ to have $d = ax + by$.

This completes the proof of the Euclid algorithm theorem.

For the example $a = 2210$ and $b = 493$, the Euclid algorithm may be written as follows:

$$
\begin{array}{r}
4 = q \\
b = 493 \overline{\smash{\big)}\, 2210} = a \\
\underline{1972} \qquad 2 = q_1 \\
r = \quad 238 \overline{\smash{\big)}\, 493} \\
\underline{476} \qquad 14 = q_2 \\
r_1 = \quad 17 \overline{\smash{\big)}\, 238} \\
\underline{238} \\
r_2 = \quad 0.
\end{array}
$$

Since $r_2 = 0$, we know that $r_1 = 17 = (2210, 493)$. To find x and y we have only to eliminate r from the equations, as follows:

$$17 = b - 2r = b - 2(a - 4b) = -2a + 9b,$$

hence we may take $x = -2$ and $y = +9$. In performing such an elimination it is convenient to retain letters for the r's, a, and b, and to substitute actual numbers only for the q's.

If a and b are positive and $d = (a, b)$, then $d = (-a, b)$ and $d = (-a, -b)$, because the divisors of a and $-a$ are the same. If $a \neq 0$, then $a = (a, 0)$. Hence the symbol (a, b) is meaningful in every case except $(0, 0)$ where it is certainly meaningless, since, as was noted at the beginning of this chapter, every integer is a divisor of 0.

6.4. Relatively prime integers

If a greatest common divisor of the integers a and b is a unit, then a and b are said to be *relatively prime*. Thus 8 and 15 are relatively prime, although neither is itself a prime.

Theorem 1: The integers a and b are relatively prime if and only if there exist integers x and y such that $ax + by = 1$.

Proof: (A) If x and y exist so that $ax + by = 1$ and if D is any common divisor of a and b, say, $a = PD$ and $b = QD$, then $(Px + Qy)D = 1$ shows that D must be a unit, hence $d = (a, b) = \pm 1$.

(B) If $(a, b) = \pm 1$, then the Euclid algorithm theorem guarantees the existence of integers x and y such that $ax + by = 1$.

Corollary 1.1:   If $(a, b) = d$ and $a = Ad$, $b = Bd$, then $(A, B) = 1$.

Proof: By the Euclid algorithm theorem integers x and y exist so that $d = ax + by$. Then from $d = (Ax + By)d$ we obtain $1 = Ax + By$. From part (A) of Theorem 1 it follows that $(A, B) = 1$.

Corollary 1.2:   If $(a, b) = 1$ and $(a, c) = 1$, then $(a, bc) = 1$.

Proof: From part (B) of Theorem 1, x_1 and y_1 exist so that $ax_1 + by_1 = 1$, and x_2 and y_2 exist so that $ax_2 + cy_2 = 1$. Then

$$1 = 1 \cdot 1 = (ax_1 + by_1)(ax_2 + cy_2)$$
$$= a(x_1 a x_2 + x_1 c y_2 + b y_1 x_2) + bc(y_1 y_2).$$

Thus integers $x_3 = x_1 a x_2 + x_1 c y_2 + b y_1 y_2$ and $y_3 = y_1 y_2$ exist so that $ax_3 + bcy_3 = 1$. Hence by part (A) of Theorem 1 we have $(a, bc) = 1$.

In the exercises of Chapter 6 many other consequences of Theorem 1 are suggested.

In much of our later work we shall find that the following theorem and its corollaries are fundamental.

Theorem 2:   If a and b are relatively prime and if a divides bc, then a must divide c.

Proof: Since $(a, b) = 1$, there exist integers x and y such that $1 = ax + by$. Hence $c = c(ax + by) = acx + bcy$. But the second hypothesis that a divides bc, say $bc = aP$, shows that $c = a(cx + Py)$, so a divides c.

EXERCISES

6.1.   If $d = (a, b)$ and m is a unit, show that $d' = md$ is also a greatest common divisor of a and b by establishing (*1*) and (*2*) for d'.

6.2.   Use the Euclid algorithm to find $d = (a, b)$ and to find x and y such that $d = ax + by$ in each of the following cases:
(a) $a = 3367$, $b = 3219$; (b) $a = 11063$, $b = 11951$;
(c) $a = 12019$, $b = 561$; (d) $a = 1337$, $b = -501$.

6.3.   If $d = (a, b) = ax + by$, prove that x and y are relatively prime. (Hint: Consider Corollary 1.1.)

6.4.   In $d = (a, b) = ax + by$ show that x and y are not unique. (Hint: Add and subtract abk.)

6.5.   If $d = (a, b)$ and $a = Ad$, $b = Bd$, and if $ax + by = aX + bY$, prove that $X = x + Bt$, $Y = y - At$. (Hint: Consider Corollary 1.1 and Theorem 2.)

6.6.   If s and t are any integers and if $sa + tb = R$, show that $d = (a, b)$ must divide R. If R has no factors except units which will divide both a and b, then $(a, b) = 1$.

6.7.   Show that for all values of k the integers $a = 22k + 7$ and $b = 33k + 5$ are relatively prime. (Hint: Apply EX. **6.6** with suitable values of s and t.)

6.8.   Prove that $(ka, kb) = k(a, b)$ for any integer $k \neq 0$. [Hint: Make good use of (*1*) and (*2*) and Corollary 1.1.]

6.9.   If $(a, b) = 1$, show that $(a + b, a - b) = 2$ or 1 depending upon whether a and b are of the same or opposite parity. (Hint: Use EXS. **6.6** and **6.8**.)

6.10. If $(a, b) = 1$, use Corollary 1.2 and induction on t to show that $(a, b^t) = 1$. If $(a, b) = 1$, show that $(a^s, b^t) = 1$.

6.11. If $(a, b) = 1$, use Theorem 1 to prove that $(a + ub, b) = 1$ for any integer u.

6.12. Extend the definition in **6.2** and define $d = (a, b, c)$. Prove that $d = (a, b, c) = ((a, b), c)$.

6.13. If $(a, b, c) = \pm 1$, then a, b, c are said to form a relatively prime triple. Prove by examples that a relatively prime triple can occur with none, one, two, or three of the pairs a, b or b, c or c, a being a relatively prime pair.

6.14. Give a new proof of EX. **6.10** patterned on the proof of Corollary 1.2 and using the binomial theorem on $(ax + by)^{s+t-1}$.

6.15. A student's proof of Corollary 1.2 was marked wrong because he started with $1 = ax + by$ and $1 = ax + cy$. Was the criticism justified?

Someone asked Euclid "But what
shall I get by learning these things?"
Euclid called his slave and said
"Give him three coins, for he
must make gain out of what he learns."
—STOBAEUS

CHAPTER 7

More about greatest common divisors

7.1. Recursion formulas for computation of x, y so that $d = (a, b) = ax + by$

It is desirable for theoretical and computational purposes to have a mechanical scheme for performing eliminations from the equations of the Euclid algorithm.

Toward this end we reconsider the Euclid algorithm, and after setting $r_{-2} = a$ and $r_{-1} = b$, we write the following equations:

(7.1) $\qquad r_{i-2} = q_i r_{i-1} + r_i, \qquad i = 0, 1, 2, \ldots, k;$

where

$$0 < r_k < r_{k-1} < \cdots < r_1 < r_0 < |b| \leqslant |a|$$

and where $r_{k-1} = q_{k+1} r_k$, so that $d = r_k = (a, b)$ as in **6.3**.

Let x_i, y_i be entered recursively in the following chart

q		q_0	q_1	q_2	$\cdots$	q_k	q_{k+1}
x	0	1	x_1	x_2	$\cdots$	x_k	x_{k+1}
y	1	q_0	y_1	y_2	$\cdots$	y_k	y_{k+1}

by defining $x_{-1} = 0$, $y_{-1} = 1$, $x_0 = 1$, $y_0 = q_0$ and using the formulas:

$$(7.2) \quad x_i = x_{i-2} + x_{i-1}q_i, \quad y_i = y_{i-2} + y_{i-1}q_i, \quad i = 1, 2, \ldots, k + 1.$$

For the example in **6.3** the entries are readily determined:

$$x_1 = 0 + 1 \cdot 2 = 2, \quad y_1 = 1 + 4 \cdot 2 = 9;$$
$$x_2 = 1 + 2 \cdot 14 = 29, \quad y_2 = 4 + 9 \cdot 14 = 130;$$

so the completed chart is as follows:

q		4	2	14
x	0	1	2	29
y	1	4	9	130

Lemma 1: The following relation holds for $i = 0, 1, 2, \ldots, k + 1$:

$$(7.3) \qquad ax_i - by_i = (-1)^i r_i.$$

Proof: Let M be the set of integers i in the range $0 \leqslant i \leqslant k + 1$ for which (7.3) holds.

(I) When $i = 0$ we have $ax_0 - by_0 = a \cdot 1 - bq_0 = r_0 = (-1)^0 r_0$ by (7.1). When $i = 1$ we see from (7.2) that $x_1 = 0 + 1 \cdot q_1 = q_1$ and $y_1 = 1 + q_0 q_1$; hence $ax_1 - by_1 = aq_1 - b(1 + q_0 q_1) = (a - bq_0)q_1 - b = r_0 q_1 - b = (-1)^1 r_1$ by (7.1).

(II) We assume that (7.3) is correct for $i = 0, 1, \ldots, j$, where $1 \leqslant j \leqslant k$ and prove that (7.3) holds for $i = j + 1$. From (7.2) we have

$$ax_{j+1} - by_{j+1} = a(x_{j-1} + x_j q_{j+1}) - b(y_{j-1} + y_j q_{j+1})$$
$$= (ax_{j-1} - by_{j-1}) + q_{j+1}(ax_j - by_j).$$

Then from the induction hypothesis for $i = j - 1$ and $i = j$ we have

$$ax_{j+1} - by_{j+1} = (-1)^{j-1} r_{j-1} + q_{j+1}(-1)^j r_j = (-1)^{j+1}(r_{j-1} - q_{j+1}r_j).$$

But from the Euclidean algorithm (7.1) we know $r_{j-1} = q_{j+1}r_j + r_{j+1}$, so

$$ax_{j+1} - by_{j+1} = (-1)^{j+1} r_{j+1}.$$

From (I) and (II) and the principle of (limited) induction we conclude that M contains all the integers $0, 1, 2, \ldots, k + 1$.

Lemma 2: The following relation holds for $i = 0, 1, 2, \ldots, k + 1$:

$$(7.4) \qquad x_{i-1}y_i - y_{i-1}x_i = (-1)^{i+1}.$$

Proof: Let M be the set of integers i in the range $0 \leqslant i \leqslant k + 1$ for which (7.4) holds.

(I) When $i = 0$ we have $x_{-1}y_0 - y_{-1}x_0 = 0 \cdot q_0 - 1 \cdot 1 = -1 = (-1)^{0+1}$.

(II) We assume that (7.4) holds for $i = 0, 1, \ldots, j$, where $0 \leqslant j \leqslant k$ and prove that (7.4) holds for $i = j + 1$. From (7.2) we have

$$x_j y_{j+1} - y_j x_{j+1} = x_j(y_{j-1} + y_j q_j) - y_j(x_{j-1} + x_j q_j)$$
$$= -(x_{j-1}y_j - y_{j-1}x_j) = -(-1)^{j+1} = (-1)^{j+2},$$

where in the penultimate step we have used the induction hypothesis for the case $i = j$.

From (I) and (II) and the principle of induction it follows that M contains all the integers $0, 1, 2, \ldots, k + 1$.

Theorem: If $d = (a, b)$ with $a = Ad$ and $b = Bd$, then a solution x, y of $d = ax + by$ is given by $x = (-1)^k x_k$ and $y = (-1)^{k+1}y_k$. If a, b, and d are positive, then $A = y_{k+1}$ and $B = x_{k+1}$.

Proof: (A) From **6.3** we know $d = r_k$, and from (7.3) of Lemma 1 when $i = k$ we have $(-1)^k r_k = ax_k - by_k$ which we rewrite in the form

$$d = r_k = a(-1)^k x_k + b(-1)^{k+1}y_k$$

to see that $x = (-1)^k x_k$ and $y = (-1)^{k+1}y_k$ is one solution of $d = ax + by$.

(B) In (7.1) we have $r_{k+1} = 0$; hence from (7.3) when $i = k + 1$ we have $0 = ax_{k+1} - by_{k+1} = (Ax_{k+1} - By_{k+1})d$ from which we obtain the relation

$$(7.5) \qquad\qquad Ax_{k+1} = By_{k+1}.$$

From Corollary 1.1 in **6.4** we know $(A, B) = 1$; hence from (7.5) and Theorem 2 in **6.4** we know A divides y_{k+1}.

From the relation (7.4) of Lemma 2 when $i = k + 1$ we have $x_k y_{k+1} - y_k x_{k+1} = (-1)^{k+2}$. From Theorem 1 in **6.4** it follows that $(x_{k+1}, y_{k+1}) = 1$. Hence from (7.5) and Theorem 2 in **6.4**, y_{k+1} divides A.

Since each of y_{k+1} and A divides the other, it follows that $y_{k+1} = \pm A$. If a and d are positive so that A is positive, then only the $+$ sign can hold, for all the q_i are positive (when both a and b are positive) and therefore all the y_i from (7.2) are positive. With $y_{k+1} = A$, it follows from (7.5) that $x_{k+1} = B$, which completes the proof of the theorem.

In a later chapter we shall find that the recursion formulas (7.2) are fundamental computational devices in the study of continued fractions.

7.2.   Illustrative example

Let us consider as an example $a = 533$, $b = 299$. The equations of the Euclid algorithm are represented by the following long divisions.

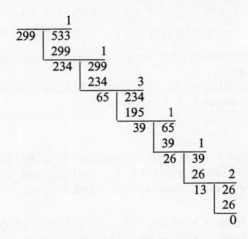

Evidently $d = 13$. Determination of x and y by straightforward elimination is somewhat tedious, as follows:

$$d = 13 = 39 - 26 = (234 - 3\cdot65) - (65 - 39)$$
$$= 234 - 4\cdot65 + (234 - 3\cdot65) = 2\cdot234 - 7\cdot65$$
$$= 2\cdot234 - 7(b - 234) = 9\cdot234 - 7b = 9(a - b) - 7b = 9a - 16b,$$

hence $x = 9$ and $y = -16$.

By the recursion formula method the computations (7.2) are simple enough to be done mentally and entered successively in the chart:

q		1	1	3	1	1	2
x	0	1	1	4	5	9	23
y	1	1	2	7	9	16	41

Not only are $x = 9$ and $y = -16$ readily determined, but also the completed chart contains a built-in checking device, for unless $a = y_{k+1}d$

$= 41 \cdot 13 = 533$ and $b = x_{k+1}d = 23 \cdot 13 = 299$ some mistake has been made.

7.3.   Other algorithms

In the discussion of the preceding sections we have supposed that a "standard" Euclid algorithm has been used, i.e., an algorithm in which the remainders are "least positive" remainders. Lamé has shown that the number of divisions in such a standard algorithm will not exceed five times the number of digits in the smaller number b (with computations in the base 10).

But there is no compulsion to use least positive remainders. Thus if $a = qb + r$, $0 < r < b$, we also have the possibility of using $a = (q + 1) b + r'$, where $|r'| = b - r$ satisfies $0 < |r'| < b$. If one, say r^*, of r and $|r'|$ is the smaller, then a second step of the algorithm, $b = q_1 r^* + r_1$, $0 \leqslant |r_1| < r^*$ would seem to have the possibility of a smaller remainder than in the standard algorithm and hence the discovery in fewer steps of $d = (a, b)$. An algorithm which at each step uses that one of the remainders which is smallest in absolute value has been shown by Kronecker to be at least as short as any other algorithm (and often, as examples show, there is considerable gain over the standard algorithm in the use of this "least absolute value "algorithm). Further discussion of these matters may be found in the book by Uspensky and Heaslet listed in the bibliography.

Even if some Euclid algorithm other than the standard one is used, a list of the successive quotients can still be used in (7.2) to find X, Y solving $d = aX + bY$, for there was nothing about the derivation of those formulas to require positive remainders. But, of course, different algorithms may lead to different solutions X, Y.

For example, consider the following algorithm:

$$
\begin{array}{r}
2 \\
\overline{299 \,\big|\, 533} \\
598 \qquad -5 \\
\overline{-65 \,\big|\, 299} \\
325 \qquad 3 \\
\overline{-26 \,\big|\, -65} \\
-78 \qquad -2 \\
\overline{13 \,\big|\, -26} \\
-26 \\
\overline{0.}
\end{array}
$$

Then using (7.2) with $q_0 = 2, q_1 = -5, q_2 = 3, q_3 = -2$, we find

q		$+2$	-5	$+3$	-2
x	0	1	-5	-14	23
y	1	$+2$	-9	-25	41

hence we may take $X = -14$, $Y = 25$. Inasmuch as $-14 = 9 - 23$, $25 = -16 + 41$, this solution is seen to be compatible with the solution $x = 9, y = -16$ previously obtained (see EX. **6.5**).

Still another computational device may be suggested, based essentially on the least absolute value algorithm. To avoid trivial cases suppose that b does not divide a and that $0 < b < |a|$. By the division algorithm compute

(1) $$a - qb = r, \quad 0 < r < b;$$

(2) $$a - (q + 1)b = -r', \quad 0 < r' = b - r < b.$$

Let $D = (r, r')$. From (1) and (2) it is clear that $d = (a, b)$ divides both r and r'; hence d divides D. But $b = r + r'$ and $a = qb + r = (q + 1)r + qr'$, so it is clear that $D = (r, r')$ divides both a and b; hence D divides d. Therefore $D = \pm d$. Thus the problem of finding $d = (a, b)$ may be replaced by the problem of finding $d = (r, r')$, where both $0 < r < b < |a|$ and $0 < r' < b < |a|$ so that smaller numbers are involved. Perhaps by inspection d as well as s and t can be found so that $d = sr - tr'$. Then if we add s times (1) to t times (2) we have

(3) $$(s + t)a - (sq + t(q + 1))b = d,$$

so that $X = s + t, Y = -(s + t)q - t$ solves $aX + bY = d$.

If the numbers r and r' are not sufficiently small to provide obvious solutions of d, s, t, the process can be repeated beginning with r and r'. The process will terminate as usual in a finite number of steps, because of the decreasing nonnegative character of the numbers involved, with the discovery of a trivial case where one member of the pair is 0 and the other is d.

In practice there is no need to memorize the formulas for X and Y. For example, to compute $d = (533, 299)$ we proceed step by step as indicated by the arrows:

(1) $533 - 1 \cdot 299 = 234$ $\}$ $\rightarrow$ $(1)'$ $234 - 3 \cdot 65 = 39$ $\}$ $\rightarrow$ but here,
(2) $533 - 2 \cdot 299 = -65$ $\}$ $\quad$ $(2)'$ $234 - 4 \cdot 65 = -26$ $\}$ $\quad$ obviously $(?)$,
(3) $\begin{cases} 9 \cdot 533 - 16 \cdot 299 = 13 \\ X = 9, \quad Y = -16 \end{cases}$ $\leftarrow$ $\begin{cases} (3)' \; 2 \cdot 234 - 7 \cdot 65 = 13 \\ s = 2, \quad t = 7 \end{cases}$ $\leftarrow$ $\begin{cases} 39 - 26 = 13 = (39, 26) \\ s' = 1, \quad t' = 1 \end{cases}$

7.4.   Application of the well-ordering principle

In the preceding sections we have emphasized the computational aspects of the Euclid algorithm method. By actually producing them we have shown in several ways the existence of $d = (a, b)$ and integers x and y so that $d = ax + by$. In rather marked contrast to such a *constructive* proof, let us give now a short proof devoted purely to *existence*. For clarity let us restate the proposition.

Theorem: For any given integers a and b, not both zero, there exists an integer $d = (a, b)$ which can be written in the form $d = ax + by$ for suitably chosen integers x and y.

Proof: Let S be the set of all positive integers which can be written in the form $as + bt$ where s and t are integers. Since a and b are not both zero, suppose $a \neq 0$. Then one or the other of $a \cdot 1 + b \cdot 0 = a$ and $a(-1) + b \cdot 0 = -a$ is positive and in the set S. Hence the set S is not empty, and by the well-ordering principle **L.3** the set S contains a least element d, which being in the set S is necessarily of the form $d = ax + by$ for certain integers x and y.

We shall prove that this least element d has the required properties (*1*) and (*2*) of **6.2** so that $d = (a, b)$.

(*1*) By the division algorithm $a = qd + r$ where either $r = 0$ or $0 < r < d$. If $0 < r < d$, then from

$$r = a - qd = a - q(ax + by) = a(1 - qx) + b(-qy)$$

we see that with $s = 1 - qx$ and $t = -qy$ the integer r is in the set S. But $0 < r < d$ contradicts the minimal property assumed for d. Hence $r = 0$, and $a = qd$ shows that d divides a. Similarly, we may show that d divides b. This completes the proof of (*1*).

(*2*) Let D be any common divisor of a and b, say $a = PD$, $b = QD$. From $d = ax + by = (Px + Qy)D$ we find that D divides d. Hence d has property (*2*). This completes the proof of the theorem.

In retrospect we can see that the various algorithms of **6.3** and **7.3** are just systematic ways of determining the members d and $-d$ of the set $\{as + bt\}$ for which $d \neq 0$ and $|d|$ is minimal.

EXERCISES

For each of the following cases complete EXS. **7.1**, **7.2**, and **7.3**.

   (a) $a = 5371$, $b = 4387$; (b) $a = 21571$, $b = 8547$;
   (c) $a = 9003$, $b = 4001$; (d) $a = 9250$, $b = 1517$.

Find d, x, y so that $d = (a, b) = ax + by$:

7.1. Using the "standard" algorithm and (7.2).

7.2. Using the "least absolute value" algorithm and (7.2).

7.3. Using the (1)-(2)-(3) method at the end of 7.3.

7.4. Check Lemma 1 and Lemma 2 for the example in **7.2**.

7.5. For the x_i, y_i defined in (7.2) prove that $(x_i, y_i) = 1$.

7.6. In the proof of (1) in **7.4** show "similarly" that d divides b.

7.7. For fixed integers a and b, not both zero, show that the least positive $d = ax + by$ of the set S' of all integers of the form $as + bt$ divides *every* member of the set S'. Show that S' coincides with the set of all multiples of d.

CHAPTER 8

The fundamental theorem of arithmetic

8.1. The fundamental lemma

Although we can prove the following lemma as a corollary of Theorem 2
in **6.4**, for emphasis on the basic character of the lemma we shall repeat
the entire proof.

Fundamental lemma: If a prime p divides a product ab, then p must
divide at least one of the integers a or b.

Proof: Suppose p divides b, then the lemma is true. Next, suppose
p does not divide b; then $(p, b) = 1$, because the only divisors of the prime
p are $+p$, $-p$, $+1$, -1. Hence by the theorem of the preceding lesson
there exist integers x and y such that $1 = bx + py$. Multiplying by a,
we find $a = abx + apy$. Since by hypothesis p divides ab and since
obviously p divides p, it follows from the last equation that p divides a,
which completes the proof.

Corollary: If a prime p divides a product $a_1 a_2 \ldots a_n$, then p must
divide at least one of the factors $a_1, a_2, \ldots, a_n$.
The proof of the corollary is left as one of the exercises.

47

8.2. The fundamental theorem

We are now in a position to establish what is justly described as the fundamental theorem of the arithmetic of ordinary integers.

The fundamental theorem of arithmetic: Any given positive integer n, other than 1, can be written uniquely as follows:

$$n = p_1^{a_1} p_2^{a_2} \ldots p_k^{a_k}$$

where k is a positive integer, where each p_i is a prime integer, where each a_i is a positive integer, and where $1 < p_1 < p_2 < \cdots < p_k$.

(It is understood that the choice of k and the p_i and the a_i will vary with different n. We shall refer to this representation as "writing n in standard form.")

Proof: (A) We shall show that there exists at least one such representation by making an induction argument on n. Let M be the set of all positive integers $n \geqslant 2$ for which the theorem holds.

(I) M contains 2, for 2 is itself a prime.

(II) Suppose that M contains the integers $2, 3, \ldots, n$. Then we can show that M must contain $n + 1$. If $n + 1$ is a prime, then the desired representation is already found. If $n + 1$ is composite, then $n + 1 = bc$ with $1 < b$ and $1 < c$, hence with $c < bc$ and $b < bc$. Thus since $1 < b < n + 1$ and $1 < c < n + 1$, it follows that the induction hypothesis applies to both b and c. By combining the representations for b and c, grouping like primes together and rearranging the combined set of primes in natural order with new labels, if necessary, we arrive at a representation of $n + 1$ of the desired form. By (I), (II), and the principle of mathematical induction, it follows that M contains all positive integers $n \geqslant 2$.

(B) Suppose that there exist two standard representations for a given integer n, say

$$n = p_1^{a_1} p_2^{a_2} \ldots p_k^{a_k} = q_1^{b_1} q_2^{b_2} \ldots q_m^{b_m}$$

where the p_i and q_i are primes and $1 < p_1 < p_2 < \cdots < p_k$ and $1 < q_1 < q_2 < \cdots < q_m$. It will be no essential restriction to suppose $m \geqslant k$. By the fundamental lemma and corollary of the preceding section it follows that the *prime* p_1 must divide some factor q_i, and since q_i is itself a *prime* that $p_1 = q_i$; but $q_i \geqslant q_1$, hence $p_1 \geqslant q_1$. But similarly, the corollary shows that the prime q_1 must divide some factor p_j, and since p_j is a prime, it follows that $q_1 = p_j$; however, $p_j \geqslant p_1$, hence $q_1 \geqslant p_1$. Thus it now follows that $p_1 = q_1$. Now suppose that $b_1 \geqslant a_1$, then $p_1^{a_1} = q_1^{a_1}$ may be divided out of the equation which we are studying to leave the following equation:

$$p_2{}^{a_2} \ldots p_k{}^{a_k} = q_1{}^{b_1 - a_1} q_2{}^{b_2} \ldots q_m{}^{b_m}.$$

If $b_1 > a_1$, the prime q_1, by the same arguments as before, must equal some p_j, $j \geqslant 2$; but since $q_1 = p_1 < p_j$, $j \geqslant 2$, we have arrived at a contradiction; therefore $b_1 = a_1$. A similar argument suffices if we suppose initially that $a_1 \geqslant b_1$.

Repeating this same kind of argument, we are step by step led to the following conclusions: $p_2 = q_2$, $a_2 = b_2$; $p_3 = q_3$, $a_3 = b_3$; $\ldots$; $p_k = q_k$, $a_k = b_k$. At this stage the equation being studied reduces (in case $m > k$) to the following:

$$1 = q_{k+1}{}^{b_{k+1}} \ldots q_m{}^{b_m}$$

but this is a contradiction, since a prime q is not a divisor of 1. Hence $m = k$, and the proof of the uniqueness of the representation is complete.

In many texts the fundamental theorem is stated in this way: "Every positive integer, except 1, can be represented uniquely as a product of primes, *except for order*." By making the rather natural agreement to collect like primes and to arrange the primes in ascending order, we have replaced the italicized phrase by the condition $1 < p_1 < p_2 < \cdots < p_k$.

8.3.   Critique

The theorem in **8.2** is called the *fundamental theorem of arithmetic* because in the further study of the theory of numbers, we use this unique factorization at almost every stage of the development. The need for presenting a proof of this theorem, however obvious the result may seem, will be apparent in a later chapter where we shall describe, briefly, systems of *algebraic integers* (our present system of natural integers being a special case) which contain a zero, units, primes, and composite integers; yet in some of these systems the fundamental theorem fails. In the higher algebra courses one of the chief concerns is to provide a remedy for this anomaly. One reason for the failure is that in some of these systems the fundamental lemma of **8.1** is lacking; since that fundamental lemma depended in its turn on the concept of a greatest common divisor introduced in Chapter 6, it may not be too surprising to learn that the remedy which is applied in the higher courses is to supply a suitable generalization of the notion of a greatest common divisor. It is true that Zermelo has shown that the fundamental theorem of **8.2** for the natural integers can be proved by an induction argument without using the lemma of **8.1** and without using the greatest common divisor theorem; but we have preferred to present here the traditional order of proof because it does suggest in a better way what later generalizations should be made.

However, proceeding from Zermelo's proof, or working back from our proof above of the fundamental theorem, we discover that because of the unique factorization all the possible divisors of a number are immediately obtainable from the standard form. For if

$$n = p_1{}^{a_1}p_2{}^{a_2}\ldots p_k{}^{a_k},$$

then every possible positive divisor s of n is obtained by considering

$$s = p_1{}^{b_1}p_2{}^{b_2}\ldots p_k{}^{b_k} \qquad \text{where } 0 \leqslant b_i \leqslant a_i.$$

Thus the greatest common divisor of two given integers can be found by writing each of these integers in standard form, selecting those primes which are *common* factors, say $P_1, P_2, \ldots, P_t$, and forming

$$d = P_1{}^{m_1}P_2{}^{m_2}\ldots P_t{}^{m_t},$$

where m_i is the *minimum* exponent of P_i as one compares the exponents of P_i in the two given integers.

For example, if $a = 2520 = 2^3 \cdot 3^2 \cdot 5 \cdot 7$ and $b = 4950 = 2 \cdot 3^2 \cdot 5^2 \cdot 11$, then $d = (a, b) = 2 \cdot 3^2 \cdot 5 = 90$.

Theoretically this construction of d is very easy, but practically it depends upon finding the standard representation, and as we shall show in the next chapter this assignment may be very difficult. Hence, as we have tried to emphasize earlier, the Euclid algorithm for finding d is, in general, to be preferred, for it avoids completely the question of finding prime factors.

8.4.   Least common multiple

If $m = qa = rb$, then m is called a *common multiple* of a and b.

If *(1)* m is a common multiple of a and b; and
   (2) every common multiple of a and b is a multiple of m;

then m is called a *least common multiple* of a and b and is designated by $m = [a, b]$.

(These definitions should be compared carefully with those in **6.2** in order to appreciate their "dual" nature.)

Directly from the definitions and from the notion of unique factorization into primes, it follows that if a and b are written in standard form, then the standard form for m is

$$m = Q_1{}^{M_1}Q_2{}^{M_2}\ldots Q_u{}^{M_u}$$

where the Q's include *all* prime factors of both a and b and where M_i is the *maximum* exponent of Q_i as one compares the exponents of Q_i in a and b.

For example, referring to the factorizations in the example of **8.3**, we see that $[2520, 4950] = 2^3 \cdot 3^2 \cdot 5^2 \cdot 7 \cdot 11 = 138600$.

This method of constructing $[a, b]$ depends on finding prime factors. A way of avoiding this difficulty is suggested by the following identity.

Theorem: If $d = (a, b)$ and $m = [a, b]$, then $md = ab$.

Proof: If $a = Ad$ and $b = Bd$, then $ab = AdBd$, so we can establish the theorem by showing that $m' = AdB$ is actually $[a, b]$.

(*1*) Since $m' = AdB = aB = Ab$, it is clear that m' is a common multiple of a and b.

(*2*) Let M be any common multiple of a and b, say $M = aS = bT$. Then $AdS = BdT$ so that $AS = BT$. From Theorem 1 of **6.4** we know $(A, B) = 1$; hence from Theorem 2 of **6.4** we see that B divides S, say $S = BU$. Then $M = aS = aBU = m'U$ so that M is a multiple of m'.

From (*1*) and (*2*) we have $m' = [a, b]$, so the proof is complete.

With the aid of the theorem we see that a way of finding $m = [a, b]$, without finding all prime factors, is to determine d, and hence B, by the Euclid algorithm and then to take $m = aB$.

8.5. Zermelo's proof of the fundamental theorem

The following proof of the fundamental theorem makes use of two forms **L.1** and **L.3** of the principle of mathematical induction.

Let M be the set of all integers n for which $n \geqslant 2$ and which are "normal" in the sense that they satisfy the fundamental theorem by having a unique factorization as a product of positive prime factors, except for order.

(I) The integer 2 is normal since it is a prime.

(II) We assume that every integer i in the range $2 \leqslant i \leqslant n - 1$ is normal and prove that n is normal. If n is prime, there is nothing more to prove. If n is composite, let S be the set of all divisors d of n satisfying the condition $d \geqslant 2$. The set S is not empty, for S contains at least n itself. By **L.3** the set S contains a least element, say p, which must be a prime; for if $p = ab$ is composite with $1 < a < p$, then a belongs to S, contradicting the minimal property of p. Since n is composite and $p > 1$, in $n = pn_1$ we have $1 < n_1 < n$. Therefore, by the induction hypothesis,

n_1 is normal. Hence $n = pn_1$ is the only factorization of n involving the prime p.

Suppose that n is "abnormal" by having a second factorization $n = qn_2$ where q is the least prime factor of the second factorization. Then $q > p$ and n_2 is not divisible by p, for n has only one factorization involving p. Furthermore, $n_2 > 1$, since n is composite.

Consider $m = n - pn_2 = (q - p)n_2 = p(n_1 - n_2)$.

Since $q > p$ and $n_2 > 1$, it follows that $1 < m < n$. Therefore, by the induction hypothesis, m must be normal. Hence p, being a prime divisor of m, must divide either $q - p$ or n_2.

But if p divides $q - p$, then p must divide q, contradicting the fact that q is a prime and $q > p$. Furthermore, p does not divide n_2, since the factorization $n = qn_2$ does not involve p.

This contradiction shows that n must be normal.

From (I), (II), and **L.1** we conclude that M contains all integers n for which $n \geqslant 2$, and the fundamental theorem is established.

EXERCISES

For EXS. **8.1**, **8.2**, and **8.3**, use the following data:
   (a) $a = 2625$, $b = 2205$;   (b) $a = 8277$, $b = 9548$;
   (c) $a = 5040$, $b = 15092$;   (d) $a = 24633$, $b = 15453$.

8.1.   Find the standard representations for a and b.

8.2.   Find (a, b) and $[a, b]$ using the P- and Q-forms in **8.3** and **8.4**.

8.3.   Find (a, b) by the Euclid algorithm and then find $[a, b]$ from the identity $md = ab$ in **8.4**.

8.4.   Using the P- and Q-forms in **8.3** and **8.4** prove that $ab = (a, b)[a, b]$.

8.5.   Prove the corollary in **8.1**, using induction on $n \geqslant 2$.

8.6.   Prove that $[a, b] = ab$ if and only if a and b are relatively prime.

8.7.   Show that $m = [a, b]$ is unique only up to a unit factor.

8.8.   Prove that $[ka, kb] = k[a, b]$.

8.9.   Extend the definition of **8.4** to the case of the least common multiple $m = [a, b, c]$ of three given integers and prove that $m = [a, b, c] = [[a, b], c]$.

8.10.   Produce examples to show that $(a, b, c)[a, b, c]$ can be less than or equal to abc.

8.11.   Show that $(a, b, c)[a, b, c]$ cannot be greater than abc.

8.12.   Show that $(a, b, c)[a, b, c] = abc$ if and only if a, b, c are relatively prime *in pairs*.

8.13.   Use the maximum and minimum exponent discussion in **8.3** and **8.4** to show (a) $([a, b], c) = [(a, c), (b, c)]$; (b) $[(a, b), c] = [(a, c), [b, c]]$.

8.14.   Use EX. **8.13** and induction on k to show
   (a) $([m_1, \ldots, m_{k-1}], m_k) = [(m_1, m_k), \ldots, (m_{k-1}, m_k)]$;
   (b) $[(m_1, \ldots, m_{k-1}), m_k] = ([m_1, m_k], \ldots, [m_{k-1}, m_k])$.

8.15. Discuss the principle of "multiplicative induction" which follows. "Let M be a set of positive integers n for which a proposition $P(n)$ is true. If (I) M contains 1 and (II) if M contains n, then M contains $n' = np$ for every prime p; then M contains every positive integer." [Hint: Apply the fundamental theorem. For examples the proof of (II) will usually fall into two cases where $(n, p) = 1$ and $(n, p) = p$.]

CHAPTER 9

Prime and composite integers

9.1. Some questions

Motivated by the fundamental theorem discussed in the previous lesson,
it is natural for us to ask questions like the following:

(*1*) How can one prepare a list of prime and composite integers
which are $\leqslant n$, where n is a given integer?

(*2*) How can one determine whether a given integer n is prime or
composite?

(*3*) Are there infinitely many distinct primes?

The answer to the last question being "Yes," we then ask:

(*4*) Is it possible to give a formula for the nth prime?

(*5*) Is it possible to find a polynomial $f(x)$ which will represent only
primes for all integral values of x?

(*6*) Are there infinitely many "prime twins," i.e., pairs of integers,
k and $k + 2$, both of which are primes?

(*7*) Are there arbitrarily long sequences of integers, all of which are
composite?

54

9.2. The sieve of Eratosthenes

Of ancient origin is the device of preparing a list of prime numbers less than a given limit by writing down all the integers up to that limit and then in a systematic way eliminating all the composite integers. One such device is ascribed to Eratosthenes (276–194 B.C.).

For example, with a limit of $n = 100$, we first set down a list of the integers from 2 to 100. Recognizing that 2 is a prime, but that all proper multiples of 2 are composite, we cross out $4, 6, 8, \ldots, 100$. The next number not crossed out is 3, which must be a prime for the only possible proper factor is 2, and 3 is not a multiple of 2 else it would have been crossed out. Recognizing that all proper multiples of 3 are composite, we cross out $6, 9, 12, \ldots, 99$—although it is not actually necessary to cross out 6, 12, $18, \ldots, 96$ again, since they are already crossed out, being multiples of 2. The next number not crossed out is 5; this number must be a prime, for if it were composite, it would have to have as a proper factor a prime less than 5, namely, either 2 or 3; but since 5 is not crossed out, it is not a multiple of 2 or 3. Crossing out all multiples of 5, not previously crossed out, namely: 25, 35, 55, 65, 85, 95, we find, by the same reasoning as before, that the next number not crossed out must be a prime; it is 7. The only multiples of 7, not previously crossed out, are 49, 77, 91, and these we now cancel. Now, unless we have been analyzing the sieve process carefully, we are due for a surprise—*all* the *remaining* numbers which have survived the sieve are *primes*! The sieve appears as follows:

```
 2  3  4  5  6  7  8  9 10 11 12 13 14 15 16 17 18 19 20
21 22 23 24 25 26 27 28 29 30 31 32 33 34 35 36 37 38 39 40
41 42 43 44 45 46 47 48 49 50 51 52 53 54 55 56 57 58 59 60
61 62 63 64 65 66 67 68 69 70 71 72 73 74 75 76 77 78 79 80
81 82 83 84 85 86 87 88 89 90 91 92 93 94 95 96 97 98 99 100
```

We are always sure to reach the end of the sieve process when we have crossed out the proper multiples of p' where p' is the largest prime such that $p' \leqslant \sqrt{n}$. This follows because if $s = ab$ is composite at least one (and in fact usually just one) of the factors a and b must be $\leqslant \sqrt{s}$; otherwise if $a > \sqrt{s}$ and $b > \sqrt{s}$, we would find $s = ab > (\sqrt{s})^2 = s$, an obvious contradiction. Hence if s is not crossed out when the proper multiples of p' (and of all the smaller primes) have been eliminated, then s must be a prime. For not having been crossed out in this or any of the previous steps, s can have no nonunit factor $\leqslant \sqrt{n}$; and since $s \leqslant n$, s can have no nonunit factor $\leqslant \sqrt{s}$; but as we have just demonstrated above, such an s cannot be composite.

Thus one answer to questions (*1*) and (*2*) has been provided. It is, of course, not too satisfactory an answer. For example, if we let the function $\pi(x)$ indicate the number of positive prime integers less than or equal to x, then our answer to (*1*) demands the making of $\pi(\sqrt{n})$ sieving steps and our answer to (*2*) demands perhaps the making of as many as $\pi(\sqrt{n})$ divisibility tests. Thus to prove that a number like $2^{127} - 1$ is a prime, would not be feasible by this method.

In general, no really satisfactory test has been found to answer the question (2) whether a given integer is prime or composite, but in the course of this book, we will point out various criteria which give impractical complete answers (like the above sieve process) or incomplete practical answers.

Essentially by the sieve method, but also with the aid of other theorems and, in recent years, with the aid of advanced mechanical computers, various mathematicians have prepared extensive tables of primes and of factors. The tables in the usual handbooks will serve for ordinary problems. For more extended numerical investigations, the student should become acquainted with the work of D. N. Lehmer:

> *Factor table for the first ten millions containing the smallest factor of every number not divisible by 2, 3, 5 and 7 between the limits 0 and 10,017,000.* Carnegie Institution of Washington Publication 105, 1909.
>
> *List of prime numbers from 1 to 10,006,721.* Carnegie Institution of Washington Publication 165, 1914.

Useful as they are, such tables are, of course, inadequate to handle problems like the one proposed above concerning

$$2^{127} - 1 = 170, 141, 183, 460, 469, 231, 731, 687, 303, 715, 884, 105, 727$$

for this number is considerably beyond the range of existing tables. Yet by clever devices, Lucas was able to show in 1876 that this number (known as M_{127}) is indeed a prime, and until recent years it remained the largest number known to be a prime (the student should compare this remark with the theorem of the next section which will show the *existence* of infinitely many primes).

9.3. The number of primes is infinite

For the theorem used as the title of this section and providing the answer to question (*3*), many, many proofs have been given, some simple, some erudite. We will present three of reasonable simplicity.

Proof 1 using $p! + 1$. If we recall the definition of $n!$ (see EX. **2.12**), then it is especially easy to describe Euclid's proof that there are infinitely many distinct primes. For suppose that the prime p is the largest prime. We shall show that this supposition is false by studying the number $M = p! + 1 = (1 \cdot 2 \cdot 3 \ldots p) + 1$. Evidently M is not divisible by any of the numbers $2, 3, 4, \ldots, p$ because there is a remainder 1 in each of these cases; hence M is not divisible by any prime $\leqslant p$. However, by the fundamental theorem in **8.2**, M is either (A) itself a prime or (B) is a product of primes. In either case we see that there must exist a prime larger than the prime p. Hence there is no largest prime p. Hence there must be infinitely many distinct primes.

In the preceding proof the student is cautioned to note the possibility of either (A) or (B). For example, $3! + 1 = 7$, a prime; but $5! + 1 = 121$, a composite number. However, 121 is the square of 11 and 11 is a prime larger than 5, so the proof is as correct in this case as in the former. In neither case is the prime uncovered by the proof necessarily the *next* prime, witness the two examples just given.

Proof 2 using integers of the form $6x - 1$. We can show that there are infinitely many primes among the integers of the arithmetic progression $A: 5, 11, 17, 23, 29, 35, \ldots$, the general form for an integer of this sequence being $6x - 1$. For if we suppose that $P_1, P_2, \ldots, P_k$ are the first k primes belonging to A, arranged in natural order, then we can prove the existence of a still larger prime belonging to A. Consider the integer

$$M = 6P_1P_2 \ldots P_k - 1.$$

Consider the standard form of M as in **8.2**. Since M is odd and not a multiple of 3, it follows that all the prime factors of M are of the form $6x + 1$ or $6x - 1$, for there are no odd primes > 3 of the form $6x \pm 3$, all of these latter numbers (except 3) being obviously composite. However, the product of any number of primes of the form $6x + 1$ is again a number of the form $6x + 1$. In order for M to have the form $6x - 1$, as it does, M must have *at least one* prime factor p of the form $6x - 1$. However, this prime p must be larger than P_k, because none of $P_1, P_2, \ldots, P_k$ is a factor of M, since each of these when tried as a factor leaves a remainder of -1. Hence P_k is not the largest prime in A, and A must contain infinitely many primes. The result just given is a special case of the celebrated theorem of Dirichlet that if a and b are given *relatively prime* integers, then the arithmetic progression made up of all integers of the type $ax + b$ contains infinitely many primes (see Dickson, *Modern Elementary Theory of Numbers*).

Proof 3 using generalized Fermat numbers. Let a be any fixed positive integer with $a \geqslant 2$. Then if $a^s + 1$ is a prime, it is necessary, but not sufficient, that s have the form $s = 2^z$. To prove this remark we need to observe that if q is odd, and $q > 1$, then $a^q + 1$ has the nontrivial factor

$a + 1$ and $a^{2^z q} + 1$ has the nontrivial factor $a^{2^z} + 1$. Both of these results follow by letting $q = 2n + 1$ and $r = a$ or $r = a^{2^z}$ in the identity which follows:

$$r^{2n+1} + 1 = (r + 1)(r^{2n} - r^{2n-1} + \cdots + r^2 - r + 1).$$

This last relation may be established by induction on n (see EX. **9.5**).

Hence if looking for primes of the form $a^s + 1$, we need examine only the numbers $F_m = a^{2^m} + 1$, which we shall describe as generalized Fermat numbers, in memory of an incorrect but provocative conjecture of Fermat, who believed in the case when $a = 2$ that all the numbers F_m were primes (however, a hundred years later Euler showed that $F_5 = 2^{32} + 1$ is composite).

We shall show, for each a, that there are infinitely many distinct primes to be found *among the factors* of the F_m. Our method is to show that *any two* members F_m and F_n of the sequence of generalized Fermat numbers going with a fixed a, *have at most a prime factor 2 in common*, for then the infinite sequence of F_m must have an infinite number of distinct primes appearing as prime factors.

By induction on $m \geqslant 1$ we shall show that

(9.1) $F_m - 2 = (a - 1)F_0 F_1 \ldots F_{m-1}.$

(I) When $m = 1$, we have $F_1 - 2 = a^2 - 1 = (a - 1)(a + 1) = (a - 1)F_0.$

(II) We assume (9.1) is correct for the case m and consider

$$F_{m+1} - 2 = (a^{2^m})^2 - 1 = (a^{2^m} - 1)(a^{2^m} + 1) = (F_m - 2)F_m.$$

Applying the induction hypothesis (9.1) for the case m, we find

$$F_{m+1} - 2 = (a - 1)F_0 F_1 \ldots F_{m-1} F_m.$$

From (I), (II), and **L.2** the proof of (9.1) is complete.

From the identity (9.1) it follows that $(F_n, F_m - 2) = F_n$ for $n = 0, 1, \ldots, m - 1$. For any such n let $d = (F_n, F_m)$. Since d divides F_n, it follows that d divides $F_m - 2$; but since d also divides F_m, then d can divide $F_m - 2$ only if d divides 2. If a is even, each F_i is odd and hence $d = 1$; but if a is odd, each F_i is even and hence $d = 2$. This completes the proof.

9.4.   Distribution of the primes

All the tables and all the known theorems indicate that the primes occur in a very irregular way within the sequence of all integers. For example, as far as any tables have been extended there always occur, now and again, "prime twins," i.e., a pair of successive odd integers x and $x + 2$, both of which are primes, such as 101 and 103, 107 and 109, 137 and 139, etc. But as yet no complete answer is available to question (6) as to whether there are infinitely many prime twins.

Question (7) is an easier one with a positive answer, for it can be shown that there are arbitrarily long sequences of integers all of which are composite. Thus if given the integer n, we have but to consider the n numbers running from $(n + 1)! + 2$ to $(n + 1)! + n + 1$ to have at hand a sequence of n successive, composite integers. However, sequences of n composite numbers usually occur much earlier in the tables; for example, there are 13 composite numbers from 114 to 126.

Many amateur mathematicians have sought formulas which would answer question (4) and show directly what integer is the nth prime; or which would show the $n + 1$ prime, if one knew the nth prime. Most professional mathematicians who have worked on this problem say that the weight of evidence is to the effect that no such formulas can be found. Perhaps the greatest progress has been made in the study of the function $\pi(x)$, giving the number of primes less than or equal to x. Of course, if the exact form of $\pi(x)$ were known, the previous problems could be answered at once. But the progress of which we speak is of a different kind and belongs to what might be called the advanced theory of numbers, where analytic methods based on infinite series and various integrals of the calculus have made it possible to estimate the value of $\pi(x)$ for "sufficiently large" values of x.†

Of a somewhat different, but still rather fruitless, nature is the search for formulas, like Fermat's incorrect one, which will yield only primes, even if they won't give all the primes. The person who first studied the function $f(x) = x^2 - x + 41$ must have been excited as he substituted $x = 1, 2, \ldots, 40$ to find that he obtained forty primes. Had he been a laboratory scientist, he might have shouted "Eureka!" But being only a mathematician, he substituted $x = 41$, and then went out for some coffee.

Of a similar exciting and then disappointing nature is the function $f(x) = x^2 - 79x + 1601$.

In view of these examples it may be of interest to answer question (5) in a definitely negative way and to prove that a polynomial $f(x)$ which is not a constant and which has integer coefficients cannot be prime for all integral values of x, and is composite for infinitely many integral values of x. The proof demands only a little familiarity with the properties of polynomials.

Since $f(x)$ is not a constant, $|f(k)| > 1$, for some integer k. Set $y = f(k)$ and consider $f(ty + k)$. There are several ways of showing that $f(ty + k)$

---

† For example, see Trygve Nagell, *Introduction to Number Theory*, Chapter VIII. New York, Wiley, 1951.

$= yQ + f(k)$, where Q is a polynomial in t, y, k with integer coefficients (see EX. **9.9**). Hence $f(ty + k) = y(Q + 1)$ is divisible by $y = f(k)$ for all values of t. Since $f(x)$ is not a constant, $f(ty + k)$ increases in absolute value for t sufficiently large; therefore, for such sufficiently large values of t, the complementary factor $Q + 1$ is not a unit, and hence $f(ty + k)$ is composite. Since $ty + k$ becomes arbitrarily large with t, the latter having, say, the same sign as y, it follows that $f(x)$ fails to represent just primes in an infinity of cases and in fact for all x of the form $x = ty + k$ when t is sufficiently large.

EXERCISES

9.1. Show that $\pi(\sqrt{210}) = 6$, listing the six primes concerned.

9.2. Apply the sieve process to only the interval 190 to 210 (recall that just $\pi(\sqrt{210})$ steps are required) and find all primes and all prime twins in this interval.

9.3. Modify Euclid's proof that there are infinitely many primes by supposing the kth prime to be the largest and using $M = (p_1 p_2 \ldots p_k) + 1$, where $p_1, p_2, \ldots, p_k$ are the first k primes, to arrive at a contradiction.

9.4. By a slight variation of *Proof 2* in **9.3**, show that there are infinitely many primes in the arithmetic progression 3, 7, 11, 15, ... of integers of the form $4x - 1$.

9.5. By induction on n, prove that
$$r^{2n+1} + 1 = (r + 1)(1 - r + r^2 - \cdots + r^{2n}).$$

9.6. Prove that $a^s - 1$ is composite if $a > 2$ and $s > 1$ (see EX. **2.4**).

9.7. Prove that $2^s - 1$ is composite if s is composite (see EX. **2.4**).

9.8. Show that there can be no prime triplets, i.e., three successive odd integers, each a prime, except 3, 5, 7.

9.9. If $f(x) = a_0 + a_1 x + \cdots + a_n x^n$ with integer coefficients, use EX. **2.12** to show that $f(ty + k) = yQ + f(k)$ where Q is a polynomial in t, y, k having integer coefficients.

9.10. Give a different proof of EX. **9.9**, using the division algorithm for polynomials with y as the divisor and R, free from y, as the remainder; then set $y = 0$ to show $R = f(k)$.

9.11. Illustrate EX. **9.9** when $f(x) = x^2 - 79x + 1601$, showing that $Q = t(ty + 2k - 79)$. With $k = 1$, $y = f(1)$, $t = 1$, show that $f(1524) = 1523 \cdot 1447$.

9.12. A sieve for odd numbers, Consider the set C of all numbers $C(r, s) = 2rs + r + s$, where r and s are positive integers. Prove that for $K > 0$ an odd number $p = 2K + 1$ is a prime if and only if K is not in the set C. (For convenience the numbers of C may be arranged in rows and columns; the elements of the rth row are then the terms of an arithmetic progression with first term $3r + 1$ and common difference $2r + 1$.)

9.13. Using the notation of EX. **9.3**, show that the $p_{k+1} - 2$ integers following M are composite.

9.14. In a dozen different ways show that there are infinitely many composite numbers. [For example, consider $\{a^k, a \geqslant 2, k \geqslant 2\}$; or $\{2k, k \geqslant 2\}$; or $\{2p, \text{ where } p \text{ is prime}\}$; or the positive answer to question (7); or the behavior of $f(ty + k)$ in **9.4**.]

9.15. What is the maximum value of n for which $\pi(\sqrt{n}) = 6$?

CHAPTER 10

The number-theoretic functions
$\tau(n)$ and $\sigma(n)$

10.1. $\tau(n)$, the number of divisors of n

Let us seek a function $\tau(n)$ to give the *number* of positive integer divisors of any given positive integer n. As we shall discover, such a function must be of a very different character from the functions usually studied in algebra or analysis, for it depends in a critical way not only upon the value of n, but also upon the standard representation of n, as in **8.2**, and the standard representation changes radically as we pass from n to $n + 1$. Hence we shall describe $\tau(n)$, and any other function whose range depends upon the standard form of n, as a *number-theoretic* function, the adjective intended to emphasize the special nature of the function.

If n is written in standard form as

$$n = p_1^{a_1} p_2^{a_2} \ldots p_k^{a_k}$$

then all the positive integer divisors of n are given, without repetition, by the form

$$d = p_1^{b_1} p_2^{b_2} \ldots p_k^{b_k}$$

where for each value of i, the b_i runs independently through the following range of values: $b_i = 0, 1, 2, \ldots, a_i$.

Now, by a well-known combinatorial principle, it follows that if b_1 can be chosen in $a_1 + 1$ ways, if b_2 can be chosen in $a_2 + 1$ ways, ..., and if b_k can be chosen in $a_k + 1$ ways, then $b_1, b_2, \ldots, b_k$ all together can be selected in a number of ways given by the product $(a_1 + 1)(a_2 + 1)\ldots(a_k + 1)$.

Hence we find that the number $\tau(n)$ of positive integer divisors of n is given exactly by

$$\tau(n) = (a_1 + 1)(a_2 + 1)\ldots(a_k + 1).$$

[This covers all cases where $n > 1$, see **8.2**, and it is easy to confirm that $\tau(1) = 1$.]

For example, $2520 = 2^3 \cdot 3^2 \cdot 5 \cdot 7$, hence

$$\tau(2520) = (3 + 1)(2 + 1)(1 + 1)(1 + 1) = 48,$$

so 2520 has exactly 48 distinct positive integer divisors.

10.2. $\sigma(n)$, the sum of the divisors of n

It is clear from the preceding discussion that the *sum* $\sigma(n)$ of all the distinct positive integer divisors of a given positive integer $n > 1$ is given by the following product:

$$\sigma(n) = (1 + p_1 + p_1{}^2 + \cdots + p_1{}^{a_1})$$
$$(1 + p_2 + \cdots + p_2{}^{a_2})\cdots(1 + p_k + \cdots + p_k{}^{a_k})$$

because in this product each of the divisors d of n, described in the previous section, appears once and only once as a summand, when the product has been expanded.

(When $n = 1$, we see directly that $\sigma(1) = 1$.)

With the aid of EX. **2.4**, inasmuch as each $p_i > 1$, we find that $\sigma(n)$ can also be written in the following form:

$$\sigma(n) = \frac{p_1{}^{a_1 + 1} - 1}{p_1 - 1} \frac{p_2{}^{a_2 + 1} - 1}{p_2 - 1} \cdots \frac{p_k{}^{a_k + 1} - 1}{p_k - 1}.$$

For example, $2520 = 2^3 \cdot 3^2 \cdot 5 \cdot 7$, hence we find that

$$\sigma(2520) = \frac{2^4 - 1}{2 - 1} \frac{3^3 - 1}{3 - 1} \frac{5^2 - 1}{5 - 1} \frac{7^2 - 1}{7 - 1} = 15 \cdot 13 \cdot 6 \cdot 8 = 9360,$$

so the sum of all the positive integer divisors of 2520 is exactly 9360.

10.3.   Perfect numbers

Number mysticism has played an important part in the history of the theory of numbers. One vestige of the influence of numerology is in the use of the adjectives *deficient*, *perfect*, and *abundant* to describe integers for which $\sigma(n) < 2n$, $\sigma(n) = 2n$, and $\sigma(n) > 2n$, respectively.

A rather fascinating, but unfinished, chapter of the theory concerns the determination of all perfect numbers: the first part concerns the discovery of all *even* perfect numbers with a creditable part by Euler and a doubtful portion by Mersenne; the second, unfinished part concerns the as yet unsolved problem as to whether there are any *odd* perfect numbers.

Let $n = 2^{k-1}A$ be an even perfect number, $k \geqslant 2$ and A odd. By definition we must have $\sigma(n) = 2n$ or $\sigma(2^{k-1}A) = 2^k A$. Since $(2^{k-1}, A) = 1$, we may apply EX. **10.2** to see that $\sigma(2^{k-1}A) = \sigma(2^{k-1})\sigma(A)$. By the formula in **10.2**, we know that $\sigma(2^{k-1}) = 2^k - 1$, hence we arrive at the following condition:

$$(2^k - 1)\sigma(A) = 2^k A.$$

Let us write $\sigma(A) = A + X$, where X is the sum of all the positive divisors of A which are less than A. Then the condition displayed above reduces to the form $(2^k - 1)X = A$. This implies that X is a divisor of A; moreover, since $k \geqslant 2$, X is less than A; thus X, which is supposed to be the sum of all, divisors of A less than A, must include X itself. But $X = X + Y$ implies $Y = 0$, so A has *only one* divisor X less than A; however, the only integers with this property are primes; therefore A is an odd prime, $X = 1$, and A must have the form $2^k - 1$. We have thus arrived at Euler's conclusion: the only possible even perfect numbers must have the form $n = 2^{k-1}p$ where $p = 2^k - 1$ is an odd prime.

Conversely, to complete the argument, we must check that every such number *is* a perfect number; but this check is very easy, for by section **10.2** we find

$$\sigma(n) = \sigma(2^{k-1}p) = (2^k - 1)(p + 1) = p2^k = 2n.$$

The result just given suggests a search for all primes of the form $M_k = 2^k - 1$, since each prime so discovered will provide a corresponding perfect number $P_k = 2^{k-1}M_k$. The study of numbers of the type M_k is known as the study of *Mersenne numbers* after Mersenne (1588–1648) who made a number of correct and several incorrect statements about which ones of these numbers are composite and which prime. As EX. **9.7** shows, M_k is composite if k is composite, hence the search for Mersenne primes (and for even perfect numbers) is narrowed to the case where k is prime. The simplest cases are as follows:

$$M_2 = 3, P_2 = 6; \quad M_3 = 7, P_3 = 28;$$
$$M_5 = 31, P_5 = 496; \quad M_7 = 127, P_7 = 8128.$$

The next Mersenne primes are M_{13}, M_{17}, M_{19}, M_{31}, M_{61}, M_{89}, M_{107}, and M_{127}. Concerning the last of these we have already made some remarks at the close of **9.2**.

The best results about odd perfect numbers are of the type that if there are any such numbers they must have more than a certain number of distinct prime factors. Imperfect though such results may be, they are yet sufficient to indicate that if any odd perfect numbers exist they will be large numbers and not found by mere guesswork.

EXERCISES

10.1. Compute $\tau(4950)$ and $\sigma(4950)$.

10.2. Assuming the formulas in **10.1** and **10.2**, prove that $\tau(ab) = \tau(a)\tau(b)$ and $\sigma(ab) = \sigma(a)\sigma(b)$ whenever $(a, b) = 1$.

10.3. Show $\tau(n)$ is odd if and only if n is a square.

10.4. Show $\tau(x) = q$ has infinitely many solutions x for every given integer $q > 1$. Use **9.3**.

10.5. Make a table of values of $\sigma(p^a) = (p^{a+1} - 1)/(p - 1)$ where p is a prime and $\sigma(p^a) < 100$.

10.6. Find all solutions of $\sigma(x) = 72$. Use EX. **10.5**.

10.7. Let n be called *multipliperfect* if $\sigma(n) = kn$, where k is an integer with $k \geqslant 3$. Prove that $n = 120$ and $n = 672$ are multipliperfect numbers.

10.8. Use the definition in EX. **10.7** and show that $n = 14,182,439,040$ is a multipliperfect number. (Descartes.)

10.9. Find a common property of $\sigma(81)$, $\sigma(343)$, $\sigma(400)$.

10.10. Let a pair of positive integers A and B be called *amicable* if $\sigma(A) = A + B = \sigma(B)$. Prove that 220 and 284 are amicable.

10.11. Prove that the *product* of all the positive divisors of n is given by $n^{\tau(n)/2}$. Compare with EX. **10.3**.

It is with mathematics not otherwise than
it is with music, painting or poetry.
—P. J. MOEBIUS

CHAPTER 11

Multiplicative number-theoretic functions

11.1. Multiplicative number-theoretic functions

A number-theoretic function $f(n)$ is defined to be *multiplicative* if and only if $f(ab) = f(a)f(b)$ for all positive integers a, b for which $(a, b) = 1$.

For example, both $\tau(n)$ and $\sigma(n)$ are multiplicative, as may be seen from their formulas developed above, see EX. **10.2**. The functions $f(n) = 1$ and $f(n) = n$ are other simple examples of multiplicative functions.

If $f(n)$ is multiplicative, it follows since $(a, 1) = 1$, that $f(a) = f(a \cdot 1) = f(a)f(1)$ and hence that $f(1) = 1$ provided that $f(a) \neq 0$ for at least one value of a. For $n > 1$ we can apply the fundamental theorem to write n in standard form as $n = p_1^{a_1}p_2^{a_2}\dots p_k^{a_k}$ where the p_i are distinct primes. Since the factors $p_i^{a_i}$ are relatively prime in pairs, it follows that an expression for a function $f(n)$, which is known to be multiplicative, can be found by investigating the value of $f(p^a)$ where p^a is a power of a prime.

Of special interest is the following theorem, which shows how new multiplicative functions may be generated from known multiplicative functions.

Theorem 1: If $f(n)$ is a multiplicative number-theoretic function, then so also is $F(n)$ where $F(n) = \sum f(d)$, summed over all positive divisors d of n.

66

Proof: By definition

$F(a) = \sum f(d)$ summed over the set S of all divisors d of a,

$F(b) = \sum f(d')$ summed over the set S' of all divisors d' of b,

$F(ab) = \sum f(d'')$ summed over the set S'' of all divisors d'' of ab.

Let S^* be the set of all numbers of the form dd' where d ranges over S and d' over S'. The relation $d''k'' = ab$ shows that any prime factor of d'' must divide either a or b, hence d'' has the form $d'' = dd'$ where d divides a and d' divides b. Thus every number in S'' is in S^*. Conversely, every number in S^* is in S'', for from $a = dk$, $b = d'k'$, we find $ab = dd'kk'$, so that dd' is a divisor of ab. However, the sets S'' and S^* are not, in general, identical, for S'' is defined in such a way as to have no duplications, whereas S^* may have duplications.

We can show that S^* has no duplications under the assumption that $(a, b) = 1$. For it is clear that (d, d') divides (a, b), hence if $(a, b) = 1$, then $(d, d') = 1$ for all d in S and all d' in S'. Consequently an equality $dd' = d_1 d_1'$ implies since $(d, d_1') = 1$ that d divides d_1, and since $(d_1, d') = 1$ that d_1 divides d; hence $d = d_1$ and $d' = d_1'$. Thus the factors d and d' of a number of S^* are uniquely determined.

By hypothesis $f(n)$ is multiplicative; under the assumption that $(a, b) = 1$, we have seen that $(d, d') = 1$; combining these remarks we may write $f(d)f(d') = f(dd')$. Under the hypothesis that $(a, b) = 1$, we have identified the sets S^* and S'', so we may write

$$F(a)F(b) = \sum_{S} f(d) \sum_{S'} f(d') = \sum_{S^*} f(dd') = \sum_{S''} f(d'') = F(ab).$$

This is, of course, precisely the requirement which shows $F(n)$ to be multiplicative.

11.2.   Another development of $\tau(n)$ and $\sigma(n)$

As an initial application of Theorem 1 in **11.1** we can develop the formulas for $\tau(n)$ and $\sigma(n)$ in a new way.

We have mentioned above that $f(n) = 1$ is a multiplicative function. This is easy to see since $f(ab) = 1 = 1 \cdot 1 = f(a)f(b)$ for all a, b, including, therefore, the cases when $(a, b) = 1$. By applying the theorem we know that $F(n) = \sum f(d)$ must be multiplicative. However, we see that $\sum f(d) = 1 + 1 + \cdots + 1$ with as many summands as there are positive integral divisors of n; hence $F(n)$ is what we have previously called $\tau(n)$. By this approach we know a priori from Theorem 1 that $\tau(n)$ is multiplicative. Consequently by investigating

$$\tau(p^a) = f(1) + f(p) + f(p^2) + \cdots + f(p^a) = a + 1$$

we are able to conclude that for $n = p_1{}^{a_1}p_2{}^{a_2}\ldots p_k{}^{a_k}$,

$$\tau(n) = (a_1 + 1)(a_2 + 1)\ldots(a_k + 1).$$

This develops the formula for $\tau(n)$ in a way entirely independent of that given in **10.1**.

Similarly, we may show that $f(n) = n$ is a multiplicative function, for $f(ab) = ab = f(a)f(b)$ for all a, b, including the required cases where $(a, b) = 1$. It follows from Theorem 1 that $F(n) = \sum f(d) = \sum d$ is multiplicative and we see that $F(n)$ is what we have previously called $\sigma(n)$. By this approach we know a priori that $\sigma(n)$ is multiplicative. We therefore investigate

$$\sigma(p^a) = f(1) + f(p) + f(p^2) + \cdots + f(p^a)$$
$$= 1 + p + p^2 + \cdots + p^a = \frac{(p^{a+1} - 1)}{(p - 1)}$$

and conclude that for $n = p_1{}^{a_1}p_2{}^{a_2}\ldots p_k{}^{a_k}$,

$$\sigma(n) = \frac{p_1{}^{a_1+1} - 1}{p_1 - 1}\frac{p_2{}^{a_2+1} - 1}{p_2 - 1} \cdots \frac{p_k{}^{a_k+1} - 1}{p_k - 1}.$$

which agrees with the result established by different reasoning in **10.2**.

11.3.   The Moebius function, $\mu(n)$

If $n > 1$ is written in standard form as $n = p_1{}^{a_1}p_2{}^{a_2}\ldots p_k{}^{a_k}$, where each p_i is a prime, $1 < p_1 < p_2 < \cdots < p_k$, and $a_i \geqslant 1$, define the Moebius function $\mu(n)$ as follows:

if any $a_i > 1$, define $\mu(n) = 0$;   if every $a_i = 1$, define $\mu(n) = (-1)^k$.

For $n = 1$, define $\mu(1) = 1$.

Theorem 2:   The Moebius function $\mu(n)$ is multiplicative.

Proof: If $a = 1$, then $\mu(ab) = \mu(b) = 1\cdot\mu(b) = \mu(a)\mu(b)$. If $a > 1$ and $b > 1$ and if $(a, b) = 1$, then the standard form for ab, except for order, can be obtained by juxtaposing a and b, so that we have, say, $ab = p_1{}^{a_1}\ldots p_k{}^{a_k}q_1{}^{b_1}\ldots q_s{}^{b_s}$ with the p's distinct from the q's. If $\mu(ab) = 0$, either some $a_i > 1$ or some $b_i > 1$.

In the first case, say, $\mu(a) = 0$, thus $\mu(a)\mu(b) = 0 = \mu(ab)$; and similarly in the second case, when $\mu(b) = 0$. If $\mu(ab) \neq 0$, then every $a_i = 1$ and every $b_i = 1$. Consequently, $\mu(a) = (-1)^k$ and $\mu(b) = (-1)^s$.

Thus $\mu(a)\mu(b) = (-1)^k(-1)^s = (-1)^{k+s} = \mu(ab)$, since $(a, b) = 1$ implies the p's are distinct from the q's. In every case for which $(a, b) = 1$, it has been shown that $\mu(ab) = \mu(a)\mu(b)$; hence $\mu(n)$ is multiplicative.

Corollary 2.1: If $G(n) = \sum \mu(d)$, summed over all the positive divisors of n, then $G(n)$ is multiplicative and $G(n) = 0$ when $n > 1$.

Proof: Since we have just shown that $\mu(n)$ is multiplicative, by Theorem 1 in **11.1** we know that $G(n)$ is multiplicative. It follows that $G(1) = 1$ and that $G(n)$ for $n > 1$ can be found by first evaluating $G(p^a)$ for any prime p. But in $G(p^a) = \mu(1) + \mu(p) + \mu(p^2) + \cdots + \mu(p^a)$ we have $\mu(p^i) = 0$ when $i > 1$, so the first two summands determine the complete value. Since $\mu(1) = 1$ and $\mu(p) = -1$, we find $G(p^a) = 0$ when $a \geqslant 1$. Hence $G(n) = G(p_1^{a_1})\ldots G(p_k^{a_k}) = 0$ when $n > 1$.

Theorem 3: If $F(n)$ and $f(n)$ are number-theoretic functions such that (1) for every $n \geqslant 1$, $F(n) = \sum f(d)$, summed over the positive divisors of n, then using the Moebius function $\mu(n)$ and the notation $dd' = n$, we have (2) $f(n) = \sum \mu(d')F(d)$ summed over the positive divisors d of n.

Proof: (A) We shall show by induction on n that the first n equations (1) define $f(n)$ completely and uniquely.

(I) When $n = 1$, equation (1) reduces to $F(1) = f(1)$.

(II) Assume that the first $n - 1$ equations have determined $f(i)$ uniquely for $i = 1, 2, \ldots, n - 1$. Then the equation (1) for the case n may be rewritten as follows: $f(n) = F(n) - \sum' f(d)$, where the sum $\sum'$ is over all divisors d of n satisfying $1 \leqslant d < n$. By the induction hypothesis each $f(d)$ for $1 \leqslant d < n$ is already uniquely determined by the first $n - 1$ equations (1). Hence $f(n)$ is uniquely determined.

From (I), (II), and **L.1** the proof of (A) is complete.

(B) From part (A) we know $f(n)$ exists and is uniquely defined by (1). We shall show that $f(d)$ given by (2) does satisfy (1). Because only a finite number of summands are concerned, we may rearrange the following summations to find

$$\sum f(d) = \sum\left\{\sum \mu(d_1')F(d_1)\right\} = \sum\left\{\sum \mu(d_2)\right\}F(d_1) = \sum G(d_1{}^*)F(d_1).$$

The outer sum in each case is over all the positive divisors d (or d_1) of n, with $dd' = n$ (or $d_1 d_1{}^* = n$). The inner sum in the first instance, in agreement with (2), is over all the positive divisors d_1 of d with $d_1 d_1' = d$. The inner sum in the second instance is over all the positive divisors d_2

of d_1^*; hence the sum in question is exactly $G(d_1^*)$ of the Corollary to Theorem 2.

For example, if $n = 6$, the rearrangement is as follows:

$$
\begin{aligned}
f(1) + f(2) + f(3) + f(6) &= \mu(1)F(1) + \{\mu(1)F(2) + \mu(2)F(1)\} \\
&\quad + \{\mu(1)F(3) + \mu(3)F(1)\} \\
&\quad + \{\mu(1)F(6) + \mu(2)F(3) + \mu(3)F(2) \\
&\quad\quad\quad\quad\quad\quad\quad\quad\quad\quad + \mu(6)F(1)\} \\
&= \{\mu(1) + \mu(2) + \mu(3) + \mu(6)\}F(1) \\
&\quad + \{\mu(1) + \mu(3)\}F(2) + \{\mu(1) + \mu(2)\}F(3) \\
&\quad + \mu(1)F(6) \\
&= G(6)F(1) + G(3)F(2) + G(2)F(3) \\
&\quad + G(1)F(6).
\end{aligned}
$$

Since Corollary 2.1 shows that $G(n) = 0$ when $n > 1$ and that $G(1) = 1$, it follows that $\sum f(d) = G(1)F(n) = F(n)$, so ($I$) is satisfied. This completes the proof of Theorem 3.

Corollary 3.1: In the application of Theorem 3 if $n = p_1^{a_1}\dots p_k^{a_k}$, then

$$
(3) \quad f(n) = F(n) - \sum_1 F\left(\frac{n}{p_{i_1}}\right)
$$
$$
+ \sum_2 F\left(\frac{n}{p_{i_1}p_{i_2}}\right) + \cdots + (-1)^k F\left(\frac{n}{p_1 p_2 \dots p_k}\right).
$$

The typical entry in (3) is $(-1)^r \sum_r F(n/p_{i_1}\dots p_{i_r})$ in which $\sum_r$ is defined for $r = 1, 2, \dots, k$ as a sum over all the ways of selecting r distinct primes from the k distinct prime factors of n.

Proof: We know that $\mu(d') = 0$ if $d' = p_1^{b_1}\dots p_k^{b_k}$ has any $b_i > 1$. Hence in the formula (2) of Theorem 3 wherein $f(n) = \sum \mu(d')F(d)$ the only terms which will not vanish are those in which either $d' = 1$ and $d = n$, or $d' = p_{i_1}\dots p_{i_r}$ and $d = n/d' = n/p_{i_1}\dots p_{i_r}$. In the first case $\mu(1) = 1$, so the term $F(n)$ appears in (2). In the second case $\mu(p_{i_1}\dots p_{i_r}) = (-1)^r$, so the term $(-1)^r F(n/p_{i_1}\dots p_{i_r})$ appears in (2). By collecting together all terms of the same type, using the $\sum_r$ notation, we obtain from (2) the formula (3).

11.4. Definition and formula for Euler's phi-function

The Euler phi-function (sometimes called the *totient* function) is a widely used number-theoretic function, almost always indicated by $\phi(n)$. For

$n = 1$, we define $\phi(1) = 1$, and when $n > 1$, we define $\phi(n)$ to be the *number of positive integers less than n* and *relatively prime* to *n*.

For example, since the only positive integers less than 12 and relatively prime to 12 are 1, 5, 7, 11, it follows that $\phi(12) = 4$. Similarly, $\phi(1) = 1$, $\phi(2) = 1$, $\phi(3) = 2$, $\phi(4) = 2$, $\phi(5) = 4$, $\phi(6) = 2$, etc. But we desire a formula which will allow us to compute the value of $\phi(n)$ directly from the standard form of *n*, without actually listing all the numbers less than *n* and relatively prime to *n*.

In this lesson we shall give two derivations of the formula for $\phi(n)$; in a later lesson we shall give yet another derivation.

For the first derivation we shall begin by stating and proving the theorem which is the correct generalization of the following example:

$$12 = \phi(1) + \phi(2) + \phi(3) + \phi(4) + \phi(6) + \phi(12) = 1 + 1 + 2 + 2 + 2 + 4.$$

Theorem: For any positive integer n, $n = \sum \phi(d)$, where the summation extends over all the positive divisors d of n.

Proof: The theorem is obvious for $n = 1$, since $1 = \phi(1)$. Consider $n > 1$. For every positive integer $x \leqslant n$, $(x, n) = d$, where d is a uniquely determined divisor of *n*. On this basis alone the *n* numbers $1, 2, \ldots, n$ are divided into mutually exclusive *d*-classes. From $(x, n) = d$ we have $x = kd, n = d'd$, with $(k, d') = 1$ and with $k \leqslant d'$ since $x \leqslant n$. The case $k = d'$ is exceptional for from the condition $(k, d') = 1$ this case can arise only when $d' = 1$. Hence in all cases we find that there are exactly $\phi(d')$ choices for k, and hence $\phi(d')$ integers x which belong to the *d*-class. Thus by the use of the *d*-classes we have found $n = \sum \phi(d')$ where $d'd = n$ and the summation is over all divisors d of n. However the set of numbers $\{d'\}$ is simply the set $\{d\}$ in another order, hence we are justified in writing $n = \sum \phi(d') = \sum \phi(d)$ which completes the proof.

Thus in the example given above,

$\phi(12) = 4$ indicates 4 integers in the 1-class: 1, 5, 7, 11;
$\phi(6) = 2$ indicates 2 integers in the 2-class: 2, 10;
$\phi(4) = 2$ indicates 2 integers in the 3-class: 3, 9;
$\phi(3) = 2$ indicates 2 integers in the 4-class: 4, 8;
$\phi(2) = 1$ indicates 1 integer in the 6-class: 6;
$\phi(1) = 1$ indicates 1 integer in the 12-class: 12.

Of course, this theorem is "tailor-made" so that the theorem and corollary in **11.3** may be applied to obtain the following result.

Theorem: If *n* is written in standard form as

$$n = p_1{}^{a_1} p_2{}^{a_2} \ldots p_k{}^{a_k}$$

where each p_i is a prime, $1 < p_1 < p_2 < \cdots < p_k$, and $a_i \geqslant 1$, then

$$\phi(n) = n \left(\frac{p_1 - 1}{p_1}\right)\left(\frac{p_2 - 1}{p_2}\right) \cdots \left(\frac{p_k - 1}{p_k}\right).$$

Proof: We have just shown that $n = \sum \phi(d)$ summed over all the positive divisors of n. We can apply Corollary 3.1, and because $F(n) = n$ is so very simple, we find that (3) becomes

$$\phi(n) = n - \sum_1 \frac{n}{p_{i_1}} + \sum_2 \frac{n}{p_{i_1}p_{i_2}} - \cdots + (-1)^k \frac{n}{p_1 p_2 \cdots p_k}.$$

From each term we can factor n, and then we can rewrite the remaining sum as a product (see EX. **11.7**)

$$\phi(n) = n \left(1 - \frac{1}{p_1}\right)\left(1 - \frac{1}{p_2}\right) \cdots \left(1 - \frac{1}{p_k}\right)$$

which can be converted easily to the form given in the theorem.

For example: since $12 = 2^2 3$, $\phi(12) = 12(1/2)(2/3) = 4$; and since $8316 = 2^2 3^3 7(11)$, it follows that

$$\phi(8316) = 2^2 3^3 7(11)(1/2)(2/3)(6/7)(10/11) = 2^4 3^3 5 = 2160.$$

Interpreting this last example, we know that there are 2160 positive integers less than 8316 and relatively prime to 8316; and we have obtained this figure of 2160 in a way far more satisfactory than mere counting.

11.5.   More about multiplicative functions

The following theorem is both an extension of Theorem 3 and a converse of Theorem 1.

Theorem 4:   If the hypothesis (*1*) for $n \geqslant 1$, $F(n) = \sum f(d)$, summed over all the positive divisors d of n, is supplemented by the hypothesis that $F(n)$ is multiplicative, then $f(n)$ is multiplicative.

Proof: (A) We have already proved in Theorem 3 that $f(n)$ is uniquely defined by the equations (*1*).

(B) Since $F(n)$ is multiplicative, $F(1) = 1$. By (*1*) we have $f(1) = F(1) = 1$.

We shall make an induction proof on $n = ab$, where we assume, of course, that $(a, b) = 1$. The fundamental theorem guarantees that there is such a representation for every positive integer n.

When $(a, b) = 1$, we have shown in **11.1** that the set S'' of all positive divisors d'' of ab is exactly the same as the set S^* formed of integers dd' where d runs over the set S of positive divisors d of a and where d' runs over the set S' of positive divisors d' of b. Furthermore we know $(d, d') = 1$.

(I) When $ab = 1$, then $a = 1 = b$. Since we have noted above that $f(1) = 1$, it follows in this case that $f(ab) = f(a)f(b)$.

(II) The induction hypothesis regarding $n = ab$ with $(a, b) = 1$ will be that $f(dd') = f(d)f(d')$ if $(d, d') = 1$ and $dd' < ab$.

From the hypothesis that $F(n)$ is multiplicative we have $F(a)F(b) = F(ab)$. From (*1*) and the remarks above about the sets S'' and S^* it follows that

$$\sum_S f(d) \sum_{S'} f(d') = \sum_{S''} f(d'') = \sum_{S^*} f(dd').$$

By the induction hypothesis it follows that the expanded product on the left contains, with possibly one exception, exactly the same summands as does the sum on the right. But this forces the remaining terms on each side to be the same, namely, $f(a)f(b) = f(ab)$.

No matter what particular representation $n = ab$ with $(a, b) = 1$ is chosen, arguments (I) and (II) are valid; since there are for each n only a finite number of these representations, it follows that the induction argument is complete and that $f(n)$ is multiplicative.

Corollary 4.1: In the application of Theorem 4, if $n = p_1^{a_1} \ldots p_k^{a_k}$, then

$$(4) \qquad f(n) = (F(p_1^{a_1}) - F(p_1^{a_1 - 1})) \cdots (F(p_k^{a_k}) - F(p_k^{a_k - 1})).$$

Proof: Since Theorem 4 shows that $f(n)$ is multiplicative, it is only necessary to show how to evaluate $f(p^a)$ where p is a prime and $a \geqslant 1$. From (2) in Theorem 3 we know $f(p^a) = \mu(1)F(p^a) + \mu(p)F(p^{a-1})$ because the only divisors of p^a are of the form p^i and $\mu(p^i) = 0$ when $i \geqslant 2$. Furthermore, $\mu(1) = 1$ and $\mu(p) = -1$. Thus $f(p^a) = F(p^a) - F(p^{a-1})$, and (4) is established.

We shall use Corollary 4.1 to obtain an independent development of the formula for $\phi(n)$. The first theorem in **11.4** shows that $n = \sum \phi(d)$ which fits the hypothesis (*1*). The function $F(n) = n$ was shown in **11.2** to be multiplicative. By Theorem 4 it follows that $\phi(n)$ is multiplicative. Since $F(p^a) - F(p^{a-1}) = p^a - p^{a-1} = p^a \left(\dfrac{p-1}{p} \right)$, we may use (4) to write

$$\phi(n) = n \left(\frac{p_1 - 1}{p_1} \right) \cdots \left(\frac{p_k - 1}{p_k} \right).$$

EXERCISES

11.1. Use the theorem in **11.1** and develop a formula for $\tau_1(n) = \sum \tau(d)$, summed over the positive divisors d of n.

11.2. Develop a formula for $\tau_2(n) = \sum \tau_1(d)$, where $\tau_1(n)$ is defined in EX. **11.1**.

11.3. If $n = p_1^{a_1} p_2^{a_2} \ldots p_k^{a_k}$ is in standard form and if s is a fixed integer, define $f(n) = s^k$ for $n > 1$ and $f(1) = 1$. Prove that $f(n)$ is multiplicative.

11.4. Develop a formula for $F(n) = \sum f(d)$ where $f(n)$ is defined in EX. **11.3**.

11.5. Referring to Corollary 3.1 if p, q, and r are distinct primes and $n = p^3 q^2 r$, write out the eight terms on the right side of (3).

11.6. Referring to Corollary 3.1 show that 2^k terms appear on the right side of (3). [Hint: The number of combinations of k objects taken r at a time is given by $\binom{k}{r}$ which appears in EX. **2.12**.]

11.7. By an induction argument on $k \geqslant 1$, justify the identity
$$(1 - x_1)\ldots(1 - x_k)$$
$$= 1 - \sum_1 x_{i_1} + \sum_2 x_{i_1} x_{i_k} - \cdots + (-1)^k x_1 x_2 \ldots x_k.$$

11.8. Show from the formula in **11.4** that $\phi(n)$ is even for $n > 2$.

11.9. Find $\phi(72)$, $\phi(210)$, and $\phi(p^t)$ where p is a prime.

11.10. Show that the *sum* of all integers less than n and relatively prime to n is given by $n\phi(n)/2$ for $n \geqslant 2$.

11.11. Prove that if $(a, b) = 1$, then $\phi(ab) = \phi(a)\phi(b)$, using the formula for $\phi(n)$ in **11.4**.

11.12. Construct a table (46 entries) of all values of $A^k(A - 1) < 5000$ where A is a prime and $k \geqslant 1$.

11.13. Find all solutions of $\phi(n) = 60$, using EX. **11.12**.

11.14. Show that the numbers $a = 242, 244, 246, 248$ form a sequence of four consecutive even numbers such that there are no solutions of $\phi(n) = a$.

11.15. Review **11.2** and apply Theorem 3 to obtain
$$1 = \sum \mu(d')\tau(d) \quad \text{and} \quad n = \sum \mu(d')\sigma(d).$$

Rewrite these formulas in the form (3) and check them with $n = 24$, 27, 30.

CHAPTER 12

The bracket function

12.1.   Definition of the bracket function

With any real number x we may associate a uniquely determined *integer*, called the *integral part of x* and designated $[x]$ which may be read "bracket x," by requiring that $[x]$ be an integer for which

$$[x] \leqslant x < [x] + 1.$$

For example:

$$[14/3] = 4, \ [-7] = -7, \ [\sqrt{10}] = 3,$$
$$[-\sqrt{10}] = -4, \ [\pi] = 3, \ [-\pi] = -4.$$

As a consequence of the definition it follows immediately that

$$x = [x] + \theta \qquad \text{with } 0 \leqslant \theta < 1.$$

For example, the division algorithm $a = qb + r$, $0 \leqslant r < b$, may be rewritten $a/b = q + r/b$, $0 \leqslant r/b < 1$. Since q is an integer and since r/b satisfies the condition required for θ, we have a new way of specifying the quotient in the division algorithm when $b > 0$, namely, $q = [a/b]$.

The following properties of the bracket function may be readily established.

75

B.1: If m is an integer, $[x + m] = [x] + m$.

Proof: From $x = [x] + \theta$, $0 \leqslant \theta < 1$, it follows that $x + m = [x] + m + \theta$; since $[x] + m$ is an integer, **B.1** must hold.

B.2: $[x] + [-x] = 0$, or -1, according as x is, or is not, an integer.

Proof: If x is an integer, $[x] = x$, and $[-x] = -x$, hence $[x] + [-x] = x - x = 0$. If x is not an integer, then

$$x = [x] + \theta, \ 0 < \theta < 1; \ \text{hence} \ -x = -[x] - \theta = -1 - [x] + (1 - \theta)$$

with $0 < 1 - \theta < 1$ and with $-1 - [x]$ an integer. Therefore $[-x] = -1 - [x]$, or otherwise expressed, $[x] + [-x] = -1$.

B.3: $[x + y] \geqslant [x] + [y]$.

Proof: Let $x = [x] + \theta_1$, $0 \leqslant \theta_1 < 1$; $y = [y] + \theta_2$, $0 \leqslant \theta_2 < 1$. Then $x + y = [x] + [y] + \theta_1 + \theta_2$ with $[x] + [y]$ an integer and with $0 \leqslant \theta_1 + \theta_2 < 2$. Either $0 \leqslant \theta_1 + \theta_2 < 1$ and $[x + y] = [x] + [y]$; or $1 \leqslant \theta_1 + \theta_2 < 2$ and $[x + y] = [x] + [y] + 1$. But in either case, **B.3** holds.

B.4: If n is a positive integer, then $[[x]/n] = [x/n]$.

Proof: Let $x = [x] + \theta$, $0 \leqslant \theta < 1$. By the division algorithm find q and r so that $[x] = qn + r$, $0 \leqslant r \leqslant n - 1$. Then $[x]/n = q + r/n$ with q an integer and with $0 \leqslant r/n < 1$; hence $[[x]/n] = q$. But $x/n = (qn + r + \theta)/n = q + (r + \theta)/n$ with q an integer and with $0 \leqslant (r + \theta)/n \leqslant (n - 1 + \theta)/n < 1$; hence $[x/n] = q$. Comparing these two results we find that we have established **B.4**.

12.2. An interesting exercise

For the purpose of the following exercise we shall assume the reader has had some experience with real numbers and knows that these numbers may be divided into two classes: the rational numbers, or ordinary fractions, of the form p/q where p and q are integers with $q \neq 0$; and the irrational numbers which are those real numbers which are not rational, such as $\sqrt{2}$ and π. These concepts are explained in detail in a later chapter.

Exercise: If a and b are positive irrational numbers such that $1/a + 1/b = 1$, then the two series $[an]$ and $[bn]$ for $n = 1, 2, \ldots$ represent *all* positive integers *without repetition*.

For example: If $a = \sqrt{2}$, then $b = 2 + \sqrt{2}$. The a-series begins $[a] = 1$, $[2a] = 2$, $[3a] = 4$, $[4a] = 5$, $[5a] = 7$, $[6a] = 8$, $[7a] = 9$, $[8a] = 11$, etc.; while the b-series begins with $[b] = 3$, $[2b] = 6$, $[3b] = 10$, etc., exactly complementing the a-list.

Proof: Since a and b are positive with $1/a + 1/b = 1$, it follows that both $a > 1$ and $b > 1$.

(A) We shall show that there is *no repetition* of integers in the series $[an]$ and $[bn]$, $n = 1, 2, \ldots$.

(A.1) In the series $[an]$ there is no repetition, for we have

$$[an] < an < a(n + 1) - 1 < [a(n + 1)];$$

the first inequality follows since a and (therefore) an are irrational; the second inequality follows from $1 < a$. Similarly there is no repetition in the series $[bn]$.

(A.2) For all positive integers n and m we can show $[an] \neq [bm]$. For if we suppose the integer $x = [an] = [bm]$, then

$$an - 1 < x < an \quad \text{or} \quad n - 1/a < x/a < n,$$
$$bm - 1 < x < bm \quad \text{or} \quad m - 1/b < x/b < m.$$

Adding the latter inequalities of each line and using $1/a + 1/b = 1$, we find $n + m - 1 < x < n + m$, so that the *integer* x lies between two successive integers, which is an obvious contradiction.

(B) Next we can show that no integer x is omitted in *both* sequences $[an]$ and $[bm]$. For if we suppose x to be such an integer, then there must exist integers n and m such that

$$an < [an] + 1 \leqslant x \leqslant [a(n + 1)] - 1 < a(n + 1) - 1$$

or

$$n < x/a < n + 1 - 1/a;$$

$$bm < [bm] + 1 \leqslant x \leqslant [b(m + 1)] - 1 < b(m + 1) - 1$$

or

$$m < x/b < m + 1 - 1/b.$$

Adding the latter inequalities of each line and using $1/a + 1/b = 1$, we find $n + m < x < n + m + 1$, which is a contradiction.

Establishing (A) and (B) completes the proof of the exercise.

12.3. $\tau(n)$ and the bracket function

The following theorem shows a connection between $\tau(n)$ and the bracket function.

Theorem: For any positive integer n, the following equation holds:

$$\tau(1) + \tau(2) + \cdots + \tau(n) = [n/1] + [n/2] + \cdots + [n/n].$$

Proof: The proof makes use of the interesting device of counting in two different ways the number of solutions in positive integers d of the set of equations

$$dx = 1, \; dx = 2, \; dx = 3, \ldots, \; dx = n.$$

First, consider the set of equations in the order just given. Certainly in the equation $dx = k$, each factor of k leads to a suitable d, and k has exactly $\tau(k)$ factors. As $k = 1, 2, \ldots, n$, we find that the total number of solutions d agrees with the left side of the equation which we are trying to establish.

Secondly, consider the equations with $x = 1, 2, \ldots, n$, and with k restricted to the range $1 \leqslant k \leqslant n$. Then the equations and corresponding solutions may be grouped as follows:

$$
\begin{aligned}
&d1 = k; \; k = 1, 2, \ldots, 1[n/1]; \quad d = 1, 2, \ldots, [n/1]; \\
&d2 = k; \; k = 2, 4, \ldots, 2[n/2]; \quad d = 1, 2, \ldots, [n/2]; \\
&d3 = k; \; k = 3, 6, \ldots, 3[n/3]; \quad d = 1, 2, \ldots, [n/3]; \\
&\cdots \; ; \quad \cdots \qquad\qquad\quad ; \qquad \cdots \qquad\qquad ; \\
&dn = k; \; k = n = \qquad n[n/n]; \quad d = 1 = \qquad [n/n].
\end{aligned}
$$

From this point of view we find that the total number of solutions d agrees with the right side of the initial equation.

For example, let us consider $n = 10$;

$$
\begin{aligned}
\tau(1) + \tau(2) &+ \cdots + \tau(10) \\
&= 1 + 2 + 2 + 3 + 2 + 4 + 2 + 4 + 3 + 4 = 27, \\
[10/1] + [10/2] &+ \cdots + [10/10] \\
&= 10 + 5 + 3 + 2 + 2 + 1 + 1 + 1 + 1 + 1 = 27.
\end{aligned}
$$

12.4. Definition and evaluation of $E(p, n)$

By $E(p, n)$ we mean the exponent of the prime p in the standard form of $n!$.

For example, $E(2, 4) = 3$, $E(3, 4) = 1$, and $E(5, 4) = 0$, because $4! = 1 \cdot 2 \cdot 3 \cdot 4 = 24 = 2^3 3$. But what we desire is a formula for determining with some rapidity the value, for example, of $E(3, 101)$, where it is not practical to begin by actually writing $101!$ in standard form.

Theorem: If $p^k \leqslant n < p^{k+1}$ we may use the bracket function to evaluate

$$(12.1) \qquad E(p, n) = [n/p] + [n/p^2] + \cdots + [n/p^k].$$

Proof: Suppose s is an integer in the range $2 \leqslant s \leqslant n$ and that s is divisible by p^i, but not by p^{i+1}. Then the contribution i of s to $E(p, n)$ is correctly counted by *(12.1)*, for $[n/p^j]$ counts the number of integers less than or equal to n which are multiples of p^j. But s is such a multiple for $j = 1, 2, \ldots, i$ and is counted once in $[n/p]$, once again in $[n/p^2]$, ..., and finally counted once in $[n/p^i]$—a total count of i. Since the maximum value of i is k for any factor s in $n!$, the count provided by *(12.1)* is complete.

For purposes of computation we can improve *(12.1)* by using **B.4** of **12.1**. Let us set $n_i = [n/p^i]$. Then

$$n_{i+1} = [n/p^{i+1}] = [(n/p^i)/p]$$

and by **B.4** we may write

$$n_{i+1} = [[n/p^i]/p] = [n_i/p].$$

From *(12.1)* we have $E(p, n) = n_1 + n_2 + \cdots + n_k$; hence with the aid of the present observations we may write

$$(12.2) \qquad E(p, n) = [n/p] + [n_1/p] + [n_2/p] + \cdots + [n_{k-1}/p],$$

where it is understood that, although by definition $n_i = [n/p^i]$, we shall here use $n_1 = [n/p]$ and $n_{i+1} = [n_i/p]$.

For example, using *(12.1)* we may write

$$E(3, 101) = [101/3] + [101/9] + [101/27] + [101/81]$$
$$= 33 + 11 + 3 + 1 = 48,$$

or using *(12.2)* we may write, recursively,

$$E(3, 101) = [101/3] + [33/3] + [11/3] + [3/3]$$
$$= 33 + 11 + 3 + 1 = 48.$$

12.5. $E(p, n)$ and representation of n to the base p

If n is written in the base p as in Chapter 5, say

$$n = (a_k \ldots a_1 a_0)_p = a_0 + a_1 p + a_2 p^2 + \ldots a_k p^k,$$

it is evident, since each a_i satisfies $0 \leqslant a_i < p$, that the computation of the n_i, defined in the previous section, can be explicitly indicated, as follows:

$$n_1 = [n/p] = a_1 + a_2 p + \cdots + a_k p^{k-1};$$
$$n_2 = [n_1/p] = a_2 + a_3 p + \cdots + a_k p^{k-2}; \ldots;$$
$$n_{k-1} = a_{k-1} + a_k p; \quad n_k = a_k.$$

However, these computations can be avoided because of the following relations:

$$n = n_1 p + a_0; \; n_1 = n_2 p + a_1; \; n_2 = n_3 p + a_2; \; \ldots;$$
$$n_{k-1} = n_k p + a_{k-1}; \; n_k = a_k;$$

for if these equations are added together we find, employing (*12.2*), that

$$n + E(p, n) = pE(p, n) + a_0 + a_1 + \cdots + a_k.$$

If we solve this last equation for $E(p, n)$ we obtain the following useful formula, due to Legendre:

(*12.3*) $E(p, n) = (n - (a_0 + a_1 + \cdots + a_k))/(p - 1).$

For example, since $(101)_{10} = 81 + 2 \cdot 9 + 2 = (10202)_3$, we find with the aid of (*12.3*) that

$$E(3, 101) = (101 - (2 + 0 + 2 + 0 + 1))/(3 - 1) = 96/2 = 48.$$

EXERCISES

12.1. For all real x from -2 to $+2$ draw the graphs of (a) $y = [x]$; (b) $y = [x] + [-x]$; (c) $y = [x]^2$; (d) $y = [x^2]$. From your answer to (a) explain why the bracket-function is sometimes called the *step-function*.

12.2. Illustrate **12.2** when $a = \sqrt{3}$.

12.3. Illustrate **12.3** when $n = 20$.

12.4. Prove that for any positive integer q and any real x

$$[x] + [x + 1/q] + [x + 2/q] + \cdots + [x + (q - 1)/q] = [qx].$$

(Hint: Let $x = [x] + \theta$, $0 \leqslant \theta < 1$, and consider $s = [q\theta] \leqslant q\theta < s + 1$.)

12.5. Use **12.3** to establish that

$$\tau(n) = 1 + \sum ([n/d] - [(n - 1)/d])$$

where the summation runs from $d = 1$ to $d = n - 1$.

12.6. Prove that

$$\tau(n) = [\sqrt{n}] - [\sqrt{n - 1}] + 2 \sum ([n/d] - [(n - 1)/d])$$

where the summation runs from $d = 1$ to $d = [\sqrt{n - 1}]$.

12.7. Whereas $[x]$ represents the "largest integer less than or equal to x," show that $[x + 1/2]$ is a "nearest integer to x."

12.8. Prove that $f(x) = |x - [x + \frac{1}{2}]|$ has the property $f(x + m) = f(x)$ for every integer m.

12.9. For values of $k = 0, 1, 2$, draw the graphs of

$$2^k y_k = |2^k x - [2^k x + \frac{1}{2}]|$$

from $x = 0$ to $x = 2$. Then draw the graph of $y = y_0 + y_1 + y_2$.

12.10. Use (*12.3*) and compute $E(10, 10202)$ with all the given numbers and all computations to the base 3. Check the result with the example following (*12.3*).

12.11. Compute $E(5, 101)$ by each of (*12.1*), (*12.2*), (*12.3*).

12.12. Show that $E(2, n) \geqslant E(5, n)$ for all n.

12.13. Use EX. **12.11** and **12.12** to answer the question: "In how many zeros does 101! end?"

12.14. Compute $E(3, 1001)$ by (*12.2*) and (*12.3*).

12.15. Use **B.3** of **12.1** and (*12.1*) to prove that $(a + b)!/a!b!$ is an integer. Compare with EX. **2.12**.

12.16. Use EX. **12.15** to prove that the product of b consecutive positive integers is divisible by $b!$.

The invention of the symbol ≡ by
Gauss affords a striking example of the
advantage which may be derived from
an appropriate notation and marks an
epoch in the development of the science
of arithmetic.—G. B. MATHEWS

CHAPTER 13

Introduction to the congruence notation

13.1. Definition of congruence modulo m

Let m be a fixed positive integer; then we shall define the integer a to be congruent to the integer b modulo m, written

$$a \equiv b \bmod m$$

and read "a is congruent to b mod m," if and only if

$$a - b = km$$

where k is an integer.

For example:

$$17 \equiv 2 \bmod 5, \text{ because } 17 - 2 = (3)5;$$
$$-8 \equiv 2 \bmod 5, \text{ because } -8 - 2 = (-2)5;$$
$$17 \equiv -8 \bmod 5, \text{ because } 17 - (-8) = (5)5.$$

This notation is due to Gauss, and, as we shall see in this and later chapters, the comment quoted above the chapter head is well justified. Remembering Gauss, we shall denote the following series of theorems about the congruence notation by **G.1**, **G.2**, etc.

G.1: We find $a \equiv b \bmod m$ if and only if a and b have the same remainder R, $0 \leqslant R < m$, when divided by m.

Proof: If $a \equiv b \bmod m$, so that $a - b = km$, with k an integer, and if $b = qm + R$, $0 \leqslant R < m$, then $a = b + km = (q + k)m + R$ has the same remainder as b. Conversely, if $a = Qm + R$, $b = qm + R$, $0 \leqslant R < m$, then $a - b = (Q - q)m$, with $Q - q$ an integer, hence $a \equiv b \bmod m$.

13.2. Congruence modulo *m* is an equivalence relation

Within a mathematical system there may be various relations between the elements of the system. If $a, b, \ldots$ are elements of a mathematical system S, then we say that a relation **E** between the elements, written $a \mathbf{E} b$ and read "*a* is **E** to *b*" or written $a \mathbf{E} b$ and read "*a* is not **E** to *b*," is an *equivalence relation* if and only if **E** satisfies the following requirements:

E.1: **E** is *determinative*: for any two elements a, b in S, either $a \mathbf{E} b$ or $a \mathbf{E} b$, but not both of these.

E.2: **E** is *reflexive*: if a is in S then $a \mathbf{E} a$.

E.3: **E** is *symmetric*: if a and b are in S and if $a \mathbf{E} b$, then $b \mathbf{E} a$.

E.4: **E** is *transitive*: if a, b, and c are in S and if $a \mathbf{E} b$ and $b \mathbf{E} c$, then $a\mathbf{E} c$.

If S is the set of all integers, then one of the most striking examples of an equivalence relation, other than the ordinary equality, is the notion of congruence modulo m.

G.2: Congruence modulo m is an equivalence relation for integers.

Proof: **E.1:** By its very definition congruence is *determinative* for the difference $a - b$ of any two given integers a and b either is or is not a multiple of m; or we may refer to **G.1** and comment that either a and b do have the same remainder R, $0 \leqslant R < m$, when divided by m, or they do not have the same remainder.

E.2: Congruence is *reflexive* because for every integer a we have $a - a = (0)m$, and 0 is an integer, hence $a \equiv a \bmod m$.

E.3: Congruence is *symmetric*, for if $a \equiv m \bmod m$ so that $a - b = km$, where k is an integer, then $b - a = (-k)m$ with $-k$ an integer, hence $b \equiv a \bmod m$.

E.4: Congruence is *transitive*, because $a \equiv b$, and $b \equiv c \bmod m$ imply $a - b = km$ and $b - c = Km$, where k and K are integers; then by addition we find $a - c = (k + K)m$ with $k + K$ an integer, hence $a \equiv c \bmod m$.

Every equivalence relation of a set divides the set into mutually exclusive classes of "equal" elements. In this case we see, from **G.1** and **G.2**, that under congruence modulo m, all the integers are divided into exactly m classes, corresponding to the possible remainders $R = 0, 1, \ldots,$ $m - 1$, and we see that each "R-class" contains infinitely many integers, namely, $qm + R$, where $q = 0, \pm 1, \pm 2, \ldots$.

These classes are commonly called *residue classes*, where we are using the word "residue" in the same sense as "remainder." Any set of m numbers, one and only one from each residue class, constitutes a *complete residue system*.

13.3.   Addition and multiplication of residue classes

We shall define the "sum" of the a-class, modulo m, and the b-class, mod m, to be the residue class containing $a + b$. Similarly, we define the "product" of the a-class and the b-class, mod m, to be the class containing ab.

When in a mathematical system a new operation is defined, there are two of its properties to be investigated and established before the new operation can be regarded as very useful.

First we must ask if the operation is "closed" by which we mean to require that the result of the operation be an element of the system.

Secondly we must check whether the operation is "well defined" by which we mean to refer to the particular equivalence relation **E** being used in the system and to require that if each of the elements on which the operation is performed be replaced by an equivalent element and the operation be performed anew, then the second result must be equivalent to the first result.

For the operations with residue classes which we have defined above, it is clear that both operations are "closed"—the result in each case being a certain residue class. It is now necessary to show that these operations are "well defined."

Thus if a is replaced by an "equal" element A: i.e., any member of the a-class; and if b is replaced by an "equal" element B: i.e., any member of the b-class, it is necessary to show that the definitions are of such a nature that the "sum" and "product" found by using a and b are "equal," respectively, to the "sum" and "product" found by using A and B. Otherwise, the proposed definitions are useless.

G.3: Addition and multiplication of residue classes modulo m, defined by

$$(a\text{-class}) + (b\text{-class}) = ((a + b)\text{-class}),$$
$$(a\text{-class})(b\text{-class}) = (ab\text{-class}),$$

are well defined.

Proof: We must show that if $a \equiv A$, and $b \equiv B \bmod m$, then $a + b \equiv A + B$, and $ab \equiv AB \bmod m$. By hypothesis we have $a - A = km$ and $b - B = Km$, where k and K are integers, whence by addition we find $(a + b) - (A + B) = (k + K)m$, and since $k + K$ is an integer, it follows that $a + b \equiv A + B \bmod m$. We may write the equations resulting from the hypothesis in the form $a = A + km$ and $b = B + Km$, whence by multiplication we find

$$ab \overset{.}{=} AB + AKm + kmB + kmKm,$$
$$ab - AB = (AK + kB + kmK)m,$$

and since $AK + kB + kmK$ is an integer, it follows that $ab \equiv AB \bmod m$. Thus both addition and multiplication of residue classes are well defined operations.

By way of illustration let us consider a complete residue system modulo 5, with the corresponding classes partly indicated as shown below:

$$0 \equiv \ldots, -10, -5, 0, 5, 10, \ldots \bmod 5$$
$$1 \equiv \ldots, -9, -4, 1, 6, 11, \ldots$$
$$2 \equiv \ldots, -8, -3, 2, 7, 12, \ldots$$
$$3 \equiv \ldots, -7, -2, 3, 8, 13, \ldots$$
$$4 \equiv \ldots, -6, -1, 4, 9, 14, \ldots$$

Theorem **G.3** implies that any member of the 2-class added to any member of the 4-class must give a result in the 1-class, for $2 + 4 = 6 \equiv 1 \bmod 5$. Similarly, any member of the 2-class multiplied by any member of the 4-class must give a result in the 3-class, for $2 \cdot 4 = 8 \equiv 3 \bmod 5$. The complete addition and multiplication tables mod 5 are as follows:

+	0	1	2	3	4
0	0	1	2	3	4
1	1	2	3	4	0
2	2	3	4	0	1
3	3	4	0	1	2
4	4	0	1	2	3

·	0	1	2	3	4
0	0	0	0	0	0
1	0	1	2	3	4
2	0	2	4	1	3
3	0	3	1	4	2
4	0	4	3	2	1

As another exercise in the use of **G.3** we seek the remainder when $x = 2^{73} + (14)^3$ is divided by 11. With the aid of the congruence notation this problem, which would otherwise seem a fearsome one, is easily solved. First, $2^4 = 16 \equiv 5 \bmod 11$; then by **G.3**, $2^8 = (2^4)^2 \equiv 5^2 \equiv 3 \bmod 11$; $2^{10} = 2^8 4 \equiv 3 \cdot 4 = 12 \equiv 1 \bmod 11$; therefore $2^{70} = (2^{10})^7 \equiv 1^7 = 1 \bmod 11$; hence, $2^{73} = 2^{70}8 \equiv 8 \bmod 11$. Secondly, $(14)^3 \equiv 3^3 = 27 \equiv 5 \bmod 11$. Finally, $x = 2^{73} + (14)^3 \equiv 8 + 5 = 13 \equiv 2 \bmod 11$. As we have shown in **G.1** this is just another way of saying that there is an integer k so that $x = 11k + 2$ and that the desired remainder is 2. We have avoided completely the actual computation of x and k and this is a remarkable gain that can be exploited in many ways.

13.4. Casting out nines

To introduce this section we shall establish a theorem from which the main results of the section follow readily.

     G.4:   Given the polynomial

$$f(x) = a_0 + a_1 x + \cdots + a_n x^n,$$

where the coefficients are integers and given that x and y are integers such that $x \equiv y \bmod m$, then

$$f(x) \equiv f(y) \bmod m.$$

Proof: The result in **G.4** is a corollary to **G.3**. Thus $x \equiv y \bmod m$ and **G.3** together imply that $x^i \equiv y^i \bmod m$; from **G.2** we have $a_i \equiv a_i \bmod m$; hence by **G.3**, $a_i x^i \equiv a_i y^i \bmod m$; summing with respect to i, employing **G.3**, we find that $f(x) \equiv f(y) \bmod m$.

As an immediate application of **G.4** we can prove the following theorem:

     G.5:   Any positive integer written to the base 10 is congruent to the sum of its digits modulo 9.

Proof: If the polynomial $f(x)$ in **G.4** is restricted by insisting that $0 \leqslant a_i < 10$, $i = 0, 1, \ldots, n - 1$; $0 < a_n < 10$; then $F = f(10)$ is a suitable way of representing any desired positive integer. If in **G.4** we take $m = 9$, $x = 10$, and $y = 1$, we have $F = f(10) \equiv f(1) \bmod 9$; but $f(1) = a_0 + a_1 + \cdots + a_n$ is the sum of the digits of F, so this completes the proof.

By repeatedly applying **G.4** we may find the least positive residue R of $F \bmod 9$, so that $F \equiv R \bmod 9$ and $0 \leqslant R < 9$. For example, by

G.5, $3275 \equiv 3 + 2 + 7 + 5 = 17$; then applying **G.5** again, we find $17 \equiv 1 + 7 = 8$; hence by the transitive property in **G.2**, we know $3275 \equiv 8$ mod 9. Actually part of this work is superfluous since the $2 + 7$ occurring in the first step is a multiple of 9 and may be "cast out" immediately.

By properly interpreting **G.3**, **G.4**, **G.5**, we have at hand the results frequently taught (without proof) in elementary school arithmetic, under the name "casting out nines," as a check on operations with integers.

First, for each number F used in a problem we compute its least positive residue F' mod 9 by repeated use of **G.5** and casting out of nines. Next, the assigned operations are performed on the given integers F, G, H, etc., until the result X is obtained. Then the same operations are performed on F', G', H', etc., until the result X' is found. Now as **G.3** and **G.4** show, if all the computations are correctly performed, we must find $X \equiv X'$ mod 9.

Conversely, however, if $X \equiv X'$ mod 9, it does *not* follow that the answer X is correct (although this erroneous conclusion is sometimes taught), for it is clear from the congruence point of view that any number of errors involving multiples of 9 may have been made, and that these errors will escape the supposed check. Thus the casting out of nines affords only a *partial* check on the accuracy of arithmetical calculations; it will detect errors if the errors are not multiples of 9.

This method of checking is illustrated in the following problems:

$$3275 \equiv 8 \bmod 9$$
$$\underline{676} \equiv 1$$
$$\overline{19650} \quad 8$$
$$22925$$
$$\underline{19650} \quad \Big| \quad \text{partial check}$$
$$\overline{2213900} \equiv 8$$

$$1635 \equiv 6 \bmod 9$$
$$173 \equiv 2$$
$$9919 \equiv 1$$
$$325 \equiv 1$$
$$\underline{617} \equiv 5$$
$$6 \equiv \overline{12669} \quad \overline{15} \equiv 6$$
$$\text{partial check}$$

If the integers are expressed in the base b and if the operations are carried out in that base, then it follows by the same arguments as used above with $m = b - 1, x = b, y = 1$, that a partial check on the operations may be obtained by "casting out $(b - 1)$'s." The following examples illustrate operations in the base "6" checked by "casting out fives":

$$3211 \equiv 2 \bmod 5$$
$$\underline{531} \equiv 4$$
$$\overline{3211} \quad \overline{12} \equiv 3$$
$$14033$$
$$\underline{24455} \quad \nearrow \quad \text{partial check}$$
$$\overline{3033441} \equiv 3$$

$$1534 \equiv 3 \bmod 5$$
$$152 \equiv 3$$
$$5515 \equiv 1$$
$$325 \equiv 0$$
$$\underline{514} = 0$$
$$2 \equiv \overline{13332} \quad \overline{11} \equiv 2$$
$$\text{partial check}$$

EXERCISES

13.1. What modulus is involved in each of the following situations: (a) the calendar for days of the week; (b) the landlubber's clock for hours; (c) the seaman's clock for hours; (d) the minutes of an hour; (e) degree measurement of angular position in a revolution?

13.2. Assuming that addition of integers is commutative and associative, prove that the addition of residue classes mod m is commutative and associative.

13.3. Replace the word "addition" in EX. **13.2** by "multiplication."

13.4. If $(a, m) = d$ and $A \equiv a$ mod m, show that $(A, m) = d$. State this result in terms of residue classes.

13.5. Construct addition and multiplication tables for the residue classes mod 6. *Compare* the addition table mod 6 with the addition table mod 5 (given in **13.3**); *contrast* the multiplication table mod 6 with the multiplication table mod 5.

13.6. Find the remainder when 3^{40} is divided by 23.

13.7. Prove that $M_{37} = 2^{37} - 1$ is divisible by 223.

13.8. Prove that an integer is divisible by 3, or by 9, if and only if the sum of its digits is divisible by 3, or by 9, respectively.

13.9. Using the notation in G.4 and G.5, prove that an integer $F = f(10)$ is divisible by 11 if and only if $f(-1)$, the alternating sum of its digits, is divisible by 11.

13.10. Show that a representation of an integer F in the base "1000," say $F = g(1000)$, can be obtained from the usual representation in the base "10," say $F = f(10)$, by grouping the digits of the latter representation in suitable triplets. Prove that F is divisible by 7, 11, or 13 if and only if the alternating sum $g(-1)$ is divisible by 7, 11, or 13, respectively.

13.11. Apply the tests of EXS. **13.8**, **13.9**, and **13.10**, to the integer 847, 963, 207.

13.12. Show that if a is odd, then $a^{2^n} \equiv 1$ mod 2^{n+2}.

13.13. Compute $X = (4353)^3 + 1734$ and cheçk (partially!) by casting out nines.

Some derive the same sort of stimulus
from a technical monograph as others find
in a detective novel—to which, in fact,
it may bear some sort of esoteric
resemblance. It is all a question of
taste, and taste is a thing which no one
person can decide for another.—R. CURLE

CHAPTER 14

Linear congruences

14.1.   Special residue classes

Much the same terminology may be used in describing residue classes
modulo m as was used for the integers themselves. This is particularly
true for the addition of residue classes.

Addition of residue classes is commutative and associative (EX. **13.2**).

The 0-class is the "zero" for addition mod m, because by **G.3**
(0-class) + (a-class) = $(0 + a)$-class = a-class, for every a.

The $(-a)$-class is the "negative" of the a-class, because by **G.3**
$((-a)$-class) + (a-class) = $((-a) + a)$-class = 0-class, for every a.

The congruence $a + x \equiv b \bmod m$ has a unique class of solutions,
namely, the $(b - a)$-class (see EX. **14.1**).

For the multiplication of residue classes mod m the terminology is the
same as for integers, and a few of the properties are the same, but not
all.

Multiplication of residue classes is commutative and associative
(EX. **13.3**).

The 1-class is the "identity" for multiplication mod m, because by **G.3**
(1-class)(a-class) = $(1 \cdot a)$-class = a-class, for every a.

The 0-class is an "annihilator" for multiplication mod m, because by
G.3 (0-class)(a-class) = $(0 \cdot a)$-class = 0-class, for every a.

89

An a-class is called a "unit" class if and only if there exists a b-class such that (a-class)(b-class) = 1-class. The b-class is then called the "inverse" of the a-class.

For example, modulo 5 all the nonzero classes are units, with 2 and 3 each the inverse of the other, and with 1 and 4 each self-inverse. But modulo 6, only the classes containing 1 and 5 are units.

In the sequel we shall show that the number of distinct unit classes modulo m is given by $\phi(m)$, the Euler phi-function of **11.4**.

In the residue class system modulo m there may exist residue classes which are "proper divisors of zero," which is a sharp contrast with the system of integers. For example, if $m = 6$, $a = 2$, $b = 3$, then $ab \equiv 0$ mod m does not imply that either $a \equiv 0$ or $b \equiv 0$.

This possibility poses some difficulties in discovering a valid cancellation law for the multiplication of residue classes and in finding a complete solution of the linear congruence $ax \equiv b$ mod m. To these topics we devote the next sections.

14.2.   The restricted cancellation law

For the ordinary integers we know that if $a \neq 0$, then $ab = ac$ implies $b = c$, hence "cancellation" or the "cancellation law" is valid for all nonzero integers.

For residue classes mod m, it is natural to ask: "If a is not in the 0-class, does it follow from $ab \equiv ac$ mod m, that $b \equiv c$ mod m?"

An immediate answer of "No!" is provided by the following example:

$(2)(1) \equiv (2)(3)$ mod 4 with $2 \not\equiv 0$ mod 4 and yet $1 \not\equiv 3$ mod 4.

As the nearest substitute for this anomaly we have the following theorem:

G.6:   If $ab \equiv ac$ mod m, $d = (a, m)$, $m = m_1 d$, then $b \equiv c$ mod m_1.

Proof: By hypothesis with $ab - ac = km$, $d = (a, m)$, $m = m_1 d$, $a = a_1 d$, we find $a_1(b - c) = km_1$. But since $(a_1, m_1) = 1$, it follows that $k = Ka_1$, whence $b - c = Km_1$ and therefore $b \equiv c$ mod m_1.

G.6.1:   The cancellation law mod m is valid for a-classes for which $(a, m) = 1$.

Proof: In **G.6**, if $(a, m) = 1$, then $m_1 = m$. It only remains to prove (see EX. **13.4**) that if $(a, m) = 1$, then every member A of the a-class has the property $(A, m) = 1$. But if $A \equiv a \bmod m$, then $A = a + km$. Let $(A, m) = (a + km, m) = d$; then d divides m and also divides $a + km$, hence d divides a; but this implies that d divides $(a, m) = 1$, and hence $d = 1$.

Conversely, if $(a, m) = d$, where $1 < d < m$, then it is possible to find a case where the cancellation law fails. For if $a = a_1 d$, $m = m_1 d$, consider how $da_1 \equiv d(a_1 + m_1) \bmod m$ and $d \not\equiv 0 \bmod m$, yet $a_1 \not\equiv a_1 + m_1 \bmod m$; because if $a_1 \equiv a_1 + m_1 \bmod m$, we would have $m_1 \equiv 0 \bmod m$; but m cannot be a divisor of m_1, for with $d > 1$ we have $0 < m_1 = m/d < m$.

14.3. Various residue systems

As we showed in **13.2** there are exactly m residue classes under congruence modulo m, and any set of m integers, one and only one from each residue class, constitutes, by definition, a *complete residue system*.

If the integers $x_1, x_2, \ldots, x_m$ of a complete residue system also satisfy the added condition $0 \leqslant x_i < m$, we have what is called a *least positive residue system*.

If m is odd and $0 \leqslant |x_i| \leqslant [m/2]$, we have an *absolutely least residue system*: if m is even, we modify this definition by allowing $+m/2$, but deleting $-m/2$.

Thus if $m = 6$:

$$\begin{array}{ll}\text{a complete residue system is} & 3, 4, 5, 6, 7, 8; \\ \text{the least positive system is} & 0, 1, 2, 3, 4, 5; \\ \text{the absolutely least system is} & -2, -1, 0, 1, 2, 3.\end{array}$$

A *reduced residue system* contains, by definition, just those members of a complete residue system for which the cancellation law is valid. Hence by **G.6.1** and by the definition of $\phi(m)$ it follows that a reduced residue system contains exactly $\phi(m)$ classes, determined by integers a for which $(a, m) = 1$.

For example, when $m = 6$, a reduced residue system contains just two classes represented, say, by 1 and 5.

14.4. The linear congruence $ax \equiv b$ mod m, in "theory"

In the following theorems the words "unique solution" must be interpreted carefully to mean one residue class, not one integer. There may be two solutions unequal in the usual sense, but "equal" in the sense of being "congruent, modulo m." For example, to solve $2x \equiv 1 \mod 5$, we run through a complete residue system 0, 1, 2, 3, 4 and find that 3 is the "unique" solution. Of course 8 and 13 are also solutions, but they are not counted as different, because each of these is congruent to 3 modulo 5.

G.7:   If $(a, m) = 1$, then $ax \equiv b \mod m$ has a unique solution.

Proof: We return to the Euclid algorithm theorem, for since $(a, m) = 1$, we know there exist integers s and t such that $as + mt = 1$ and then $a(sb) + m(tb) = b$. Hence we find that $x = sb$ is a solution of the given congruence, for we have $ax - b = (-tb)m$ which implies $ax \equiv b \mod m$. If X is any other solution, so that $aX \equiv b \mod m$, then we see by **G.2** that $aX \equiv ax \mod m$; then since $(a, m) = 1$, we may apply **G.6** to see that $X \equiv x \mod m$; so the solution is unique.

G.7.1:   If $(a, m) = d$, then $ax \equiv b \mod m$ has no solution when d is not a divisor of b; but if d divides b, there are exactly d solutions.

Proof: Since the congruence is equivalent to $ax + mk = b$ in integers x and k, the existence of solutions x and k requires that $d = (a, m)$ divide b. Suppose then that this requirement is satisfied and let $a = a_1 d$, $m = m_1 d$, $b = b_1 d$; then according to **G.6** the congruence $ax \equiv b \mod m$ reduces to $a_1 x \equiv b_1 \mod m_1$. But $(a_1, m_1) = 1$, hence **G.7** is applicable and hence this new congruence has a unique solution mod m_1, say X. Every integer in the X-class mod m_1 has the form $X + sm_1$, and these constitute all the possible solutions of $ax \equiv b \mod m$. In particular, this set includes the solutions

$$X, \; X + m_1, \; X + 2m_1, \ldots, X + (d - 1)m_1$$

which are d in number. Every solution $X + sm_1$ must be congruent mod m to one of the solutions listed; for if we set $s = qd + r$, $0 \leqslant r < d$, then $X + sm_1 = X + (qd + r)m_1 = X + qm + rm_1 \equiv X + rm_1 \mod m$, and $X + rm_1$ is in the list. The solutions listed are distinct mod m, for they are of the form $X + r_i m_1$ where the r_i form a complete residue system mod d. Then if $X + r_i m_1 \equiv X + r_j m_1 \mod m$, we find by **G.3** that $r_i m_1 \equiv r_j m_1 \mod m$ and then by **G.6** that $r_i \equiv r_j \mod d$; hence $i = j$.

For example, we solve $39x \equiv 65 \mod 52$ as follows: since $a = 39$, $m = 52$, $(a, m) = 13$, $b = 65 = 5 \cdot 13$, there must be 13 distinct solutions; the "reduced" congruence is $3x \equiv 5 \mod 4$, with the unique solution $x \equiv 3 \mod 4$; hence $x = 3, 7, 11, 15, 19, 23, 27, 31, 35, 39, 43, 47, 51$, are the 13 distinct solutions of the original congruence.

As a related example, we note that $39x \equiv 64 \mod 52$ has *no* solution, since 64 is *not* a multiple of 13.

G.7.2:   There are exactly $\phi(m)$ unit classes modulo m.

Proof: By definition the a-class is a unit class if and only if $ax \equiv 1$ mod m has a solution. By **G.7.1** there cannot be a solution unless (a, m) divides 1, i.e., unless $(a, m) = 1$; and by **G.7** there is a solution in each such case. Within a complete residue system, say $0 \leqslant a \leqslant m - 1$, there are exactly $\phi(m)$ values of a for which $(a, m) = 1$; so the proof is complete.

14.5.   The linear congruence $ax \equiv b \bmod m$, in "practice"

We regard **G.7** and **G.7.1** as existence theorems—clarifying the situation as to whether there will be solutions of $ax \equiv b \bmod m$ and how many solutions to expect. Actually, of course, the proofs are constructive if one is willing to go back to the Euclidean algorithm and the elimination schemes for finding s and t such that $a_1 s + m_1 t = 1$. In practice— especially if the numbers are reasonably small—the solutions may be obtained much more rapidly by working directly with the congruences— with due precautions for the anomalies contained in **G.6** and **G.7.1**.

In simplest outline we may perform steps like the following in any desired succession:

(*1*) By **G.3** we replace integers by others in the same residue classes which are smaller in absolute value or which have simple desired factors.

(*2*) If we multiply a given congruence by any desired integer k, then the new congruence by **G.3** will have at least as many solutions as the original; but if we make sure that $(k, m) = 1$, then by **G.6.1** the new congruence has exactly the same solutions as the given congruence.

(*3*) From a given congruence we can cancel a common factor and obtain a reduced congruence in accord with **G.6** or **G.6.1**. Of course, after solving the reduced congruence, we must remember to determine all solutions of the original congruence, as in the example following **G.7.1**.

(*4*) If at any stage we find a congruence of the type $ax \equiv b \bmod m$ where a common factor of a and m fails to divide b, we must declare "no solution" by the first part of **G.7.1**.

The above steps are used in solving the following examples.

Example 1: $91x \equiv 98 \bmod 119$.

Divide by 7; reduce modulus:	$13x \equiv 14 \bmod 17$
Replace, anticipating next step:	$-4x \equiv -3 \equiv -20$
Divide by -4:	$x \equiv 5 \bmod 17$
Return to original problem:	$x \equiv 5, 22, 39, 56, 73,$
	$90, 107 \bmod 119$.

Example 2: $6x \equiv (10)^k \bmod 21$.

No solution! because $(6, 21) = 3$ does not divide $2^k 5^k$.

Example 3: $131x \equiv 21 \bmod 77$.

Replace: $54x \equiv 21$

Divide by 3: $18x \equiv 7$

Multiply by 4; anticipate next step: $72x \equiv 28$

Replace, anticipate: $-5x \equiv 28 \equiv 105$

Divide by -5: $x \equiv -21 \equiv 56$.

Example 4: $37x \equiv b \bmod 53$.

Begin by solving for A, $37A \equiv 1$

   the "inverse" of 37 mod 53. $-16A \equiv 1 \equiv 54$

                                  $8A \equiv -27 \equiv 26 \equiv 132$

                                  $2A \equiv 33 \equiv 86$

                                  $A \equiv 43$

Multiply by A, $37Ax \equiv bA$, $x \equiv bA \equiv 43b \bmod 53$.

In Example 4 the solution of $37A \equiv 1 \bmod 53$ by the Euclid algorithm would appear as follows:

$$
\begin{array}{r|l}
 & 1 \\
37 & \overline{53} \\
 & 37 \quad 2 \\
 & \overline{16} \quad \overline{37} \\
 & \; 32 \quad 3 \\
 & \; \overline{5} \quad \overline{16} \\
 & \quad 15 \quad 5 \\
 & \quad \overline{1} \quad \overline{5}
\end{array}
$$

	1	2	3	5
0	1	2	7	37
1	1	3	10	53

From $7 \cdot 53 - 10 \cdot 37 = 1$,

$A \equiv -10 \equiv 43 \bmod 53$.

EXERCISES

14.1.   Show that $a + x \equiv b \bmod m$ has a unique solution.

14.2.   Solve the following linear congruences:

     (a) $16x \equiv 25 \bmod 19$; (b) $51x \equiv 37 \bmod 34$; (c) $37x \equiv 51 \bmod 34$; (d) $66x \equiv 121 \bmod 737$; (e) $117x \equiv 45 \bmod 360$; (f) $513x \equiv -17 \bmod 1163$.

14.3.   Show that all units mod 8 are self-inverse.

14.4.   Find all units and inverse pairs mod m for (a) $m = 16$; (b) $m = 17$; (c) $m = 18$; (d) $m = 72$.

14.5.   Prove that the product of two units is a unit.

14.6.   If a is a unit and A is the inverse of a, show that $ax \equiv b \bmod m$ has the unique solution $x \equiv Ab \bmod m$.

14.7. To find an integer in the 1-class mod 53 and divisible by 16 use $u = 1 + 53t$ where t is a solution of $1 + 53t \equiv 0$ mod 16. This reduces to $1 + 5t \equiv 0$ mod 16, solvable by inspection. Use this idea to solve $37A \equiv -16A \equiv 1$ mod 53 in a way different from that in Example 4.

14.8. In solving $ax \equiv b$ mod m we may replace a by a' with $|a'| \leqslant m/2$. In the b-class mod m we can find $b' = b + mx_1$ divisible by a', if we can solve $mx_1 \equiv -b$ mod a'. In the latter congruence we may replace m by m' where $|m'| \leqslant |a'/2|$. Develop these ideas into an algorithm for solving $ax \equiv b$ mod m. (Compare with 7.3.)

14.9. Solve the following congruences: (a) $371x \equiv 1$ mod 401; (b) $33x \equiv 1$ mod 91; (c) $101x \equiv 1$ mod 507.

CHAPTER 15

Diophantine equations of the first degree

15.1. The equation $ax + by = n$

The problem we propose here is that of finding all pairs of integers x, y which satisfy the equation

(15.1) $$ax + by = n,$$

in which a, b, and n are given integers.

Because we restrict our attention to *integer* solutions, we shall describe the problems as a *Diophantine* equation in honor of Diophantus of the third century. However this is a modern agreement since Diophantus would have sought all fractional solutions. Sometimes such a problem is called a problem in *indeterminate analysis*, because if there are not as many equations as unknowns, there may be infinitely many solutions, and if a solution is not unique, it is often described as indeterminate.

Theorem: The equation $ax + by = n$ *has a solution* in integers, say X, Y, if and only if $d = (a, b)$ divides n. In case there is a solution, then *every* solution is given by

(15.2) $$x = X + Bt, \quad y = Y - At,$$

96

where A and B are defined by $a = Ad$ and $b = Bd$, and t is an arbitrary integer.

Proof: (A) Every solution X, Y of $ax + by = n$ determines a solution of $ax \equiv n$ mod b; and conversely. For we write $aX \equiv n$ mod b if and only if there exists an integer k such that $aX - n = bk$, and with $k = -Y$, this can be rewritten as $aX + bY = n$.

(B) In **G.7.1** (with appropriate change of notation) we have shown that $ax \equiv n$ mod b has a solution if and only if $d = (a, b)$ divides n.

(C) In **G.7.1** (with B in the role of m_1) we have shown that if $n = Nd$ and if X solves $AX \equiv N$ mod B, then every solution x of $ax \equiv n$ mod b has the property $x \equiv X$ mod B. But this means $x = X + Bt$ for *some* integer t. Then

$$y = (n - ax)/b = (n - aX)/b - aBt/b = Y - AdBt/Bd = Y - At.$$

(D) If X, Y solves $ax + by = n$, then for *every* value of the integer t, $x = X + Bt$, $y = Y - At$ is also a solution. For

$$ax + by = a(X + Bt) + b(Y - At)$$
$$= aX + bY + AdBt - BdAt = n + 0 = n.$$

Corollary 1: The basic solution X, Y in (*15.2*) may be chosen in just one way, say X^*, Y^* such that $0 \leqslant X^* < |B|$.

Proof: In part (C) of the proof of the theorem, by **G.7** the congruence $AX \equiv N$ mod B with $(A, B) = 1$ has a unique solution class mod B. The corollary simply reminds us that the X-class mod B has a unique representative X^* in the least positive residue system mod B.

Corollary 2: All solutions of $ax + by = n$ in *positive* integers x, y, if there are any, can be found by solving $x > 0$, $y > 0$, simultaneously, with x, y given by (*15.2*), to find those values of t which are suitable.

If we assume that a and b are both positive, there will be at most a finite number of solutions of $ax + by = n$ in positive integers, so this restriction makes the problem a little more interesting and is considered the "cricket" requirement for most problems of this kind.

Example 1: Find the complete solution of $33x + 17y = 13$. By the congruence method we consider $33x \equiv 13$ mod 17, and readily find $-x \equiv 13$, $x \equiv -13 \equiv 4$, to see that the general solution for x is $x = 4 + 17t$. Then $17y = 13 - 33(4 + 17t)$ yields $y = -7 - 33t$.

Example 2: Find the smallest positive integer m such that there is a solution in integers for $533x + 299y = 20000 + m$; and then find how many solutions the equation has in pairs of positive integers.

From the example in **7.2** we know $(533, 299) = 13$. Since $20000 = 13 \cdot 1538 + 6$, the smallest positive value of m which will make $20000 + m$ divisible by 13 is $m = 7$. Then $n = 20007$ and the equation reduces to $41x + 23y = 1539$. As a congruence we have $41x \equiv 1539 \bmod 23$. By the method in **14.4** we quickly reduce this to $-5x \equiv -2 \equiv -25 \bmod 23$ and solve for $x \equiv 5 \bmod 23$. Therefore $x = 5 + 23t$; and $23y = 1539 - 41(5 + 23t) = 1334 - 41 \cdot 23t$ yields $y = 58 - 41t$. The divisibility of 1334 by 23 gives a check on the work, and the form $x = 5 + 23t$, $y = 58 - 41t$ agrees with (15.2) as the proper form for the complete solution of the problem $a = 533$, $d = 13$, $A = 41$, etc.

We answer the second question by solving $0 < x = 5 + 23t$ and $0 < y = 58 - 41t$ to obtain the conditions: $-5/23 < t < 58/41$, which can be satisfied if and only if the integer $t = 0$ or 1. The corresponding solutions x, y, are 5, 58 and 28, 17, which do check since $2665 + 17342 = 20007$ and $14924 + 5083 = 20007$.

15.2.   The equation $ax + by + cz = n$

The problem of this section is to find all triples of integers x, y, z, if there are any, such that

$$(15.3) \qquad\qquad ax + by + cz = n,$$

where a, b, c, and n are given integers.

If we write (15.3) in the form $ax + by = n - cz$, then according to the discussion of (15.2) there can be a solution of (15.3) for a fixed value of z if and only if $n - cz \equiv 0 \bmod d_1$ where $d_1 = (a, b)$. But by **G.7** an integer z can satisfy the latter condition if and only if $d = (d_1, c)$ divides n. Since $d = (d_1, c) = ((a, b), c) = (a, b, c)$, we see that (15.3) has a solution if and only if $d = (a, b, c)$ divides n.

Moreover, the discussion indicates how to find a complete solution. For $cz \equiv n \bmod d_1$ may be solved completely by **G.7.1**, introducing a first integral parameter, say t_1, with $z = Z + dt_1$ where $d = (d_1, c)$. Then $ax + by = n - cz$ may be solved as in (15.2), introducing a second integral parameter, say t_2. The presence of two arbitrary parameters in the final answer is not unexpected if we consider that the original equation (15.3) is doubly indeterminate.

Example: Manor Mouse was given \$104 by his wife to cover exactly the cost, including 4 per cent sales tax, of some items A, @ \$7; some items B, @ \$3; and some items C, @ \$15. Alas, poor Mouse! When he got to the store he could only recall the names of the items and that he was to get at least one of each. Find the probability, if Mouse spent all his money for certain numbers of items A, B, C and paid the tax, that he would get exactly his wife's order.

Stripped of nonessentials, the Mouse problem is that of solving the Diophantine equation $7x + 3y + 15z = 100$ for the number of solutions in positive integers. Here $a = 7, b = 3, c = 15$, and since $(a, b, c) = 1$, the problem does have solutions in integers. Since $(a, b) = d_1 = 1$, we see that $15z \equiv 100 \bmod d_1$ can be solved by any integer z, so we have $z = t_1$. Then considered mod 3 the equation reduces to the congruence $7x \equiv 100 \bmod 3$, or $x \equiv 1$; hence $x = 1 + 3t_2$. Then $3y = 100 - 15t_1 - 7(1 + 3t_2)$ yields $y = 31 - 5t_1 - 7t_2$. In summary, the complete solution is given by

$$x = 1 + 3t_2, \quad y = 31 - 5t_1 - 7t_2, \quad z = t_1.$$

To find all solutions in positive integers we study the system of inequalities $x > 0$, $y > 0$, $z > 0$. With the original equation these imply $100 > 15z$, so we find $7 > t_1 > 0$. On the one hand, $x > 0$ implies $3t_2 > -1$; hence $t_2 \geqslant 0$. On the other hand, $y > 0$ implies $31 - 5t_1 > 7t_2$. We can list the possibilities easily:

$$
\begin{array}{lll}
t_1 = 1, & 0 \leqslant 7t_2 < 26, & t_2 = 0, 1, 2, 3; \\
t_1 = 2, & 0 \leqslant 7t_2 < 21, & t_2 = 0, 1, 2; \\
t_1 = 3, & 0 \leqslant 7t_2 < 16, & t_2 = 0, 1, 2; \\
t_1 = 4, & 0 \leqslant 7t_2 < 11, & t_2 = 0, 1; \\
t_1 = 5, & 0 \leqslant 7t_2 < 6, & t_2 = 0; \\
t_1 = 6, & 0 \leqslant 7t_2 < 1, & t_2 = 0.
\end{array}
$$

Thus there are fourteen sets of solutions in positive integers. Hence the required probability is 1/14, one success out of fourteen possibilities. Mouse had better return to his spouse for written instructions!

As an example of one of the solutions referred to above, let us take $t_1 = 2$, $t_2 = 2$; then $x = 7$, $y = 7$, $z = 2$, and we check that $7(7) + 3(7) + 15(2) = 49 + 21 + 30 = 100$.

15.3. A linear Diophantine equation in four or more unknowns

It is reasonably clear that the procedure explained in **15.2** will depress a linear Diophantine equation in, say, four variables, to one involving three. Then the method in **15.2** may be applied to complete the solution. An example will illustrate the procedure adequately.

Example: Find all solutions in integers of

$$27x + 33y + 45z + 77w = 707.$$

Since $(27, 33, 45, 77) = 1$, there will be solutions in integers.

Since $(27, 33, 45) = 3$, consider the equation mod 3. Since the congruence $77w \equiv 707$ mod 3 has the solution $w \equiv 1$ mod 3, take $w = 1 + 3t_1$. The equation then reduces to $9x + 11y + 15z = 210 - 77t_1$. Here $(9, 11, 15) = 1$, so for all values of t_1 the equation is solvable for x, y, z and can be considered successfully depressed to three variables. As a matter of fact, since $(9, 11) = 1$, we can set $z = t_2$ and immediately reduce to $9x + 11y = 210 - 77t_1 - 15t_2$, an equation in two variables.

Considered mod 9 this becomes the congruence $2y \equiv 3 - 5t_1 - 6t_2$ mod 9, which may be solved by multiplying by 5, the inverse of 2 mod 9, to find $y \equiv 6 + 2t_1 + 6t_2$ mod 9. Hence $y = 6 + 2t_1 + 6t_2 + 9t_3$. Finally, $9x = 210 - 77t_1 - 15t_2 - 11(6 + 2t_1 + 6t_2 + 9t_3)$ yields the solution $x = 16 - 11t_1 - 9t_2 - 11t_3$.

At each step every possible integral solution is found, so a complete solution of the given Diophantine equation is provided by

$$x = 16 - 11t_1 - 9t_2 - 11t_3, \quad y = 6 + 2t_1 + 6t_2 + 9t_3,$$
$$z = t_2, \quad w = 1 + 3t_1,$$

where t_1, t_2, and t_3 are arbitrary integral parameters.

15.4. Systems of Diophantine equations of the first degree

If a system of two (or more) Diophantine equations of the first degree must be solved, the plan is to obtain the complete solution in integers (if any such solution exists) of one of these equations, and then to substitute this solution into the second equation to obtain a new second equation involving the parameters of the solution of the first equation. Inasmuch as the parameters must take on only integer values, a complete solution of this new second equation represents a complete solution of the system. (More equations can be handled by further successive substitutions.)

It should be noted that a given Diophantine system may be indeterminate (having solutions involving one or more parameters), determinate (having one and only one solution), or inconsistent (having no solution in integers).

To one who is familiar with the various elimination procedures used in the theory of equations which reduce a system of m linear equations in n unknowns, $m \leqslant n$, to equations in $n - m + 1$ unknowns, the procedure for Diophantine equations may seem familiar, but awkward. But it will be recognized as a procedure which at every step collects together every possible solution in integers. If one were interested in fractional solutions, say, this method would actually work (for the parameters could then be allowed to be fractions), but would be needlessly complicated.

Example: Solve the Diophantine system

$$\begin{cases} 17x + 51y + 19z = 1000, \\ 13x + 5y + 23z = 2000. \end{cases}$$

As in **15.2** let us find the complete solution of the first equation. Considered mod 17, this becomes $2z \equiv 14 \bmod 17$; so $z = 7 + 17t_1$. Then the first equation reduces to $x + 3y + 19t_1 = (1000 - 133)/17 = 51$ with the obvious solution $x = 51 - 19t_1 - 3t_2, y = t_2$; together with $z = 7 + 17t_1$ we have a complete solution of the first equation. We substitute these results in the second equation and find that to solve the whole system we must determine integers t_1 and t_2 so that

$$13(51 - 19t_1 - 3t_2) + 5t_2 + 23(7 + 17t_1) = 2000, \text{ or } 144t_1 - 34t_2 = 1176.$$

We consider $72t_1 - 17t_2 = 588$ as a congruence mod 17 and solve $4t_1 \equiv 10 \equiv 44 \bmod 17$ to find that t_1 must have the form $t_1 = 11 + 17T$. Then $72(11 + 17T) - 17t_2 = 588$ shows that $t_2 = 12 + 72T$. Finally, we return to the variables of the original system to find that a complete solution in integers is the one parameter solution which follows:

$$x = -194 - 539T, \quad y = 12 + 72T, \quad z = 194 + 289T.$$

EXERCISES

15.1. Show that $213x + 441y = 10002$ has solutions in integers, but none where both x and y are positive integers.

15.2. Find *one* solution X, Y of $3713x + 1343y = d = (3713, 1343)$ by using the Euclid algorithm. Find *all* solutions by using (*15.2*). Find a solution satisfying Corollary 1 of **15.1**.

15.3. Show that if $ax + by = n$ has any solution in integers we may assume the problem reduced to the form $Ax + By = N$ where $(A, B) = 1$ and $B > 0$.

15.4. If a and b are both positive, discuss the number of pairs x, y solving $ax + by = n$, in which x and y are both positive integers, using plane analytic geometry. (Hint: graph, intercepts, quadrants.)

15.5. Show that the example in **15.3** has just fourteen solutions in which x, y, z, w are all positive integers.

15.6. Reconsider the problem of Manor Mouse in **15.2**, supposing the prices were A @ \$13, B @ \$7, C @ \$18.

15.7. Find the complete solution in integers of $3x + 7y + 10z = 102$ and show that there are just twenty solutions in positive integers.

15.8. Find the complete solution in integers of the system:

$$3x + 7y + 10z = 102, \quad 2x + 3y + 4z = 46;$$

and determine whether there are solutions in positive integers.

15.9.   Prove by induction on $k \geqslant 2$ that

$$a_1x_1 + a_2x_2 + \cdots + a_kx_k = n$$

has a solution in integers if and only if $d = (a_1, a_2, \ldots, a_k)$ divides n.

15.10.   If a rooster is worth 5 coins, if a hen is worth 3 coins, and if three chicks are worth 1 coin, how many roosters, hens, chicks, 100 in all and at least some of each kind, will be worth 100 coins? (The Chinese problem of "One Hundred Fowls.")

15.11.   Consider $ax + by = c$ where a and b are fixed positive integers such that $(a, b) = 1$. Let s, t be any solution of $bt - as = 1$. If c is a positive integer, let $K(c)$ denote the number of solutions x, y in positive integers. Show that $K(c) = [tc/a] - [sc/b] - E(c)$ where $E(c) = 0$ or 1 depending on whether c is not, or is, a multiple of a. Brackets indicate the bracket-function of Chapter 12. (P. Barlow, 1811.)

15.12.   For $K(c)$ in EX. **15.11** show that $K(c + ab) = K(c) + 1$. Let $N(T)$ be the number of values of c such that $K(c) = T$. Prove that $N(T)$ is independent of T, if T is a *positive* integer. (Hint: Show that $K(c) = 0$ when $c < a + b$.)

15.13.   For $K(c)$ in the preceding exercises, if T is a positive integer, show that all integers c such that $K(c) = T$ must be in the interval from $L(T) = (T - 1)ab + a + b$ to $U(T) = (T + 1)ab$. Show that both $L(T)$ and $U(T)$ are values of c such that $K(c) = T$. (A. D. Wheeler, 1860.)

15.14.   In EX. **15.13** show that values of c satisfying $K(c) = T$ are consecutive only when $a = 1$ or $b = 1$.

15.15.   Show that the number of solutions in positive integers of $x + 2y + 3z = n$ is given by $1 + [n(n - 6)/12]$, where the bracket-function has been used to consolidate several separate cases.

Every common mechanic has something
to say in his craft about good and
evil, useful and useless, but these practical
considerations never enter into the purview
of the mathematician.
—ARISTIPPUS, the Cyrenaic

CHAPTER 16

Systems of linear congruences

16.1. The Chinese remainder theorem

After the interlude with Diophantine equations we return to the series of theorems about congruences. A variety of possible systems of congruences can be studied depending both upon the number of equations and unknowns and also upon the number of moduli and their relations to one another. We begin with a system which has considerable interest in itself and important application in later chapters.

Problems of the kind which can be solved by the following theorem were solved by the Chinese in ancient times, and in honor of these early contributions we term our theorem the "Chinese remainder theorem," although the notion of congruence enables us to state the theorem and solution and make the proof in a much more condensed and convenient form than was available to these ancients.

G.8: If $m_1, m_2, \ldots, m_k$ are given moduli, relatively prime in pairs, then the system of linear congruences

$$x \equiv a_1 \bmod m_1, \quad x \equiv a_2 \bmod m_2, \quad \ldots, \quad x \equiv a_k \bmod m_k$$

where a_i are given remainders, has a unique solution modulo m, where $m = m_1 m_2 \ldots m_k$.

The following proof has the advantage that it automatically constructs the unique solution X in the range $0 \leqslant X < m$, whereas other methods of proof (for example, see EX. **16.4**) may produce some other member of the X-class mod m of inconvenient form.

Proof: (A) Using induction on $k \geqslant 1$ we shall prove the existence of a solution X of the form

$$X = x_1 + x_2 m_1 + x_3 m_1 m_2 + \cdots + x_k m_1 m_2 \ldots m_{k-1},$$

where $0 \leqslant x_i \leqslant m_i - 1$ for $i = 1, 2, \ldots, k$.

(I) If $k = 1$, we see by **G.1** that $x \equiv a_1 \bmod m_1$ has a solution x_1 satisfying $0 \leqslant x_1 \leqslant m_1 - 1$.

(II) Assume that $X' = x_1 + x_2 m_1 + \cdots + x_{k-1} m_1 m_2 \ldots m_{k-2}$ has been found satisfying the first $k - 1$ congruences, with $0 \leqslant x_i \leqslant m_i - 1$ for $i = 1, 2, \ldots, k - 1$. Then $X = X' + m_1 m_2 \ldots m_{k-1} T_k$ also satisfies the first $k - 1$ congruences for every integer value of T_k. We consider the possibility of determining T_k so that $X \equiv a_k \bmod m_k$. From **G.7** we see that $X' + m_1 m_2 \ldots m_{k-1} T_k \equiv a_k \bmod m_k$ is solvable for T_k, because from the hypothesis that the m_i are relatively prime in pairs we have $(m_1 m_2 \ldots m_{k-1}, m_k) = 1$. Furthermore from **G.7**, T_k is uniquely determined mod m_k. By **G.1** we choose $x_k \equiv T_k \bmod m_k$ with $0 \leqslant x_k \leqslant m_k - 1$. Then X has the form specified and satisfies all k of the congruences.

By (I), (II), and induction the proof of (A) is complete.

(B) If Y is another solution, then by **G.2**, $Y \equiv X \bmod m_i$, for $i = 1, 2, \ldots, k$. By induction on $k \geqslant 1$ we will show $Y \equiv X \bmod m_1 m_2 \ldots m_k$.

(I) If $k = 1$, then $Y \equiv X \bmod m_1$ completes the argument.

(II) Assume we have shown $Y \equiv X \bmod m_1 m_2 \ldots m_{k-1}$. Therefore $Y - X = K m_1 m_2 \ldots m_{k-1}$. But $Y \equiv X \bmod m_k$, so $Y - X = K' m_k$. Since $(m_1 m_2 \ldots m_{k-1}, m_k) = 1$, the equation $K m_1 m_2 \ldots m_{k-1} = K' m_k$ implies, by Theorem 2 in **6.4**, that $K = K'' m_k$.

Hence $Y - X = K'' m_1 m_2 \ldots m_{k-1} m_k = K'' m$. Thus $Y \equiv X \bmod m$. By (I), (II), and induction the proof of (B) is complete.

Corollary: The solution X obtained in (A) satisfies $0 \leqslant X < m$.

Proof: The conditions $0 \leqslant x_i \leqslant m_i - 1$ for $i = 1, 2, \ldots, k$ show that

$$\begin{aligned} 0 \leqslant X &= x_1 + x_2 m_1 + x_3 m_1 m_2 + \cdots + x_k m_1 m_2 \ldots m_{k-1} \\ &\leqslant (m_1 - 1) + (m_2 - 1)m_1 + (m_3 - 1)m_1 m_2 + \cdots \\ &\qquad + (m_k - 1)m_1 m_2 \ldots m_{k-1} = m - 1. \end{aligned}$$

Example 1: Just for fun let's do the "Chinese remaining problem."

A band of 17 pirates upon dividing their doubloons in equal portions found 3 coins remaining which they agreed they ought to give to their

Chinese cook, Wun Tu. But 6 of the pirates were killed in a brawl, and now when the total fortune was divided equally among them, there were 4 coins left over which they considered giving to Wun Tu. In a shipwreck that followed only 6 of the pirates, the coins, and the cook were saved; this time an equal division left a remainder of 5 coins for the cook. Wearying of his masters' niggardliness, Wun Tu took advantage of his culinary position to concoct a potent mushroom stew so that the entire fortune in doubloons became his own. With the aid of the Chinese remainder theorem we are to find the two smallest numbers of coins which may have been the fortune of the Chinese remaining.

Stripped of embellishment, our problem is to find the two smallest positive solutions of the system of congruences:

$$x \equiv 3 \bmod 17, \quad x \equiv 4 \bmod 11, \quad x \equiv 5 \bmod 6.$$

Since 17, 11, 6 are relatively prime in pairs, **G.8** guarantees that there is a solution. Using the method in (A) we start with $x = 3 + 17T_2$, the complete solution of the first congruence, and substitute in the second congruence. Since $3 + 17T_2 \equiv 4 \bmod 11$ is solved by $T_2 \equiv 2 \bmod 11$, we have $x = 3 + 17(2 + 11T_3) = 3 + 2\cdot17 + 17\cdot11T_3$ as the complete solution of the first two congruences. Substituting in the third congruence, we must solve $3 + 2(-1) + (-1)(-1)T_3 \equiv 5 \bmod 6$. We find $T_3 \equiv 4$ mod 6 so that $T_3 = 4 + 6t$. Hence

$$x = 3 + 2\cdot17 + 4\cdot17\cdot11 + 17\cdot11\cdot6t = 785 + 1122t$$

is the complete solution of the system of three congruences. Perhaps it is symbolic that Wun Tu's fortune depends upon multiples of 1122 (Wun Wun Tu Tu!). The desired solutions are found by taking $t = 0$ and $t = 1$ with the results $x = 785$ and $x = 1907$, respectively.

Example 2: Solve the system $x \equiv a \bmod 27$, $x \equiv b \bmod 49$.

From the first congruence $x = a + 27T$. In the second congruence $a + 27T \equiv b \bmod 49$ may be solved by determining the inverse of 27 mod 49. Multiply $27A \equiv 1 \bmod 49$ by 2 and notice that $54 \equiv 5$ and $2 \equiv 100$ to see that $5A \equiv 100$ is solved by $A \equiv 20$. From $T = 20(b - a) + 49t$ we find $x = a + 27T = 540b - 539a + 27\cdot49t$ as the complete solution.

Systems like that in **G.8** in which the moduli are not relatively prime in pairs have a solution if and only if $a_i \equiv a_j \bmod (m_i, m_j)$ is satisfied for $1 \leqslant i < j \leqslant k$. (See EX. **16.7**.) The method of proof in **G.8** still applies if **G.6** and **G.7.1** are used appropriately instead of **G.7**. The solutions are unique mod m where $m = [m_1, m_2, \ldots, m_k]$.

Example 3: Solve the system $x \equiv 3 \bmod 14$, $x \equiv 5 \bmod 6$, $x \equiv 38$ mod 63.

In solving $x = 3 + 14T_2 \equiv 5 \bmod 6$, we use **G.6** to reduce this congruence to $7T_2 \equiv 1 \bmod 3$ and find $T_2 = 1 + 3T_3$. Hence $x =$

$3 + 1 \cdot 14 + 14 \cdot 3T_3$ is the complete solution of the first two congruences. To solve $3 + 14 + 14 \cdot 3T_3 \equiv 38 \bmod 63$, we use **G.6** to reduce this to $2T_3 \equiv 1 \bmod 3$; hence $T_3 = 2 + 3t$. Then

$$x = 3 + 1 \cdot 14 + 2 \cdot 14 \cdot 3 + 14 \cdot 3 \cdot 3t = 101 + 126t$$

is the complete solution of the system of three congruences.

In Example 3 if the third congruence were $x \equiv c \bmod 63$, then at the step of solving $17 + 42T_3 \equiv c \bmod 63$, we would use **G.7.1** to declare that there is a solution if and only if $21 = (42, 63)$ divides $c - 17$, i.e., if and only if $c \equiv 17 \bmod 21$. Hence 17, 38, 59 are the only permissible c-classes mod 63 if the system is to have a solution.

16.2. Systems of n linear congruences in n unknowns

In contrast to the system studied in **16.1** involving *one* unknown, but k *different* moduli, we here study a system of n linear congruences in n unknowns, say, $x_1, x_2, \ldots, x_n$, all with the *same* modulus m. If we set

$$L_i = a_{i1}x_1 + a_{i2}x_2 + \cdots + a_{in}x_n - c_i,$$

where the a_{ij} and the c_i are given integers with $i, j = 1, 2, \ldots, n$, then the system which we propose to study may be indicated by

$$L_i \equiv 0 \bmod m, \qquad i = 1, 2, \ldots, n.$$

Two such systems will be said to be *equivalent* if they have exactly the same solutions.

G.9. If $L_j' = L_j$ when $j \neq k$, but

$$L_k' = b_1L_1 + b_2L_2 + \cdots + b_kL_k + \cdots + b_nL_n,$$

where the b's are integers, then if $(b_k, m) = 1$, the system $L_i' \equiv 0 \bmod m$, $i = 1, 2, \ldots, n$, is equivalent to the system $L_i \equiv 0 \bmod m, i = 1, 2, \ldots, n$; but if $(b_k, m) > 1$, the primed system may have extraneous solutions which will not satisfy the original system.

Proof: (A) Obviously each solution of the original system is a solution of the primed system, for the only congruence which is different is the kth one; and since by hypothesis $L_i \equiv 0 \bmod m$ for $i = 1, 2, \ldots, n$, it follows by substitution that $L_k' \equiv 0 \bmod m$.

(B) Conversely, each solution of the primed system is a solution of all the congruences of the original system except possibly the kth one, because $L_i = L_i'$ when $i \neq k$. For the same reason the congruence $L_k' \equiv 0$

mod m takes the simplified form $b_k L_k \equiv 0$ mod m. Hence by **G.6** if (b_k, m) = 1, we find that we must have $L_k \equiv 0$ mod m, so that the two systems are equivalent. But if $(b_k, m) = d > 1$, then $b_k L_k \equiv 0$ mod m may be satisfied by having $L_k \equiv s(m/d)$ mod m for $s = 1, 2, \ldots, d - 1$, as well as by having $L_k \equiv 0$ mod m; such a situation shows plainly that a solution of the primed system need not be a solution of the original system and an attempt to replace the original system by the primed system may, when $(b_k, m) > 1$, introduce extraneous solutions.

The suggestion is strong that by repeated application of **G.9**, with suitable and cautious choice of the multipliers b, we may be able to replace a given system by an equivalent system of the type

$$A_i x_i \equiv B_i \text{ mod } m, \qquad i = 1, 2, \ldots, n$$

so that the solutions, if any exist, may be found by applying **G.7.1**. Since no solutions can be lost by the method, it is perhaps easier to rely on a check by substitution to delete extraneous solutions than it is to avoid the introduction of the extraneous solutions. Following the terminology of the theory of equations we may designate such a method as is proposed here as "elimination by addition and subtraction." The method is illustrated in the following example. (If the method seems haphazard, the student who is acquainted with the theory of determinants can substitute an explicit method and tests for the existence of solutions and the exclusion of extraneous solutions, see EX. **16.14**.)

Example: Solve the system $2x + 11y \equiv 5$, $x + 3y \equiv 0$ mod 15.
Using the notation of the theorem we set $L_1 = 2x + 11y - 5$, $L_2 = x + 3y$ and consider $L_1 \equiv 0$, $L_2 \equiv 0$ mod 15.
To eliminate first x and then y we consider

$$L_1' = L_1 - 2L_2 = 5y - 5 \quad \text{and} \quad L_2' = 3L_1' - 5L_2 = -5x - 15.$$

By **G.9** the system $L_1' \equiv 0$, $L_2 \equiv 0$, mod 15 is equivalent to $L_1 \equiv 0$, $L_2 \equiv 0$, mod 15, because $(1, 15) = 1$; but the system $L_1' \equiv 0$, $L_2' \equiv 0$, mod 15 may have solutions extraneous to those of the system $L_1' \equiv 0$, $L_2 \equiv 0$, mod 15, because $(5, 15) = 5 > 1$. In fact, $L_1' \equiv 0$ mod 15, or $5y \equiv 5$ mod 15, has solutions $y = 1, 4, 7, 10, 13$; and $L_2' \equiv 0$ mod 15, or $10x \equiv 0$ mod 15, has solutions $x = 0, 3, 6, 9, 12$; so that the system $L_1' \equiv 0$, $L_2' \equiv 0$, mod 15 has a grand total of 25 solutions (pairing each value of x with each value of y). However, a check reveals that only 5 of these solutions solve the original system, namely:

$$(x, y) = (0, 10); (3, 4); (6, 13); (9, 7); (12, 1).$$

The theorem **G.9** guarantees that this is the complete set of solutions of the original problem.

16.3. A cipher based on congruences

The ideas of the preceding section have been made the basis of an interesting, flexible, and, in a certain sense, unbreakable cipher.

To begin with we select for the modulus m any prime just a little larger than the number of letters in the alphabet required for the messages. Thus with the usual 26-letter English alphabet in mind, we might select $m = 29$.

Then we adjoin to the alphabet a sufficient number of useful symbols so that we can establish a one-to-one correspondence (C) between residue classes mod m and symbols of the (enlarged) alphabet. For example, to the alphabet $A, B, \ldots, Z$ we might adjoin the symbols &, ., ?, supposing that we have $m = 29$, and assign to these "letters" the residue classes $1, 2, \ldots, 26$ and $27, 28, 0$, respectively.

The purpose in choosing a *prime* modulus is to afford us a great variety of ways to choose n^2 integers a_{ij} so that the system of congruences

$(E) \quad c_i \equiv a_{i1}x_1 + a_{i2}x_2 + \cdots + a_{in}x_n \bmod m, \qquad i = 1, 2, \ldots, n$

will have a unique solution for any selection of the c_i (see EX. **16.14** for the exact conditions), namely:

$(D) \quad x_i \equiv d_{i1}c_1 + d_{i2}c_2 + \cdots + d_{in}c_n \bmod m, \qquad i = 1, 2, \ldots, n.$

The integers a_{ij} which are selected are said to form the *encipherment-matrix*; the integers d_{ij}, which can be computed if the encipherment-matrix is known, are said to form the *decipherment-matrix*.

A given message is enciphered in the following way:

(1) it is divided into groups of n letters by some pattern (P), for example, a "standard" pattern is to use n successive letters of the message as a group;

(2) the letters of a group are designated in order as $x_1, x_2, \ldots, x_n$, and each is given its numerical equivalent according to the plan (C);

(3) using the agreed upon encipherment-matrix the values of $c_1, c_2, \ldots, c_n$ are computed mod m from the congruences (E);

(4) the numerical values of $c_1, c_2 \ldots, c_n$ are replaced by their letter equivalents according to the plan (C) and this group of n letters is one group of the enciphered message.

A ciphered message is reduced to "clear" in the following way:

(1) the message is divided into successive groups of n letters; the letters of a group are designated in order as $c_1, c_2 \ldots, c_n$ and are replaced by their numerical equivalents according to the plan (C);

(2) using the computed decipherment-matrix the values of $x_1, x_2 \ldots, x_n$ are computed mod m from the congruences (D);

(3) the numerical values of $x_1, x_2, \ldots, x_n$ are replaced by their letter equivalents according to the plan (C);

(4) the various groups of n letters are arranged in proper position by reversing the pattern (P).

For example, let us take $m = 29$ and the correspondence (C) suggested above; let us take $n = 3$ and the following congruences for encipherment:

$$(E) \quad \begin{aligned} c_1 &\equiv x_1 + 5x_2 + 6x_3, \\ c_2 &\equiv 8x_1 + 2x_2 + 4x_3, \\ c_3 &\equiv 9x_1 + 7x_2 + 3x_3, \quad \text{mod } 29. \end{aligned}$$

If we follow the standard pattern (P) a message such as *HE DIED* becomes first $(8, 5, 4)$ $(9, 5, 4)$ and enciphers by (E) as $(28, 3, 3)$ $(0, 11, 12)$ so that the cipher message is *.CC?KL.*

If we solve the system of congruences (E) by the method in **16.2** we obtain (see EX. **16.15**) the following formulas for decipherment:

$$(D) \quad \begin{aligned} x_1 &\equiv 13c_1 + 17c_2 + 19c_3, \\ x_2 &\equiv 14c_1 + 13c_2 + 3c_3, \\ x_3 &\equiv 25c_1 + 25c_2 + 4c_3, \quad \text{mod } 29. \end{aligned}$$

This cipher is unbreakable in the following sense: even if the "enemy" knows the method of encipherment, the correspondence (C), and the pattern (P), he has a poor chance of guessing the key encipherment-matrix, because there exists a matrix of integers a_{ij} such that *any* message of only n letters will, when enciphered by the congruences based on that matrix, taken the form $c_1, c_2, \ldots, c_n$ of the cipher message which the "enemy" is trying to break.

For example, the correct decipherment of $\cdot CC$ by the congruences (D) above is *HED*. But it is easy to find an encipherment-matrix for which the decipherment of $\cdot CC$ would be, say, *THE*. We would have to choose the a_{ij} so that

$$\begin{aligned} a_{11}20 + a_{12}8 + a_{13}5 &\equiv 28, \\ a_{21}20 + a_{22}8 + a_{23}5 &\equiv 3, \\ a_{31}20 + a_{32}8 + a_{33}5 &\equiv 3, \quad \text{mod } 29, \end{aligned}$$

and so that the new system (E') would have a unique solution (D'). One suitable choice is

$$(E') \quad \begin{aligned} c_1 &\equiv x_1 + x_2 \quad , \\ c_2 &\equiv x_1 + 4x_2 + 25x_3, \\ c_3 &\equiv 2x_1 + 28x_2 \quad , \quad \text{mod } 29. \end{aligned}$$

Since in practice the value of n must be fairly small, the almost inevitable recursion of certain combinations of letters in exactly the same position in the n-groups would, however, probably allow the skilled cryptographer to break the cipher, particularly if he had several long messages of more than n letters to study.

EXERCISES

16.1. Solve the system $x \equiv 5 \bmod 11$, $x \equiv 6 \bmod 15$, $x \equiv 7 \bmod 19$.

16.2. Solve the system $x \equiv a \bmod 8$, $x \equiv b \bmod 25$, $x \equiv c \bmod 7$.

16.3. Find the least two positive integers with the remainders 2, 3, 2, when divided by 3, 5, 7, respectively. (Sun-Tsu, first century.)

16.4. Reconsider **G.8**. Define $M_i = m/m_i$. Show that $M_i S_i \equiv 1 \bmod m_i$ may be solved for S_i. Show that $x = \sum M_i S_i a_i$ solves the system in **G.8**.

16.5. If $x \equiv a \bmod r$ and $x \equiv b \bmod s$, show that $a \equiv b \bmod (r, s)$.

16.6. If $X \equiv x \bmod r$ and $X \equiv x \bmod s$, show that $X \equiv x \bmod [r, s]$.

16.7. Generalize **G.8** as follows: "The system $x \equiv a_i \bmod m_i$, $i = 1, 2, \ldots,$ k, has a solution if and only if $a_i \equiv a_j \bmod (m_i, m_j)$ for $1 \leqslant i < j \leqslant k$. If a solution exists, it is unique mod m where $m = [m_1, m_2, \ldots, m_k]$." (Hints: For the necessity use EX. **16.5**. For the uniqueness use EX. **16.6**. For the sufficiency use EX. **8.14**(a) to proceed recursively: for $i \geqslant 2$, assume X_{i-1} solves the first $i - 1$ congruences and solve $X_{i-1} + x_i[m_1, \ldots, m_{i-1}] \equiv a_i \bmod m_i$ for x_i. Use **8.4** and **G.7.1** to show x_i unique mod $[m_1, \ldots, m_i]/[m_1, \ldots, m_{i-1}]$, and produce a solution $X = x_1 + x_2 m_1 + x_3[m_1, m_2] + \cdots + x_k[m_1, \ldots, m_{k-1}]$ satisfying $0 \leqslant X < [m_1, \ldots, m_k]$.)

16.8. Find a least positive number having remainders 2, 3, 4, 5 when divided by 3, 4, 5, 6, respectively. (Brahmegupta, seventh century.)

16.9. Show that there exists an integer with remainders $b, b + s, \ldots, b + ks$ when divided by $m, m + t, \ldots, m + kt$, respectively, if $t = 1$ or if $t = -1$.

16.10. In solving the system: $L_1 = 3x + 7y + 3 \equiv 0$, $L_2 = 5x + 23y - 3 \equiv 0 \bmod m$, it is natural to study $L = 5L_1 - 3L_2$. If $m = 21$, why is it better to consider the new system to be $L \equiv 0$, $L_2 \equiv 0$ instead of $L_1 \equiv 0$, $L \equiv 0$? Solve the system when
(a) $m = 21$ (one solution); (b) $m = 20$ (four solutions);
(c) $m = 19$ (one solution); (d) $m = 17$ (no solution).

16.11. How many solutions do the following systems have?
(a) $mx \equiv 0$, $my \equiv 0 \bmod m$; (b) $ax \equiv c_1 a$, $by \equiv c_2 b \bmod ab$.

16.12. Solve the following system mod 29:
$$2x - 4y + z \equiv 3, \quad x + 5y - z \equiv 2, \quad 3x - y + 2z \equiv 1,$$

16.13. Solve the system in EX. **16.12** mod 24.

16.14. This exercise is intended for students who are familiar with the theory of determinants. Modify Cramer's rule so that it will apply to the solution of a system of n linear congruence in n unknowns, mod m;

and apply **G.9** to prove that there will be a *unique* solution of the system *when*

$$(D, m) = (A_{11}, m) = (A_{22}, m) = \cdots = (A_{nn}, m) = 1,$$

where D is the determinant of the a_{ij} and where A_{ii} is the cofactor of a_{ii}. Apply **G.7.1** to show that *in general* the number of solutions may vary from *none* to $(D, m)^n$.

16.15. Obtain the solution (D) mod 29 given in **16.3**, and decipher the following cipher message: *WN&VLJ*.

16.16. Solve this system mod 31 for x, y, z in terms of a, b, c:

$$a \equiv 21x + 3y + 3z, \quad b \equiv 26x + 8y + 7z, \quad c \equiv 3x + 2y + 3z.$$

What special interest would this work have if used for (E) and (D)?

16.17. Establish the formula in **11.4** for $\phi(n)$ using the "multiplicative induction" of EX. **8.15**. (Hints: $(x, np) = 1$ if and only if $(x, n) = 1$ and $(x, p) = 1$. If $(n, p) = 1$ use EX. **13.4** and **G.8**; if $(n, p) = p$ use EX. **13.4**.)

CHAPTER 17

The Euler-Fermat theorems

17.1.   Another development of the formula for $\phi(n)$

In this section we shall derive the formula for $\phi(n)$ in a way independent of the proofs in **11.4** and **11.5**. At the same time we shall have an instructive review of the concepts of complete and reduced residue systems, whose definitions we now repeat and rephrase.

Any set of integers, one and only one from each residue class, constitutes a complete residue system mod m.

Any set of integers, one and only one from each residue class, whose members are relatively prime to m constitutes a reduced residue system mod m.

112

By definition (for $m > 1$) $\phi(m)$ is the number of integers x in the range $1 \leqslant x < m$ such that $(x, m) = 1$. Hence $\phi(m)$ is the number of classes in every reduced residue system mod m.

A series of six lemmas leads to the new proof.

L.1: If $(m, n) = 1$ and if $r_1, r_2, \ldots, r_m$ and $s_1, s_2, \ldots, s_n$ are complete residue systems mod m and mod n, respectively, then the set $\{nr_i + ms_j\}$ is a set of mn integers forming a complete residue system mod mn.

Proof: (A) The set $\{nr_i + ms_j\}$ does contain mn integers, for there are m choices for i and n choices for j.

(B) We must show that no two of these numbers are congruent mod mn. Suppose $nr_i + ms_j \equiv nr_k + ms_t$ mod mn. Then it follows that $nr_i \equiv nr_k$ mod m; but since $(m, n) = 1$, we may use **G.6** to write $r_i \equiv r_k$ mod m; but since the r's form a *complete* residue system mod m, it follows that $i = k$. Similarly, we have $ms_j \equiv ms_t$ mod n, whence $s_j \equiv s_t$ mod n, whence $j = t$.

Since parts (A) and (B) fulfill the two requirements for a complete residue system mod mn, the proof of **L.1** is complete.

For example, if $m = 3$, $r_1 = 0$, $r_2 = 1$, $r_3 = 2$; and if $n = 4$, $s_1 = 0$, $s_2 = 1$, $s_3 = 2$, $s_4 = 3$; then in lexicographic order the integers of the set $\{nr_i + ms_j\}$ are as follows:

$$0, \quad 3, \quad 6, \quad 9, \quad 4, \quad 7, \quad 10, \quad 13, \quad 8, \quad 11, \quad 14, \quad 17$$

and these are readily checked as forming a *complete* residue system mod 12, albeit not a least positive residue system.

L.2: If $(m, n) = 1$ and if both $(r, m) = 1$ and $(s, n) = 1$, then $(nr + ms, mn) = 1$.

Proof: Let $(nr + ms, mn) = d$ and let p be a prime dividing d. By the *Fundamental Lemma* in **6.1** since p divides mn, p must divide, say, m; then p does not divide n, for $(m, n) = 1$; but p divides $nr + ms$ and hence divides nr; however, not being a divisor of n, p must divide r; hence p divides $(r, m) = 1$; but this is a contradiction. It must be that d has no prime divisors; in other words, $d = 1$.

L.3: If $(m, n) = 1$ and $(a, mn) = 1$, then $a = nr + ms$ where $(r, m) = 1$ and $(s, n) = 1$.

Proof: Since $(m, n) = 1$ there exist integers x and y such that $1 = mx + ny$; hence there exist integers $r = ay$ and $s = ax$ such that

$a = nr + ms$. Suppose $(r, m) = d$; then since d divides both r and m it follows that d divides a; hence d divides $(a, mn) = 1$; hence $d = 1$. Similarly, we may show $(s, n) = 1$.

L.4: If $(m, n) = 1$ and if $r_1, r_2, \ldots, r_{\phi(m)}$ and $s_1, s_2, \ldots, s_{\phi(n)}$ are reduced residue systems mod m and mod n, respectively, then the set $\{nr_i + ms_j\}$ is a set of $\phi(m)\phi(n)$ integers forming a reduced residue system mod mn.

Proof: (A) There are $\phi(m)\phi(n)$ integers in the set $\{nr_i + ms_j\}$ for there are $\phi(m)$ choices for i and $\phi(n)$ choices for j.

(B) No two of the integers in the set $\{nr_i + ms_j\}$ are congruent mod mn; for each of the reduced residue systems is part of a complete residue system; and the property in question has been proved for complete residue systems in **L.1**.

(C) Each integer $nr_i + ms_j$ is relatively prime to mn, for since the r's and s's form reduced residue systems we have $(r_i, m) = 1$ and $(s_j, n) = 1$; and the required result follows from **L.2**.

(D) Every integer a relatively prime to mn occurs in one of the classes represented by some $nr_i + ms_j$; for this is the implication of **L.3** and EX. **13.4**.

Then (A), (B), (C), (D) together show that the $\phi(m)\phi(n)$ integers of the set $\{nr_i + ms_j\}$ constitute an entire reduced residue system mod mn.

For example, if $m = 3$, $r_1 = 1$, $r_2 = 2$; and if $n = 4$, $s_1 = 1$, $s_2 = 3$; then in lexicographic order the integers of the set $\{nr_i + ms_j\}$ are as follows: 7, 13, 11, 17; if we note that $13 \equiv 1$ and $17 \equiv 5$ mod 12, it is easy to check that we have here a reduced residue system mod 12.

L.5: If $(m, n) = 1$, then $\phi(mn) = \phi(m)\phi(n)$.

Proof: A reduced residue system mod mn contains exactly $\phi(mn)$ integers; but by **L.4**, if $(m, n) = 1$, a reduced residue system mod mn contains $\phi(m)\phi(n)$ integers; hence if $(m, n) = 1$, we have $\phi(mn) = \phi(m)\phi(n)$.

The important point about the proof just given is that it is entirely independent of a priori knowledge of a formula for $\phi(n)$. Hence the "multiplicative property" expressed by **L.5** can be put to use as part of an entirely different derivation of the formula for $\phi(n)$ originally developed in Chapter 11.

L.6: If p is a prime, then $\phi(p^a) = p^a - p^{a-1}$.

Proof: The proof is made by the simple process of counting the positive integers less than p^a and relatively prime to p^a. The integers k such that

$1 \leqslant k \leqslant p^a$ and such that $(k, p^a) > 1$ must of necessity be multiples of p, so they may be listed as follows: $p, 2p, 3p, \ldots, (p^{a-1} - 1)p, (p^{a-1})p = p^a$; hence they are p^{a-1} in number. All other numbers x with $1 \leqslant x < p^a$ are $p^a - p^{a-1}$ in number and have the property $(x, p^a) = 1$; thus we have shown that $\phi(p^a) = p^a - p^{a-1}$.

Theorem: If $n > 1$ is written in standard form as

$$n = p_1^{a_1} p_2^{a_2} \ldots p_k^{a_k},$$

then

$$\phi(n) = n\left(\frac{p_1 - 1}{p_1}\right)\left(\frac{p_2 - 1}{p_2}\right) \ldots \left(\frac{p_k - 1}{p_k}\right).$$

Proof: Since $p_1^{a_1}, p_2^{a_2}, \ldots, p_k^{a_k}$ involve distinct primes, we apply **L.5** repeatedly to see that

$$\phi(n) = \phi(p_1^{a_1})\phi(p_2^{a_2}) \ldots \phi(p_k^{a_k}).$$

To each $\phi(p_i^{a_i})$ we apply **L.6** to find

$$\phi(p_i^{a_i}) = p_i^{a_i} - p_i^{a_i - 1} = p_i^{a_i}\left(\frac{p_i - 1}{p_i}\right).$$

Then the given formula follows immediately by substituting these results for $i = 1, 2, \ldots, k$, and rearranging the product in an obvious way.

17.2. The Euler-Fermat theorems

Lemma: If $r_1, r_2, \ldots, r_{\phi(m)}$ form a reduced residue system mod m and if $(a, m) = 1$, then $ar_1, ar_2, \ldots, ar_{\phi(m)}$ also form a reduced residue system mod m.

Proof: (A) There are $\phi(m)$ numbers in the set $ar_1, ar_2, \ldots, ar_{\phi(m)}$.

(B) Each ar_i is relatively prime to m, for from $(r_i, m) = 1$ and $(a, m) = 1$ it follows that $(ar_i, m) = 1$ by Corollary 1.2 in **6.4**.

(C) No two distinct ar_i and ar_k are congruent mod m, for from $ar_i \equiv ar_k \bmod m$, since $(a, m) = 1$, it would follow from **G.6** that $r_i \equiv r_k \bmod m$; but since the r's form a reduced residue system mod m, the last congruence can hold only if $i = k$.

The proof is now complete, for (A), (B), (C) together show that $ar_1, ar_2, \ldots, ar_{\phi(m)}$ satisfy all the requirements to form a reduced residue system mod m.

G.10.   Euler's theorem: If $(a, m) = 1$, then $a^{\phi(m)} \equiv 1 \bmod m$.

Proof: Let $r_1, r_2, \ldots, r_{\phi(m)}$ be a reduced residue system mod m. Since $(a, m) = 1$, it follows from the *Lemma* above that $ar_1, ar_2, \ldots,$ $ar_{\phi(m)}$ is also a reduced residue system mod m. Therefore each ar_i is congruent mod m to one and only one r_j. Multiplying these congruences together using **G.3**, we find *upon rearranging the r's on the right in natural order* that

$$a^{\phi(m)}r_1 r_2 \ldots r_{\phi(m)} \equiv r_1 r_2 \ldots r_{\phi(m)} \bmod m.$$

Since $(r_i, m) = 1$, we may employ **G.6** repeatedly to "cancel" $r_1, r_2, \ldots,$ $r_{\phi(m)}$ and find $a^{\phi(m)} \equiv 1 \bmod m$.

For example, since $\phi(9) = 6$ with 1, 2, 4, 5, 7, 8 each relatively prime to 9, it follows that

$$1 \equiv 1^6 \equiv 2^6 \equiv 4^6 \equiv 5^6 \equiv 7^6 \equiv 8^6 \bmod 9.$$

G.10.1:   Fermat's theorem: If p is a prime, then for any integer a, we have $a^p \equiv a \bmod p$.

Proof: Since all integers x such that $x \not\equiv 0 \bmod p$ satisfy $(x, p) = 1$ and since $\phi(p) = p - 1$, it follows from **G.10** that for these x we have $x^{p-1} \equiv 1 \bmod p$. Multiplying each side by x, we find $x^p \equiv x \bmod p$. But this latter congruence is satisfied also by $x \equiv 0 \bmod p$; hence the proof is complete.

For example, since 7 is a prime, it follows that $1^7 \equiv 1, 2^7 \equiv 2, 3^7 \equiv 3,$ $4^7 \equiv 4, 5^7 \equiv 5, 6^7 \equiv 6, 7^7 \equiv 7,$ mod 7. Similarly, we know $(10)^6 \equiv 1,$ $(113)^6 \equiv 1,$ mod 7, etc.

G.10.2:   If $(a, m) = 1$, then $ax \equiv b \bmod m$ is solved by $X \equiv a^{\phi(m)-1}b$ mod m.

Proof: Using **G.10** we find $aX \equiv a^{\phi(m)}b \equiv b \bmod m$, as desired.

For theoretical purposes **G.10.2** is very neat, but as a practical matter this method may be laborious, both in finding $\phi(m)$ and calculating $a^{\phi(m)-1}$. To appreciate this the student should solve some congruences $ax \equiv b \bmod m$ both by **G.10.2** and the methods suggested in **14.5**.

For example, consider $31x \equiv 45 \bmod 77$. Since $\phi(77) = 60$, we can be sure that $x \equiv (31)^{59} 45 \bmod 77$, but reducing x to the range $0 \leqslant x < 77$ is tedious; and in the time it might take us to do the first of a dozen or so multiplications and reductions, we can solve the problem directly as follows: we multiply by 2, replace 62 by -15, and divide by -15 to find $x \equiv -6 \equiv 71 \bmod 77$.

EXERCISES

17.1. Illustrate the lemmas **L.1** and **L.4** when $m = 3$ and $n = 5$.

17.2. Check Euler's theorem for $m = 12, 13, 14, 15$.

17.3. Solve the following congruences by **G.10.2** and by the methods in **14.5**:

(a) $19x \equiv 15 \bmod 24$; (b) $32x \equiv 19 \bmod 37$;

(c) $13x \equiv 1 \bmod 100$; (d) $91x \equiv 7 \bmod 700$.

17.4. Use Fermat's theorem to show that every prime, except 2 and 5, divides infinitely many of the integers: 9, 99, 999, 9999, ...

17.5. Show that for every integer n, the number $n^{13} - n$ is divisible by 2730.

17.6. Study the binomial coefficient $p!/(p - r)!r!$ where p is a prime and $0 < r < p$, and prove directly that

$$(a + b)^p \equiv a^p + b^p \bmod p$$

(but don't let any freshmen observe this heresy!).

17.7. Give an independent proof of Fermat's theorem using EX. **17.6** and mathematical induction.

17.8. Define Carmichael's lambda-function as follows: $\lambda(1) = \phi(1)$, $\lambda(2) = \phi(2)$, $\lambda(4) = \phi(4)$; $\lambda(2^a) = \frac{1}{2}\phi(2^a)$, $a > 2$; $\lambda(p^a) = \phi(p^a)$ if p is an odd prime; if m is written in standard form as $m = 2^a p_1{}^{a_1} p_2{}^{a_2} \ldots p_k{}^{a_k}$ where p_i is an odd prime, then $\lambda(m) = [\lambda(2^a), \lambda(p_1{}^{a_1}), \lambda(p_2{}^{a_2}), \ldots, \lambda(p_k{}^{a_k})]$, where the brackets indicate least common multiple. Use EX. **13.12** and **G.10** to prove that if $(a, m) = 1$, then $a^{\lambda(m)} \equiv 1 \bmod m$.

17.9. Show that $\lambda(m)$ is a divisor of $\phi(m)$. Compare $\lambda(m)$ and $\phi(m)$ when $m = 2^6 \cdot 3 \cdot 5 \cdot 7 \cdot 17 \cdot 19$.

Excellence is evident in full and adequate
solutions to problems; for whatsoever
theorem solves the most complicated
problem of the kind, does with a due reduction reach all the subordinate cases.
—E. HALLEY

CHAPTER 18

Congruences of higher degree

18.1. Theory of congruences

Let

$$F(x) = a_0 x^n + a_1 x^{n-1} + \cdots + a_n, \qquad n \geqslant 1,$$

be a polynomial with integers as coefficients and with $a_0 \not\equiv 0 \bmod m$;
then $F(x) \equiv 0 \bmod m$ will be said to be a congruence of degree $n \bmod m$.

For example, in Chapter 14 we have already discussed the case $n = 1$,
the "linear" congruence, for it is clear that $ax \equiv b \bmod m$ can be rewritten
$F(x) \equiv 0 \bmod m$ by using $F(x) = ax - b$. The restriction $a \not\equiv 0$ was not
imposed in **G.7.1**, but if $a \equiv 0$, we see that the situation is trivial.

For emphasis we repeat and expand the previous discussion of the
term "solution" of a congruence.

If there exists an integer x_1 such that $F(x_1) \equiv 0 \bmod m$, it would be
natural to define x_1 to be a solution of the congruence. However, our earlier
theorems show that if X_1 is any integer such that $X_1 \equiv x_1 \bmod m$, then
we also have $F(X_1) \equiv 0 \bmod m$. Thus if one solution can be found, then
infinitely many others can be obtained, but related to each other in an
obvious manner. To avoid this trivial duplication we therefore agree to
speak in terms of residue classes and we define the x_1-*residue class* to be a
solution of $F(x) \equiv 0 \bmod m$ if and only if $F(x_1) \equiv 0 \bmod m$.

118

If x_1 and x_2 are solutions of $F(x) \equiv 0$ mod m, they will be considered as distinct solutions if and only if $x_1 \not\equiv x_2$ mod m. Hence by the number of solutions of a congruence mod m we shall mean the maximum number of solutions incongruent in pairs.

According to this definition there cannot be more than m solutions for any given congruence, since there are only m different residue classes to be considered. If m is small, this implies that all the solutions may be found by direct substitution.

In elementary algebra courses most of our readers will have studied, at least in an introductory way, the "theory of equations" of the complex number system, beginning with linear equations and progressing to quadratics, cubics, etc. It is therefore natural that here we propose a study of the "theory of congruences," starting with the linear case and continuing to congruences of higher degree.

Many points of difference between the two theories will appear.

As explained above, for a congruence a "solution" will mean a "residue class," so each solution will actually involve infinitely many integers; and "distinct" solutions are defined to be "incongruent" solutions. In contrast a solution of a polynomial equation over the complex number system is individual; and distinct solutions are unequal solutions. However, the wider view of an "equivalence relation" which we have been emphasizing makes this situation readily understandable, for congruence of integers mod m and equality of complex numbers are two different equivalence relations: the first has infinitely many elements in each equivalence class, the second has only one element in each equivalence class.

A congruence may have no solution. For example, in **G.7.1** we noted that if $d = (a, m)$ fails to divide b, then there is no solution to the congruence $ax \equiv b$ mod m. For another example, consider $x^2 \equiv 3$ mod 5, for trying in turn each of the five possibilities 0, 1, 2, 3, 4 we fail to find a solution. In contrast, over the complex number system every polynomial equation with coefficients in the system has a solution within the system.

Again, a congruence may have more distinct solutions that its degree. Thus in **G.7.1** if $d = (a, m) > 1$, we noted that if d divides b, then there are d solutions of $ax \equiv b$ mod m, so that $d > n = 1$. Consider also the example $x^2 \equiv 1$ mod 8 which is of degree 2, but has four incongruent solutions: 1, 3, 5, 7. In contrast, a polynomial equation over the complex number system of degree n has at most n distinct solutions.

But the most striking difference is that we shall be able to give an explicit method for solving any congruence of any degree and any modulus m. (Of course, as explained above, one such "method" would be to substitute, in turn, each of the integers of a complete residue system, say, 0, 1, 2, ..., $m - 1$, and while this method is complete in a finite number of steps, it is not practical for large values of m.) In contrast, no comparable method can be found in the theory of equations for complex numbers for equations of degree greater than 4.

We must bear in mind that even if the given congruence is of degree n, there may be more than n solutions; however, a later theorem will show that this anomaly can arise only when the modulus m is composite.

To preserve the continuity of the following chain of theorems—**G.11, G.12, G.13, G.14**—we shall present all the theorems and proofs, and then begin an example in whose solution we can illustrate all the theorems.

18.2.   Reduction of the solution of congruences mod m to the solution of congruences mod p^s where p is a prime

In this section we shall use the Chinese remainder theorem to prove the following theorem:

•

G.11:   If $m > 1$ is written in standard form as $m = p_1{}^{s_1} p_2{}^{s_2} \ldots p_k{}^{s_k}$ where p_i is a prime and $1 < p_1 < p_2 < \cdots < p_k$, then the solution of $F(x) \equiv 0 \bmod m$ depends upon the solution of $F(x) \equiv 0 \bmod p_i{}^{s_i}$, for $i = 1, 2, \ldots, k$.

Proof: Obviously, if $F(x) \equiv 0 \bmod m$, then $F(x) \equiv 0 \bmod p_i{}^{s_i}$ for $i = 1, 2, \ldots, k$; so every solution of the given congruence mod m is a solution of the several congruences mod $p_i{}^{s_i}$.

Conversely, suppose that all solutions of the congruences $F(x) \equiv 0$ mod $p_i{}^{s_i}$ can be found. Let us suppose that integers $x_1, x_2, \ldots, x_k$ have been found so that

$$F(x_1) \equiv 0 \bmod p_1{}^{s_1}, \; F(x_2) \equiv 0 \bmod p_2{}^{s_2}, \ldots, F(x_k) \equiv 0 \bmod p_k{}^{s_k}.$$

Then since the $p_i{}^{s_i}$, $p_j{}^{s_j}$ are relatively prime in pairs, we are in a position to apply the Chinese remainder theorem, **G.8**, and to find an integer x such that

$$x \equiv x_1 \bmod p_1{}^{s_1}, \quad x \equiv x_2 \bmod p_2{}^{s_2}, \quad \ldots, \quad x \equiv x_k \bmod p_k{}^{s_k}.$$

Then since $F(x) \equiv F(x_i) \equiv 0 \bmod p_i{}^{s_i}$, for $i = 1, 2, \ldots, k$, it follows from EX. **16.6** that $F(x) \equiv 0 \bmod m$. Moreover, **G.8** asserts that the x which has just been found is unique mod m. Hence we have shown that each distinct set of solutions $x_1, x_2, \ldots, x_k$ of the system of several congruences leads to a distinct solution of the given congruence mod m. Thus if there are T_i incongruent solutions x_i of $F(x) \equiv 0 \bmod p_i{}^{s_i}$, then there will be

$T = T_1 T_2 \ldots T_k$ incongruent solutions x of $F(x) \equiv 0 \bmod m$. It should be noted, that if any $T_i = 0$, then, of course, $T = 0$ so that there is *no* solution mod m.

18.3. Reduction of the solution of congruences mod p^s to solutions mod p

In this section we show that the solution of a congruence mod p^s, where p is a prime and $s > 1$, can be reduced to the solution of a congruence mod p^{s-1}, hence by repeated applications of this process the solution can be reduced to the solution of a congruence mod p.

To carry out the next proof we need first to make a slight digression and consider certain consequences of the binomial theorem of EX. **2.12.** We note that if a and b are integers and if n is an integer, $n \geqslant 2$, then

(18.1) $$(a + b)^n = a^n + na^{n-1}b + b^2 Q_n(a, b)$$

where $Q_n(a, b)$ is an *integer*, depending on n, a, and b.

By repeated application of (18.1) we find that if $n \geqslant 2$, then

$$
\begin{aligned}
F(a + b) &= a_0(a+b)^n + a_1(a+b)^{n-1} + \cdots + a_{n-2}(a+b)^2 + a_{n-1}(a+b) + a_n \\
&= (a_0 a^n + a_1 a^{n-1} + \cdots + a_{n-2}a^2 + a_{n-1}a + a_n) \\
&\quad + b\{na_0 a^{n-1} + (n-1)a_1 a^{n-2} + \cdots + 2a_{n-2}a + a_{n-1}\} \\
&\quad + b^2\{a_0 Q_n(a, b) + a_1 Q_{n-1}(a, b) + \cdots + a_{n-2}Q_2(a, b)\}.
\end{aligned}
$$

Let us define a new function, $F'(x)$, read "F-prime of x" and called the "derivative of $F(x)$," derived from $F(x)$ according to the following formula:

(18.2) $$F'(x) = na_0 x^{n-1} + (n-1)a_1 x^{n-2} + \cdots + 2a_{n-2}x + a_{n-1},$$
$$n \geqslant 1.$$

In terms of $F'(x)$ we find that $F(a + b)$ may be written

(18.3) $$F(a + b) = F(a) + bF'(a) + b^2 Q$$

where $Q = a_0 Q_n(a, b) + a_1 Q_{n-1}(a, b) + \cdots + a_{n-2}Q_2(a, b)$ if $n \geqslant 2$ and $Q = 0$ if $n = 1$.

For example,

$$F(x) = 2x^3 + 3x^2 + 5x + 7,$$
$$F'(x) = 6x^2 + 6x + 5,$$
$$F(a + b) = (2a^3 + 3a^2 + 5a + 7) + b(6a^2 + 6a + 5) + b^2 Q,$$
$$Q = 6a + 2b + 3.$$

In the application which we shall make of (18.3) we shall not need to know the exact value of Q, but merely that Q is an *integer*.

G.12. If $s > 1$ the solution of $F(x) \equiv 0 \bmod p^s$, where p is a prime, depends upon the solution of $F(x) \equiv 0 \bmod p^{s-1}$.

Proof: We begin by observing that each solution x of $F(x) \equiv 0 \bmod p^s$ is obviously a solution of $F(x) \equiv 0 \bmod p^{s-1}$. Consequently all solutions of $F(x) \equiv 0 \bmod p^s$ must be included amongt† the solutions of $F(x) \equiv 0 \bmod p^{s-1}$. In other words, if x is a solution of $F(x) \equiv 0 \bmod p^s$, it must be possible for us to find a solution X of $F(x) \equiv 0 \bmod p^{s-1}$ so that $x \equiv X \bmod p^{s-1}$; i.e., x must have the form $x = X + tp^{s-1}$ for a suitably chosen integer t.

We will suppose then that all solutions X of $F(x) \equiv 0 \bmod p^{s-1}$ have been found and we shall check each of these, in turn, to see if one or more integers t can be found so that $x = X + tp^{s-1}$ will be a solution of $F(x) \equiv 0 \bmod p^s$, for we are certain from the above discussion that this is the only way solutions of the latter congruence can arise.

In the attempt to find suitable values of t we may use (*18.3*) for this equation allows us to write

$$F(x) = F(X + tp^{s-1}) = F(X) + tp^{s-1}F'(X) + t^2(p^{s-1})^2 Q$$

where Q is an integer. Since we are seeking solutions x of $F(x) \equiv 0 \bmod p^s$, and since for $s > 1$ it is clear that $(p^{s-1})^2 \equiv 0 \bmod p^s$, we are led to the following restriction on t:

$$F(X) + tp^{s-1}F'(X) \equiv 0 \bmod p^s.$$

However, by hypothesis $F(X) \equiv 0 \bmod p^{s-1}$ so there exists an integer M so that $F(X) = Mp^{s-1}$. Therefore the congruence restriction on t may be replaced by the following congruence $\bmod p$:

$$(18.4) \qquad\qquad M + tF'(X) \equiv 0 \bmod p.$$

To the congruence (*18.4*) we may apply all the results of **G.7.1**, as follows:

> there is *one* solution t if $F'(X) \not\equiv 0 \bmod p$;
> there is *no* solution t if $F'(X) \equiv 0 \bmod p$ and $M \not\equiv 0 \bmod p$;
> there are p solutions t if $F'(X) \equiv 0 \bmod p$ and $M \equiv 0 \bmod p$.

Using these results we have at hand a definite method when $s > 1$ of discovering every possible solution of $F(x) \equiv 0 \bmod p^s$ if we have previously found every solution of $F(x) \equiv 0 \bmod p^{s-1}$, so this completes the proof of **G.12**.

---

† However, the phrase "included among" must be interpreted carefully; there may be more solutions mod p^s than mod p^{s-1}, because integers congruent mod p^{s-1} may be incongruent mod p^s.

18.4. Modulo p, a prime, only congruences of degree less than p need be considered

By repeated application of **G.12**, we see that solving $F(x) \equiv 0 \bmod p^s$ reduces to solving $F(x) \equiv 0 \bmod p$. Next by using Fermat's theorem we are able to make a significant reduction in the number of congruences that need be considered. Whereas it was obvious from the start that the coefficients of the congruence are limited by the number of residue classes, it will now appear that for a prime modulus the *degree* of the congruence can also be limited.

G.13: If p is a prime, $F(x) \equiv 0 \bmod p$, may be replaced by a congruence of degree less than p.

Proof: By the division algorithm for polynomials we may write

$$F(x) = A(x)(x^p - x) + R(x)$$

where either $R(x)$ is a constant or the degree r of $R(x)$ satisfies the condition $1 \leqslant r \leqslant p - 1$. Since Fermat's theorem **G.10.1** shows $x^p - x \equiv 0 \bmod p$ for every integer x, it follows that $F(x) \equiv R(x) \bmod p$ for every integer x. Hence the solutions of $F(x) \equiv 0 \bmod p$ and $R(x) \equiv 0 \bmod p$ are exactly the same.

If $R(x) = 0$, then every integer solves $F(x) \equiv 0 \bmod p$; but if $R(x) = a \not\equiv 0 \bmod p$, then there is no solution of $F(x) \equiv 0 \bmod p$.

If $R(x) = a \not\equiv 0 \bmod p$, or if $R(x)$ is a polynomial of degree r with $1 \leqslant r \leqslant p - 1$ with leading coefficient a, of course $a \not\equiv 0 \bmod p$, then we have $(a, p) = 1$, so by **G.7** there exists an integer b so that $ab \equiv 1 \bmod p$. Then $R(x)$ may be replaced by $bR(x)$ with a leading coefficient 1, and $R(x) \equiv 0 \bmod p$ and $bR(x) \equiv 0 \bmod p$ have the same solutions. Having agreed to make the leading coefficient 1, we cannot further specify the coefficients that may appear in $R(x)$ and each may be chosen in p ways. Counting the case $R(x) = 0$, the case $R(x) = 1$, and the possibilities $1 \leqslant r \leqslant p - 1$, we find there are a total of

$$2 + p + p^2 + \cdots + p^{p-1} = 1 + (p^p - 1)/(p - 1)$$

congruences mod p which need to be considered; for any other congruence mod p may be reduced to one of these.

For example, if $p = 3$, there are just 14 congruences that need be considered corresponding to the following $R(x)$:

$$0, \quad 1, \quad x, \quad x + 1, \quad x + 2, \quad x^2, \quad x^2 + 1, \quad x^2 + 2, \quad x^2 + x,$$
$$x^2 + x + 1, \quad x^2 + x + 2, \quad x^2 + 2x, \quad x^2 + 2x + 1, \quad x^2 + 2x + 2.$$

Any other congruence mod 3 is reducible to one of the forms $R(x) \equiv 0$ mod 3. For example, $2x^4 + x^3 + x + 7 \equiv 0$ mod 3, reduces by **G.13** to $2x^2 + 2x + 1 \equiv 0$ mod 3, and if multiplied by 2 reduces to $x^2 + x + 2 \equiv 0$ mod 3, corresponding to one of the "standard" congruences mod 3 listed above.

18.5. Lagrange's theorem

The anomaly that a congruence of degree n may have more solutions than its degree can appear only when the modulus m is composite, for the following theorem due to Lagrange shows that the ordinary rule of the theory of equations for complex numbers holds for the theory of congruences when the modulus is a prime.

G.14: If p is a prime, the number of incongruent solutions of $F(x) \equiv 0$ mod p is never more than the degree of the congruence.

Proof: The proof is by induction on the degree n of the congruences.

(I) When $n = 1$, the congruences take the form $ax \equiv b$ mod p with $a \not\equiv 0$ mod p, and by **G.7** such a congruence has just one solution, for we have here, since p is a prime, that $(a, p) = 1$.

(II) Suppose the theorem has been established for all congruences of degree $< n + 1$. Consider a congruence $F(x) \equiv 0$ mod p of degree $n + 1$; and suppose, if such a thing be possible, that the congruence has $n + 2$ incongruent solutions. Let r be one of these solutions on which we fix attention and let s be any one of the other $n + 1$ solutions. By the division algorithm we may write

$$F(x) = (x - r)Q(x) + R,$$

where R is an integer and $Q(x)$ is of degree n and has integers as coefficients. Since by hypothesis $F(r) \equiv 0$ mod p, it follows by substitution that $R \equiv 0$ mod p. Also by hypothesis $F(s) \equiv 0$ mod p. Combining these observations we see that $(s - r)Q(s) \equiv 0$ mod p. Since s and r are incongruent mod p and since p is a prime, we have $(s - r, p) = 1$, hence we may invoke **G.6** to assert that $Q(s) \equiv 0$ mod p. (It is exactly at this point that the argument will break down if the modulus m is composite, for then it is possible to have $s - r \not\equiv 0$ mod m, $(s - r)Q(s) \equiv 0$ mod m, without forcing $Q(s) \equiv 0$ mod m.) But $Q(x)$ is of degree n and s is *any one* of $n + 1$ incongruent residues for each of which we have just proved that $Q(s) \equiv 0$ mod p. This is a contradiction of the induction hypothesis. Hence a congruence of degree $n + 1$ must have at most $n + 1$ incongruent solutions mod p.

By (I), (II), and the principle of mathematical induction the proof of **G.14** is complete.

18.6. An example

To illustrate the preceding theorems **G.11**, **G.12**, **G.13**, **G.14**, we propose to find the complete solution of

$$F(x) = x^7 - 14x - 2 \equiv 0 \bmod 1323.$$

Here we have $m = 1323 = 3^3 7^2$, so we begin as **G.11** suggests and consider separately

$$(1) \quad F(x) \equiv 0 \bmod 49; \qquad (2) \quad F(x) \equiv 0 \bmod 27.$$

To solve (1) we begin as **G.12** suggests and consider $F(x) \equiv 0 \bmod 7$; but to this problem we may apply the reductions suggested in **G.13**, such as $x^7 \equiv x$, $14 \equiv 0$, mod 7, to find that the congruence reduces to $x - 2 \equiv 0 \bmod 7$ with the unique solution $X \equiv 2 \bmod 7$.

Now we are ready to apply **G.12** and (18.4) so we compute $M = F(2)/7 = (128 - 28 - 2)/7 = 14$ and $F'(x) = 7x^6 - 14$. Inasmuch as $M \equiv 0 \bmod 7$ and $F'(2) \equiv 0 \bmod 7$, there are 7 suitable values for t solving $M + tF'(X) \equiv 0 \bmod 7$; hence from $x = X + 7t$, we find $x = 2, 9, 16, 23, 30, 37, 44$—the complete solution of $F(x) \equiv 0 \bmod 49$.

To solve (2) we begin by considering $F(x) \equiv 0 \bmod 3$, a congruence which reduces readily to the form $2x \equiv 2 \bmod 3$ with the unique solution $X \equiv 1 \bmod 3$.

Then $M = F(1)/3 = -5 \equiv 1 \bmod 3$ and $F'(1) = -7 \equiv 2 \bmod 3$, so that ($18.4$) becomes $1 + 2t \equiv 0 \bmod 3$ with just one solution, $t \equiv 1 \bmod 3$. Hence there is just one solution, $x = X + 3t = 4$ of $F(x) \equiv 0 \bmod 9$.

We must apply **G.12** and (18.4) once more, now with $X = 4$. Then

$$M = F(4)/9 = 16326/9 = 1814 \equiv 2 \bmod 3,$$
$$F'(4) = 7(4)^6 - 14 \equiv 1 + 1 \equiv 2 \bmod 3,$$

so that (18.4) becomes $2 + 2t \equiv 0 \bmod 3$ with just one solution $t \equiv 2 \bmod 3$. Hence there is just one solution $x = X + 9t = 4 + 9(2) = 22$, of $F(x) \equiv 0 \bmod 27$.

To finish the problem we need to apply **G.11** which means we must solve *several* problems of the form

$$x \equiv a \bmod 27, \quad x \equiv b \bmod 49.$$

But this is Example 2 of **16.1** which we solved and obtained $x \equiv 540b - 539a \bmod 1323$. Under the present circumstances with $a = 22$ and a variety of values for b we find $x \equiv 49 + 540b \bmod 1323$.

As we give b, in turn, the values 2, 9, 16, 23, 30, 37, 44, we find

$$x \equiv 1129, 940, 751, 562, 373, 184, -5, \text{mod } 1323.$$

These seven solutions represent the complete solution of

$$x^7 - 14x - 2 \equiv 0 \text{ mod } 1323.$$

18.7.   Wilson's theorem

We are now in a position to present one of the complete, but impractical, tests, mentioned in **9.2** for deciding whether a given integer n is a prime.

Wilson's theorem: A necessary and sufficient condition that n be a prime is that $(n - 1)! \equiv -1 \text{ mod } n$.

Proof: (A) If p is a prime, then by Euler's theorem **G.10** there are $p - 1$ solutions $x = 1, 2, \ldots, p - 1$ of the congruence

$$G(x) = x^{p-1} - 1 \equiv 0 \text{ mod } p.$$

On the other hand the congruence

$$H(x) = (x - 1)(x - 2) \cdots (x - (p - 1)) \equiv 0 \text{ mod } p$$

also has $p - 1$ solutions: $x = 1, 2, \ldots, p - 1$. Both $G(x)$ and $H(x)$ are of degree $p - 1$ and they have the same leading term x^{p-1}. It follows that $F(x) = G(x) - H(x) \equiv 0 \text{ mod } p$ is a congruence of degree at most $p - 2$ having $p - 1$ incongruent solutions. But this is a contradiction of Lagrange's theorem **G.14**, unless every coefficient of $F(x)$ is a multiple of p (so that $F(x)$ is not of degree $\geqslant 1$, mod p); but, in this latter circumstance, $F(x) \equiv 0 \text{ mod } p$ is also satisfied by $x = 0$. Hence we find

$$0 \equiv F(0) \equiv (-1) - (-1)^{p-1}(p - 1)! \text{ mod } p.$$

If p is odd, $p - 1$ is even, so $(-1)^{p-1} \equiv +1 \text{ mod } p$. If p is even, then $p = 2$, and $(-1)^{p-1} = -1 \equiv +1 \text{ mod } 2$. Thus for *every* prime p we find

$$(p - 1)! \equiv -1 \text{ mod } p.$$

(B) Conversely, if n is composite, then n has at least one divisor d, with $1 < d < n$, so that d divides $(n - 1)!$ and $(n - 1)! \equiv 0 \text{ mod } d$. It is therefore impossible that

$$(n - 1)! \equiv -1 \text{ mod } n$$

for this latter congruence would imply $(n - 1)! \equiv -1 \text{ mod } d$, a patent contradiction.

EXERCISES

18.1. Illustrate **G.11** in solving (a) $19x \equiv 1 \bmod 136$; (b) $19x \equiv 1 \bmod 231$.

18.2. Illustrate **G.12** in solving (a) $37x \equiv 18 \bmod 121$; (b) $37x \equiv 18 \bmod 343$.

18.3. Produce congruences of degree 6 with coefficients in the least positive residue system mod 7 having exactly N distinct roots for $N = 0, 1, 2, 3, 4, 5, 6$.

18.4. For what values of N, $0 \leqslant N \leqslant 8$, can you produce congruences of degree 3 having exactly N distinct roots mod 8? Answer: only $N = 7$ is impossible. [Hints: (A) Consider $4x^3 + 4x + R(x) \equiv 0 \bmod 8$ with $R(x) = 1, x, x^2 - x, x^3 - x^2, x^2 - 1, x^3 - x, 2x^3 - 2x, 0$. (B) If 0 is not a solution, show that 2 and 4 cannot both be solutions.]

18.5. (a) By substitution from absolutely least residue systems find all solutions of
$$x^3 + 3x^2 + 31x + 23 \equiv 0$$
mod 5 and mod 7.

(b) Using the results of (a) and **G.11**, find all solutions of the given congruence mod 35.

(c) Discuss the numbers of solutions mod 5, mod 7, and mod 35 as illustrations of **G.14**.

18.6. (a) Solve
$$x^3 + 3x^2 + x + 3 \equiv 0 \bmod 5 \qquad \text{(two solutions)}.$$

(b) Apply **G.12** and solve the same congruence mod 25 (six solutions).

(c) Apply **G.12** again and solve the same congruence mod 125 (eleven solutions).

18.7. Solve
$$x^3 + 64x^2 + x + 30 \equiv \bmod 216.$$

18.8. Solve $x^3 \equiv 13 \bmod 490$.

18.9. Show that
$$x^3 + x + 16 \equiv (x - 1)^2 x \bmod 2;$$
$$x^3 + x + 16 \equiv (x - 2)^2(x + 4) \bmod 13;$$
and then solve $x^3 + x + 16 \equiv 0 \bmod 676$.

18.10. Solve the system $x^3 + x \equiv 5 \bmod 15$, $2x^3 + x^2 + 2x \equiv 4 \bmod 65$. (Two solutions mod 195.)

18.11. If $(A, M) = 1$ and $m = p_1^{a_1} \ldots p_k^{a_k}$ is in standard form, show that y can be found so that $(A + My, m) = 1$, by setting $y_1 = 0$ if $(A, p_i) = 1$, or $y_i = 1$ if $(A, p_i) = p_i$, and solving the system $y \equiv y_1 \bmod p_1, \ldots, y \equiv y_k \bmod p_k$ as in **G.8**.

18.12. If the congruence $F(x) \equiv 0 \bmod m$ has as its leading coefficient $a \not\equiv 0 \bmod m$ and if $(a, m) = d$, prove that there is an equivalent congruence with leading coefficient d. (Hint: If $a = Ad$, $m = Md$, replace a by $d(A + My)$ where y is chosen as in EX. **18.11**.)

18.13. Illustrate the theory in **18.7** by computing $F(x) = 10x^3 - 35x^2 + 50x - 25$ when $p = 5$. Find $F(x)$ when $p = 7$.

CHAPTER 19

Exponents and primitive roots

19.1. The exponent of a modulo m

The general object of this lesson is to pursue further the implications of
Euler's theorem, with our results culminating, in case the modulus is a
prime, in a remarkable analogue of the theory of logarithms. The new
theory ties in with the preceding chapters in that it enables us to find in
a new way the solutions (and, first of all, to decide whether there are
solutions) of congruences of the type $x^n \equiv b \bmod p$, sometimes called
pure congruences.

Since Euler's theorem shows that $a^{\phi(m)} \equiv 1 \bmod m$ whenever $(a, m) = 1$,
it follows that for such an a and m there must exist a *least positive* exponent
e such that $a^e \equiv 1 \bmod m$. We shall describe this least exponent by saying
"e is the exponent of a modulo m" or that "a belongs to e modulo m."
It is important to note that the definition concerns only integers a satisfying
$(a, m) = 1$.

For example, with $a = 3$ and $m = 13$, we investigate the powers of a
and find $3 \equiv 3, 3^2 \equiv 9, 3^3 \equiv 27 \equiv 1 \bmod 13$, so we say that "3 belongs to
3 mod 13." Without such an investigation we might have applied Euler's
theorem to assert correctly that $3^{12} \equiv 1 \bmod 13$; but, as we have just seen,
it would have been wrong to conclude from this that 12 is the *least* positive
exponent which will serve our purpose.

128

G.15:   If *a* belongs to *e* mod *m*, and if $a^k \equiv 1$ mod *m*, then *e* divides *k*.

Proof: Since *e* is a minimal positive exponent such that $a^e \equiv 1$ mod *m*, it follows that $k \geqslant e$. Suppose $k = qe + r$, with $0 \leqslant r < e$. Then

$$a^r \equiv (a^e)^q a^r \equiv a^{qe+r} \equiv a^k \equiv 1 \text{ mod } m$$

But this is a contradiction of the minimal property of *e*, unless $r = 0$; but if $r = 0$, then $k = qe$, and *e* divides *k*.

G.15.1:   If *a* belongs to *e* mod *m*, then *e* divides $\phi(m)$.

Proof: By Euler's theorem $a^{\phi(m)} \equiv 1$ mod *m*, hence by **G.15** we find that *e* must divide $\phi(m)$.

G.15.2:   If $a^s \equiv a^t$ mod *m*, then $s \equiv t$ mod *e*.

Proof: It is no restriction to assume $s \geqslant t$. Then $(a, m) = 1$ implies $(a^t, m) = 1$, so that we may apply the cancellation law **G.6** to the given congruence $a^s \equiv a^t$ mod *m* to conclude that $a^{s-t} \equiv 1$ mod *m*. Hence by **G.15** it follows that *e* divides $s - t$, but this is equivalent to writing $s \equiv t$ mod *e*.

G.15.3:   If *a* belongs to *e* mod *m* and if $(e, s) = d$ with $e = Ed$, $s = Sd$, then a^s belongs to *E* mod *m*. If $1 \leqslant s < e$, there are $\phi(E)$ values of *s* such that a^s belongs to *E*.

Proof: (A) Suppose a^s belongs to *k*; then *k* is minimal and positive such that $(a^s)^k \equiv 1$ mod *m*. Then **G.15** implies $sk = et$ and thus $Sk = Et$. But $(E, S) = 1$; hence $k = EK$. So the least possible value of *k* is $k = E$. This value is indeed suitable for $(a^s)^E = a^{SdE} = (a^e)^S \equiv 1$ mod *m*.
(B) The added restriction $1 \leqslant s < e$ implies $1 \leqslant S < E$ which, together with $(E, S) = 1$, means *S* and $s = Sd$ can be chosen in $\phi(E)$ ways.

G.16:   If *p* is a prime and if *d* is a positive divisor of $p - 1$, then $x^d \equiv 1$ mod *p* has *d* distinct solutions.

Proof: Since *d* divides $p - 1$ we can write $p - 1 = kd$ and $x^{p-1} - 1 = (x^d - 1)Q(x)$ where $Q(x) = x^{(k-1)d} + x^{(k-2)d} + \cdots + x^d + 1$ has integral coefficients and is of degree $p - 1 - d$. Let *D* be the number of distinct solutions of $x^d - 1 \equiv 0$ mod *p*. By Euler's theorem, since *p* is a prime, there are $p - 1$ distinct solutions of $x^{p-1} - 1 \equiv 0$ mod *p*. Every solution r of $x^{p-1} - 1 \equiv 0 \bmod p$ that is not a solution of $x^d - 1 \equiv 0$ mod p must be a solution of $Q(x) \equiv 0 \bmod p$, because

$$0 \equiv r^{p-1} - 1 \equiv (r^d - 1)Q(r) \bmod p$$

with $r^d - 1 \not\equiv 0 \bmod p$, implies, by virtue of **G.6**, that $Q(r) \equiv 0 \bmod p$. Hence $Q(x) \equiv 0 \bmod p$ must have $p - 1 - D$ solutions. However, by Lagrange's theorem, **G.14**, we know with regard to $x^d - 1 \equiv 0 \bmod p$ that $D \leqslant d$ and with regard to $Q(x) \equiv 0 \bmod p$ that $p - 1 - D \leqslant p - 1 - d$, since the number of solutions of a congruence with a prime modulus is at most equal to its degree. But the second of these inequalities is equivalent to $d \leqslant D$, and when coupled with the first inequality, this shows that $D = d$.

G.17:   If p is a prime and if e is a positive divisor of $p - 1$, then the number of residue classes belonging to e modulo p is given by $\phi(e)$.

Proof: Let the divisors of $p - 1$ be arranged in order:

$$1 = d_1 < d_2 < \cdots < d_k < d_{k+1} < \cdots < d_{\tau(p-1)} = p - 1$$

where $\tau(n)$ is the number-theoretic function described in **10.1**. The proof will be by "limited induction" on k, i.e., an induction type of proof limited to the integers k for which $1 \leqslant k \leqslant \tau(p - 1)$.

(I) The theorem is true for $k = 1$, because $d_1 = 1$, $\phi(1) = 1$, and only the 1-class belongs to 1 mod p.

(II) Let us assume that the theorem is correct for $d_1, d_2, \ldots, d_k$, where k is limited to the range $1 \leqslant k < \tau(p - 1)$, and let us consider the next case involving d_{k+1}. We shall divide the argument into several steps:

(A) By **G.16** there are exactly d_{k+1} solutions of the congruence $x^{d_{k+1}} \equiv 1 \bmod p$.

(B) Every *proper* divisor $d_1', d_2', \ldots, d_{\tau(d_{k+1})-1}'$ of d_{k+1} is a divisor of $p - 1$ less than d_{k+1}, and hence is included in the list $d_1, d_2, \ldots, d_k$ to which the hypothesis of induction applies, hence there are $\phi(d_i')$ residue classes belonging to $d_i' \bmod p$; since d_i' is a divisor of d_{k+1} it follows that every one of the $\phi(d_i')$ residue classes belonging to $d_i' \bmod p$ is a solution of $x^{d_{k+1}} \equiv 1 \bmod p$.

(C) From steps (A) and (B) it follows that the number of residue classes belonging to $d_{k+1} \bmod p$, *not* to some *proper* divisor of d_{k+1}, is given by s where

$$s = d_{k+1} - \{\phi(d_1') + \phi(d_2') + \cdots + \phi(d_{\tau(d_{k+1})-1}')\}.$$

(D) From the theorem in **16.3** we know that

$$d_{k+1} = \phi(d_1') + \phi(d_2') + \cdots + \phi(d_{\tau(d_{k+1})-1}') + \phi(d_{\tau(d_{k+1})}')$$

where $d_{\tau(d_{k+1})}' = d_{k+1}$.

(E) Substituting from (D) into (C) we find $s = \phi(d_{k+1})$.

Hence if the theorem is true for $d_1, d_2, \ldots, d_k$ where $1 \leqslant k < \tau(p-1)$, then the theorem is true for d_{k+1}.

Then from (I), (II), and the principle of mathematical induction it follows that the theorem is true for all the $\tau(p-1)$ divisors of $p-1$, which completes the proof.

An example illustrating **G.17** is given at the close of the next section.

Since the results in **G.17** agree with those in **G.15.3**, there is a temptation to think that **G.15.3** by itself establishes **G.17**. If we knew a priori that some a belongs to $p-1 \bmod p$, this reasoning would be correct. But it is only after we have proved that some a belongs to $p-1 \bmod p$, perhaps as a corollary of **G.17**, that we can apply **G.15.3** with $e = p-1$. To this topic we devote the next section.

19.2. Primitive roots

By definition, if p is a prime and if a belongs to $p-1 \bmod p$, then a is called a *primitive root* mod p. The terminology results, of course, from comparing the congruence $x^{p-1} \equiv 1 \bmod p$ with the equation $x^{p-1} = 1$ over the complex number system, for a root of the latter equation which is not a root of $x^d = 1$ for $1 \leqslant d < p-1$ has long been called a primitive $(p-1)$ root of unity. The object of the next corollary to **G.17** is to show the *existence* of primitive roots mod p.

G.17.1: For every prime p there are $\phi(p-1)$ primitive roots.

Proof: Since p is a prime and $p-1$ is a divisor of $p-1$, it follows from **G.17** that there are $\phi(p-1)$ residue classes belonging to $p-1$ modulo p and, according to our definition, each of these classes is a primitive root mod p.

The important feature of **G.17.1** is that it guarantees for every prime the existence of at least one primitive root. The unfortunate feature of the proof is that it is an existence proof, not a constructive proof, and there seems to be no really simple way of finding a primitive root for large values of p. For small values of p a primitive root may be found by trial, and once it has been found, it can be used, together with **G.15.3** to determine to what exponent each residue class of p belongs. For if a is a primitive root mod p, then **G.15.3** shows that a^s belongs to $E = (p-1)/d$ where $d = (s, p-1)$ for $s = Sd$ for the $\phi(E)$ values of S satisfying $(S, E) = 1$ and $1 \leqslant S \leqslant E$.

For example, when $p = 13$ we find by trial that $a = 2$ is a primitive root. The table mod 13 is as follows:

$$s:\quad 1 \quad 2 \quad 3 \quad 4 \quad 5 \quad 6 \quad 7 \quad 8 \quad 9 \quad 10 \quad 11 \quad 12$$
$$a^s:\quad 2 \quad 4 \quad 8 \quad 3 \quad 6 \quad 12 \quad 11 \quad 9 \quad 5 \quad 10 \quad 7 \quad 1$$

In tabular form, the distribution into classes a^s belonging to E for various E dividing $p - 1 = 12$ is as follows:

E	d	S	s	a^s	$\phi(E)$
12	1	1, 5, 7, 11	1, 5, 7, 11	2, 6, 11, 7	4
6	2	1, 5	2, 10	4, 10	2
4	3	1, 3	3, 9	8, 5	2
3	4	1, 2	4, 8	3, 9	2
2	6	1	6	12	1
1	12	1	12	1	1

EXERCISES

19.1. Determine the exponent to which a belongs mod m:
(a) $a = 7$, $m = 15$; (b) $a = -7$, $m = 15$; (c) $a = 4$, $m = 21$;
(d) $a = -4$, $m = 21$; (e) $a = 6$, $m = 15$.
[Answer to (e): not defined!]

19.2. Prove that 1, 5, 7, 11 all belong to 1 or 2 mod 12 and that there are no residue classes belonging to $\phi(12)$ mod 12.

19.3. If there is one class a belonging to $\phi(m)$ mod m, prove that there are $\phi(\phi(m))$ classes belonging to $\phi(m)$ mod m.

19.4. Find eight residue classes belonging to 20 mod 25.

19.5. Prove that 2 is *not* a primitive root mod 17.

19.6. Prove that 3 *is* a primitive root mod 17 and then use **G.15.3** to find *all* the primitive roots mod 17.

19.7. Find a primitive root mod 19 and then use **G.15.3** to classify all the residue classes mod 19 according to the exponents to which they belong.

19.8. If a belongs to e mod m, prove that e divides $\lambda(m)$ as defined in EX. **17.8.**

19.9. If p is an odd prime and a is a primitive root mod p, prove that $p - a$ is a primitive root if and only if $p \equiv 1$ mod 4.

19.10. If q is an odd prime define $F(a, q)$ by $a^q - 1 = (a - 1)F(a, q)$. If p is a prime dividing $F(a, q)$ show that either $a \equiv 1$ mod p and $p = q$, or $a \not\equiv 1$ mod p and $p = 2qx + 1$. (Euler.) (Hint: Use **G.10** and **G.15.**)

19.11. Use EX. **19.10** and $F(q, q)$ to prove in a new way that there are infinitely many primes.

19.12. Establish the following theorems:
  (a) if $(a, m) = 1$ and $a^{m-1} \not\equiv 1 \bmod m$, then m is composite;
  (b) if a belongs to $m - 1 \bmod m$, then m is prime;
  (c) if $m - 1$ has just k distinct prime factors and $a^{m-1} \equiv 1 \bmod m$, then k tests will suffice to decide whether a belongs to $m - 1 \bmod m$.

19.13. With $a = 2$ use the ideas of EX. **19.12** to test the primality of (a) 601; (b) 6001; (c) 60,001; (d) 600,001; (e) 700,001.

19.14. If p is a prime and $p > 3$, show that the product P of the primitive roots mod p has the property $P \equiv 1 \bmod p$. (Hints: **G.15.3**, EX. **11.10**, **G.10**.)

In questions of science the authority
of a thousand is not worth the humble
reasoning of a single individual.—GALILEO

CHAPTER 20

The theory of indices

20.1. The theory of indices

If p is a prime and if a is a primitive root mod p, then the powers

$$a, a^2, a^3, \ldots, a^{p-2}, a^{p-1} \equiv 1 \bmod p$$

are $p - 1$ in number and are incongruent in pairs, for otherwise a contradiction of **G.15.2** and the fact that a is a primitive root would appear. Hence it follows that these powers represent, in some order, the nonzero residue classes mod p. In other words, if $b \not\equiv 0 \bmod p$, there exists an integer x such that $a^x \equiv b \bmod p$. We now agree, for convenience of reference, to give this x a new name; we shall write $x = \operatorname{ind}_a b$, to be read "$x$ is the index of b to the base a mod p".

In the very definition of the index the reader will no doubt recognize the close analogy with the usual definition in analysis of the logarithm of b to the base a; and in studying the following rules of indices, the reader can easily anticipate the results by thinking of the usual rules of logarithms. Just as in the study of logarithms where the base a is usually kept constant in a given discussion, so that the a is not written in the logarithms, so here, too, we will agree to dispense with the subscript a on each index, simply adopting the understanding that in a given problem or in a given set of

134

rules it is a fixed primitive root a which is being used as the base of the system of indices; but there is a further agreement here, not of concern in logarithms, that the modulus p is also being held constant.

G.18:　Rules of indices with the base a modulo p:

G.18.1:　If $b \equiv c \not\equiv 0 \bmod p$, then ind $b \equiv$ ind $c \bmod p - 1$; and conversely.

G.18.2:　If $d \equiv bc \not\equiv 0 \bmod p$, then

$$\text{ind } d \equiv \text{ind } b + \text{ind } c \bmod p - 1;$$

and conversely.

G.18.3:　If $d \equiv b^k \not\equiv 0 \bmod p$, then ind $d \equiv k$ ind $b \bmod p - 1$; and conversely.

Proof:　Every one of these rules is a direct consequence of the usual rules of exponents and of **G.15.2** with $e = p - 1$, and with $s = $ ind b, $t = $ ind c, $u = $ ind d. For example, in **G.18.1** by hypothesis and definition we have

$$a^{\text{ind } b} \equiv b \equiv c \equiv a^{\text{ind } c} \bmod p;$$

then since a belongs to $p - 1$ we apply **G.15.2** to conclude that

$$\text{ind } b \equiv \text{ind } c \bmod p - 1.$$

Conversely, from ind $b \equiv$ ind $c \bmod p - 1$ we may write ind $b = $ ind $c + K(p - 1)$ where K is an integer. Then

$$b \equiv a^{\text{ind } b} \equiv a^{\text{ind } c + K(p-1)} \equiv a^{\text{ind } c}(a^{p-1})^K \equiv a^{\text{ind } c} \equiv c \bmod p.$$

The details in proving **G.18.2** and **G.18.3** will be left as exercises for the reader.

In the following example with $p = 29$ we use the primitive root $a = 2$ and construct a complete table of indices, comparable to the usual table of logarithms. However, with logarithms it is not thought necessary usually to give a companion table of antilogarithms, because if the numbers for which logarithms are given are arranged in increasing order, then the logarithms themselves automatically appear in increasing order. But when the nonzero residue classes mod p for which indices are given are arranged in the natural order, then the indices do not appear, in general, in the natural order; hence a separate table of anti-indices is a very great convenience. In fact in constructing such tables, it is the latter table which it is most natural to form at the outset, so we give it first in the following example:

ind b	1	2	3	4	5	6	7	8	9	10	11	12	13	14	ANTI-INDICES
b	2	4	8	16	3	6	12	24	19	9	18	7	14	28	Given ind b,
ind b	15	16	17	18	19	20	21	22	23	24	25	26	27	28	mod 28; to find b,
b	27	25	21	13	26	23	17	5	10	20	11	22	15	1	mod 29.
b	1	2	3	4	5	6	7	8	9	10	11	12	13	14	INDICES
ind b	28	1	5	2	22	6	12	3	10	23	25	7	18	13	Given b, mod 29;
b	15	16	17	18	19	20	21	22	23	24	25	26	27	28	to find ind b,
ind b	27	4	21	11	9	24	17	26	20	8	16	19	15	14	mod 28.

As an example of the use of the tables of indices and the rules of indices, let us solve $21x \equiv 36 \bmod 29$.

First we note that $36 \equiv 7 \bmod 29$ and then using **G.18.1** and **G.18.2**, we have ind $21 +$ ind $x \equiv$ ind $7 \bmod 28$. From the table of indices we have $17 +$ ind $x \equiv 12 \bmod 28$, whence ind $x \equiv -5 \equiv 23 \bmod 28$. Finally, by the table of anti-indices and by an application of the converse part of **G.18.1**, we find the unique solution $x \equiv 10 \bmod 29$.

As another example, let us solve $x^{36} \equiv 36 \bmod 29$.

By Euler's theorem $x^{28} \equiv 1 \bmod 29$, and $36 \equiv 7 \bmod 29$, so the problem reduces to the simpler form $x^8 \equiv 7 \bmod 29$. By **G.18.1** and **G.18.3** we find that an equivalent problem is 8 ind $x \equiv$ ind $7 \bmod 28$; from the tables this last congruence may be written 8 ind $x \equiv 12 \bmod 28$. Since $(8, 28) = 4$ is a divisor of 12, this congruence may be solved as in **G.7.1**. First we consider 2 ind $x \equiv 3 \bmod 7$ and multiplying by 4, we discover the solution ind $x \equiv 12 \equiv 5 \bmod 7$. Therefore ind $x \equiv 5, 12, 19, 26 \bmod 28$ are the only possibilities. By the table of anti-indices and **G.18.1** it follows that $x \equiv 3, 7, 26, 22 \bmod 29$ are the respective solutions of the given problem and form the complete set of solutions.

Using the same attack, we find the congruence $x^8 \equiv 8 \bmod 29$ has *no* solution; for the equivalent linear congruence 8 ind $x \equiv$ ind $8 \equiv 3 \bmod 28$ has no solution by **G.7.1** inasmuch as $(8, 28) = 4$ does not divide 3.

It is easy to generalize from these examples.

G.18.4:   If p is a prime let N be the number of solutions x of the congruence $x^k \equiv y \bmod p$ for a fixed k with $y \not\equiv 0 \bmod p$. Let $N_1 = (k, p - 1)$. Either $N = N_1$ for the $Q_1 = (p - 1)/N_1$ values of y for which ind y is divisible by N_1. Or $N = N_2 = 0$ for all the other $Q_2 = p - 1 - Q_1$ values of y.

Proof: From **G.18.3** the congruence $x^k \equiv y \bmod p$ is solvable if and only if k ind $x \equiv$ ind $y \bmod p - 1$. But from **G.7.1** the latter congruence is solvable if and only if $N_1 = (k, p - 1)$ divides ind y; and if there are solutions, they are N_1 in number.

For extensive problem solving of this type it may be useful to know that tables of indices and anti-indices for all primes less than 100 are given in Uspensky and Heaslet.

20.2.   A slide rule for problems mod 29

Since the theory behind the ordinary slide rule is the theory of logarithms, it is reasonably clear that with the aid of the theory of indices we may construct a slide rule for the solution of all problems of the type suggested by **G.18**. As an example we shall show here how to construct a circular slide rule to be used in solving problems mod 29.

By way of preliminary discussion we need to digress for a moment and explain the possibility of defining, for real numbers, congruence modulo m where m is a fixed real number. For real numbers a and b, we shall define $a \equiv b \bmod m$ if and only if $a - b = Km$ where K is an *integer*. This notion is an equivalence relation dividing all the real numbers into mutually exclusive classes of congruent numbers.

For example, a very useful device in some problems is the notion of congruence mod 1; of course, in strict number theory this concept may not be of much use, because all the integers fall into one class, say the 0-class, mod 1; but for all fractions, say, or for all real numbers, the concept is useful, every real number a being congruent mod 1 to one and only one real number b in the interval $0 \leqslant b < 1$.

In particular, here we want to use the notation $\theta_1 \equiv \theta_2 \bmod 2\pi$ as a convenient way of saying $\theta_1 = \theta_2 + 2\pi K$ where K is an integer. For if θ_1 and θ_2 are central angles measured in radians with the same initial sides, then their terminal sides will be coincident, inasmuch as 2π radians is one revolution. In other words, to write $\theta_1 \equiv \theta_2 \bmod 2\pi$ is equivalent to the usual "equals relation" for angles.

In making a circular slide rule mod 29 we shall use five concentric circular scales, each of which we shall describe in terms of polar coordinates, the radius vector of each scale being constant, while the polar angle is in each case a function of an integral parameter, with all five functions involving the same constant $k = 2\pi/28$. The exact description of the scales is as follows:

A-scale: $r = r_1$, $\theta = kA$;
c-scale: $r = r_2$, $\theta = k$ ind c;
d-scale: $r = r_3$, $\theta = k$ ind d;
R-scale: $r = r_4$, $\theta = -k$ ind R;
Q-scale: $r = r_5$, $\theta = k$ (ind Q)/2, if ind Q is *even*.

We shall make a rule† in which $r_1 < r_2 < r_3 < r_4 < r_5$ and in which the A- and c-scales are constructed upon one circular disk, while the other scales are constructed upon another sheet, the disk being pinned to the sheet, and free to rotate, at the common center of the scales. The first four scales have the parameters A, c, d, R running from 1 to 28; and as usual in constructing a slide rule, we use the formula to locate the correct θ-position corresponding to a given value of the parameter, but we label that position *not* with the value of θ, but with the value of the parameter.

We know from **G.18.1** that if $C \equiv c$ mod 29 then ind $C \equiv$ ind c mod 28, or ind $C =$ ind $c + 28K$ where K is an integer. Hence we discover the relation

$$k \text{ ind } C = k \text{ ind } c + k28K = k \text{ ind } c + 2\pi K$$

so that with reference to the c-scale we have

$$\theta(C) \equiv \theta(c) \text{ mod } 2\pi.$$

But this is exactly the type of relation discussed earlier and shows that $\theta(C)$ and $\theta(c)$ are "equal" angles. Hence this type of slide rule automatically takes care of our need of staying within the same residue classes, mod 29 (or mod 28 in case of the A-scale), for the same position on our circular scales. It will be unnecessary, therefore, to add any labels, different from those of the nonzero residue classes mod 29 already marked.

If the disk carrying the A- and c-scales is rotated so that c-ray marked 1 falls upon the d-ray marked x, then if the d-ray marked z falls upon the c-ray marked y, it will follow that $xy \equiv z$ mod 29. Hence if any two of the three quantities x, y, z are given, the third can be found.

The proof resides in the fact that in the rotated position of the central disk we have in terms of angles:

$$\theta(z) \equiv \theta(x) + \theta(y) \text{ mod } 2\pi;$$

but in terms of the c- and d-scales this congruence implies

$$k \text{ ind } z = k \text{ ind } x + k \text{ ind } y + 2\pi K$$

where K is an integer. Multiplying by $1/k = 28/2\pi$, we arrive at the relation

$$\text{ind } z = \text{ind } x + \text{ind } y + 28K;$$

thus ind $z \equiv$ ind $x +$ ind y mod 28 and by **G.18.2** we know that this implies $xy \equiv z$ mod 29.

A ray extending from the A-scale to the c-scale obviously solves $A =$ ind c, so here in graphic form is a table of anti-indices, and with just

---

† See the tailpiece to Chapter 20 and construct a working model from the sheet facing this page.

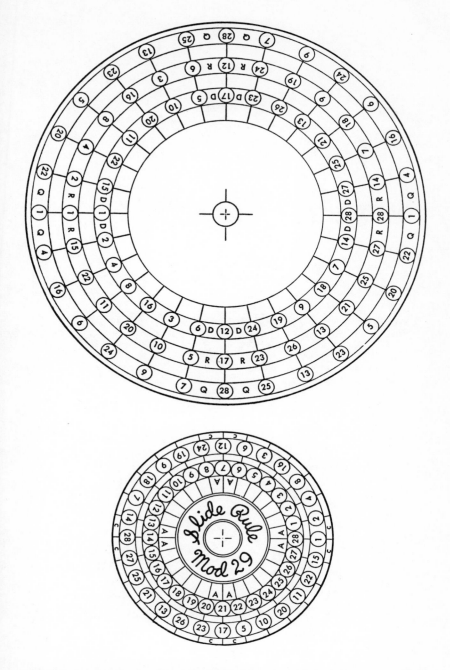

If desired, a working model of the slide rule may be constructed by mounting the above components on cardboard and combining the separate parts on a common axis.

a bit of looking (because of the c's not appearing in the natural order) it may also be considered a table of indices.

In the d- and R-scales is provided a direct solution of the congruence $dR \equiv 1 \bmod 29$, obtained by merely extending the ray from d on the d-scale to R on the R-scale.

The proof is simple since the proposed construction gives $\theta(d) \equiv \theta(R) \bmod 2\pi$, or k ind $d \equiv -k$ ind $R \bmod 2\pi$, whence

$$\text{ind } d + \text{ind } R \equiv 0 \equiv 28 \equiv \text{ind } 1 \bmod 28;$$

but this last congruence by **G.18.2** implies $dR \equiv 1 \bmod 29$.

Similarly, the d- and Q-scales provide a direct solution of the problem $d^2 \equiv Q \bmod 29$ in the *fourteen* cases where there are solutions. For from **G.18.3** we know that the given congruence is equivalent to

$$2 \text{ ind } d \equiv \text{ind } Q \bmod 28;$$

but by **G.7.1** we know that there are solutions, in fact just *two* solutions, of this latter congruence if and only if ind Q is *even*. Since this last restriction is exactly that placed on the function defining the Q-scale, the connection is fairly obvious. However, it is to be noted that $Q \equiv q \bmod 29$ implies ind $Q \equiv$ ind $q \bmod 28$ and $\theta(Q) \equiv \theta(q) \bmod \pi$, *not* 2π. Hence for a given value of Q there are found two entries on the Q-scale differing by π. If then a ray is drawn from either position of Q on the Q-scale to d_1 and d_2, respectively, on the d-scale there will be found the two solutions of $d^2 \equiv Q \bmod 29$. For the construction gives $\theta(d) \equiv \theta(Q) \bmod \pi$,

$$k \text{ ind } d \equiv k \,(\text{ind } Q)/2 \bmod \pi, \text{ or } 2k \text{ ind } d \equiv k \text{ ind } Q \bmod 2\pi,$$
$$2 \text{ ind } d \equiv \text{ind } Q \bmod 28, \text{ or } d^2 \equiv Q \bmod 29.$$

The fact that $d^2 \equiv Q \bmod 29$ has solutions for fourteen values of Q of even index and fails to have a solution for fourteen values of Q of odd index, will provide us with a good introduction to the next chapter.

EXERCISES

20.1. Use the tables in **20.1** to solve the following congruences mod 29:

$$x \equiv (12)(18), \quad 3x \equiv 7, \quad 17x \equiv (21)(25), \quad 18x \equiv 1,$$
$$x \equiv (15)^{10}, \quad x \equiv (33)^{33} \equiv 4^5, \quad x^2 \equiv 24, \quad x^2 \equiv 14,$$
$$x^3 \equiv 7, \quad x^3 \equiv 18, \quad x^5 \equiv 22, \quad x^6 \equiv 5, \quad x^{12} \equiv 7.$$

20.2. Construct tables of $s =$ ind b and $b = a^s \bmod 17$ with $a = 3$ and use these to solve the following congruences mod 17:

$$x \equiv (8)(14), \quad 13x \equiv 5, \quad 12x \equiv (9)(13), \quad x \equiv (13)^{11},$$
$$x^2 \equiv 2, \quad x^3 \equiv 2, \quad x^4 \equiv 13, \quad x^6 \equiv 16.$$

20.3. Use the tables in **20.1** to find all primitive roots mod 29.

20.4. Construct a table of indices mod 29 using $a = 3$.

20.5.   Complete the proof of **G.18.2** and **G.18.3**.

20.6.   Solve the congruences in EX. **20.1** using the slide rule mod 29.

20.7.   Why do diametrically opposite entries on the c-scale of the circular slide rule mod 29 add to give 29?

20.8.   Construct a circular slide rule mod 31.

20.9.   Construct a straight slide rule mod 29 with parallel scales, one on the stock, the other on the slide.

20.10.   Given an index system for $p = 29$, construct a circular c-scale with $r = K$, $\theta = k$ ind c, where K is any convenient radius and $k = 2\pi/28$. Let P_i be a point on the c-scale with $\theta_i = k$ ind c_i. If the chord joining P_1 to P_2 is parallel to the chord joining P_3 and P_4, prove that $c_1 c_2 \equiv c_3 c_4$ mod p. (Soreau.) (Hint: Parallel chords are bisected by the same diametral line, if not by the same radial line.)

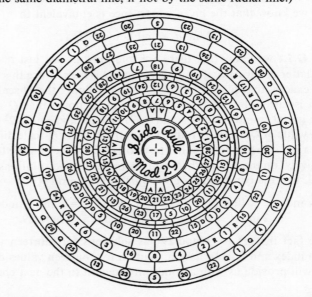

An example of the use of the slide rule mod 29. Turned to this position, the rule solves $D \equiv 16C$ mod 29 with D and C on the same ray.

CHAPTER 21

Quadratic residues
and Legendre's symbol

21.1. Quadratic congruences

The purpose of this and the following chapter is to provide a complete
test for the *existence* of solutions of the general quadratic congruence

$$ax^2 + bx + c \equiv 0 \bmod m, \qquad a \not\equiv 0 \bmod m.$$

In a sense the discussion of Chapter 20 completely solves this problem;
however, the reader will recall that by the method of that chapter a given
congruence problem mod m was reduced to a series of problems mod p,
a prime, and that the solutions mod p were to be found, presumably, by
trial of all the residue classes. This is feasible for small primes p, but
impractical for large primes. It is that defect which we propose to remedy
in the case of quadratic congruences, in the sense of providing another way
of deciding whether solutions exist.

If in the general congruence displayed above we have $b \equiv 0 \bmod m$,
then the congruence is called a pure quadratic congruence. The purpose
of the next theorem is to show that for a prime modulus the general
quadratic congruence is equivalent to a chain of two congruences: the
first of which is a pure quadratic congruence, which may or may not have
a solution, and the second of which is a linear congruence, which is always
solvable provided that the first congruence of the chain has a solution.

ıulas are remarkably like those of the quadratic formula, so
in the theory of equations for complex numbers.
ɛ the case $p = 2$ is trivially solved by trial, we shall limit ourselves
ınd the next lesson to having p represent an odd prime.

19:   If p is an odd prime and if $a \not\equiv 0 \bmod p$, then

$$ax^2 + bx + c \equiv 0 \bmod p$$

is equivalent to the chain of congruences which follows:

$$u^2 \equiv b^2 - 4ac, \qquad 2ax \equiv u - b \bmod p.$$

Proof: By the hypothesis that p is an odd prime and that $a \not\equiv 0 \bmod p$,
it follows that $(4a, p) = 1$; hence **G.6** may be employed to show that the
given congruence is equivalent to the following congruence:

$$4a^2x^2 + 4abx + 4ac \equiv 0 \bmod p.$$

By subtracting $4ac$ and adding b^2 to each side of the latter congruence we
succeed in completing the square and arriving at the equivalent congruence
which follows:

$$(2ax + b)^2 \equiv b^2 - 4ac \bmod p.$$

By setting $u \equiv 2ax + b \bmod p$, we complete the proof; for if there is no u
satisfying $u^2 \equiv b^2 - 4ac \bmod p$, then there is no x satisfying the given
congruence; and if there is a u satisfying $u^2 \equiv b^2 - 4ac \bmod p$, then
because $(2a, p) = 1$ there is an x satisfying $2ax \equiv u - b \bmod p$ and
satisfying the given congruence.

21.2.   Quadratic residues

As shown in the preceding section, the solution of the general quadratic
congruence mod m reduces finally to the solution of pure quadratic congruences modulo primes. With due notice, we now change notation and
consider as our typical problem the following pure quadratic congruence:

$$x^2 \equiv a \bmod p, \quad (a, p) = 1, \quad p \text{ an odd prime}.$$

The case $a \equiv 0 \bmod p$ is trivial, having the unique solution $x \equiv 0 \bmod p$,
and is not included in the discussion.

We begin with the following useful definitions.

If the congruence $x^2 \equiv a \bmod m$ has a solution, then a is called a
quadratic residue mod m; if there is no solution, then a is called a *quadratic
nonresidue mod m*.

For example, 1, 4, 9, 3, 12, 10 are quadratic residues mod 13, for they
are the remainders mod 13 of the squares of ± 1, ± 2, ± 3, ± 4, ± 5, ± 6,

respectively. Since this exhausts the list of possible solutions (except for the case $x \equiv 0$ leading to $a \equiv 0$ which we have agreed to exclude from the discussion, although by definition 0 is certainly a quadratic residue), it follows that the other nonzero residue classes, 2, 5, 6, 7, 8, 11 are quadratic nonresidues mod 13.

G.20: Exactly half the nonzero residues mod p are quadratic residues mod p.

Proof: This is a special case of **G.18.4** with $k = 2$ and $N_1 = (2, p - 1)$ $= 2$, so that there are $Q_1 = (p - 1)/2$ cases in which solutions of $x^2 \equiv a$ mod p exist, namely, exactly those a for which ind a is even.

G.21: The integer $a \not\equiv 0$ mod p is a quadratic residue, or a quadratic nonresidue mod p, according as

$$a^s \equiv 1 \bmod p, \quad \text{or} \quad a^s \equiv -1 \bmod p,$$

where $s = (p - 1)/2$.

Proof: By Euler's theorem, $x^{p-1} - 1 \equiv 0$ mod p has $p - 1$ solutions made up of the nonzero residue classes mod p. In factored form $x^{p-1} - 1 = (x^s - 1)(x^s + 1)$. By **G.16**, the congruence $x^s - 1 \equiv 0$ mod p has exactly s solutions. But it is easy to see that every quadratic residue mod p is a solution of $x^s - 1 \equiv 0$ mod p; for if there exists an integer x so that $x^2 \equiv a$ mod p, then $a^s \equiv x^{2s} \equiv x^{p-1} \equiv 1$ mod p, the last congruence being justified by Euler's theorem. However, by **G.20** the quadratic residues are s in number, so all the solutions of $x^s - 1 \equiv 0$ mod p are quadratic residues. Hence the remaining s solutions of $x^{p-1} - 1 \equiv 0$ mod p must be quadratic nonresidues all of which solve $x^s + 1 \equiv 0$ mod p, because by **G.16** and **G.6** the factor $x^s - 1 \not\equiv 0$ mod p may be cancelled, when x is a nonresidue.

G.21.1: The product ab is a quadratic nonresidue mod p if and only if exactly one of a or b is a quadratic nonresidue mod p.

Proof: Since $(ab)^s \equiv a^s b^s$ mod p, it follows from **G.21** that a^s and b^s are either congruent to $+1$ or -1 mod p so that $(ab)^s \equiv -1$ if and only if *just one* of a^s or b^s is congruent to -1 mod p. By **G.21** this result may be rephrased in terms of residues and nonresidues as stated in **G.21.1**.

21.3. Legendre's symbol

In explaining and carrying out tests to decide whether a given integer a is a quadratic residue or nonresidue mod p, we shall find it extremely convenient to use a special number-theoretic function known as Legendre's symbol, written (a/p), with its values defined as follows:

$(a/p) = +1$ if $a \not\equiv 0 \bmod p$ and if a is a quadratic residue mod p;

$(a/p) = -1$ if a is a quadratic nonresidue mod p.

Of course, it is essential that the user of this Legendre symbol be a bit cautious, and not interpret the symbol as a mere fraction in parentheses, for as we know already from the definition and see again in the next theorems, the properties of the symbol are quite different from those of fractions.

G.22.1:   If $a \equiv b \bmod p$, then $(a/p) = (b/p)$.

G.22.2: $(a/p) \equiv a^s \bmod p$.

G.22.3: $(ab/p) = (a/p)(b/p)$.

G.22.4: $(c^2b/p) = (b/p)$.

Proofs: If $a \equiv b \bmod p$ then $x^2 \equiv a \bmod p$ has exactly the same solutions, if any, as has $x^2 \equiv b \bmod p$, which establishes **G.22.1**.

The result in **G.22.2** is a direct consequence of the definition of the Legendre symbol and of **G.21**.

The result in **G.22.3** is a mere restatement of **G.21.1** in terms of the Legendre symbol.

G.22.4 is a special case of **G.22.3** making use of the fact that $a = c^2$ is obviously a quadratic residue so that $(c^2/p) = 1$.

For the present in evaluating Legendre's symbol, we may be content with the above theorems, but in the next chapter a much more elegant method of evaluation, avoiding computations of $a^s \bmod p$, will be explained.

For example, the question "Is 113 a quadratic residue mod 101?" should first be mentally compared with the equivalent question "Does $x^2 \equiv 113 \bmod 101$ have a solution?" and then rephrased "Find the value of $(113/101)$."

According to **G.22.1** and **G.22.4**, since $113 \equiv 12 \equiv 2^23 \bmod 101$, the problem reduces to finding $(3/101)$. Then, at this stage of our work, we must have recourse to finding the value of $3^{50} \bmod 101$, as in **G.22.2**. Since $3^5 = 243 \equiv 41 \bmod 101$, we find in turn that $3^{10} \equiv (41)^2 = 1681 \equiv 65$, $3^{20} \equiv (65)^2 = 4225 \equiv 84$, $3^{25} \equiv (84)(41) = 3444 \equiv 10$, $3^{50} \equiv (10)^2 = 100 \equiv -1$, mod 101. Therefore $(3/101) = -1$; and 3 and 12 and 113 are *not* quadratic residues mod 101.

EXERCISES

21.1.   As in **G.19**, find the chain of congruences equivalent to $2x^2 + 3x - k \equiv 0 \bmod 5$ and determine for what values of k there will be solutions.

21.2. If $x^2 \equiv a \bmod p$ has a solution x_1, show that $x_2 = p - x_1$ is also a solution. If $a \not\equiv 0$ and if p is odd show that $x_2 \not\equiv x_1$.

21.3. If p is an odd prime and if $(a/p) = 1$, prove that a is a quadratic residue mod p^n and $x^2 \equiv a \bmod p^n$ has *exactly two* solutions. Use **G.12** and induction.

21.4. If a is odd and $m \geqslant 3$, then $x^2 \equiv a \bmod 2^m$ is impossible unless $a \equiv 1 \bmod 8$.

21.5. If $a \equiv 1 \bmod 8$ and if $m \geqslant 3$, then $x^2 \equiv a \bmod 2^m$ has *exactly four* solutions. Use **G.12** and induction, noting that the four solutions are related: x_1, $x_2 = -x_1$, $x_3 = x_1 + 2^{m-1}$, $x_4 = -x_1 + 2^{m-1}$.

21.6. Prove that $(-1/p) = +1$ if and only if p has the form $p = 4K + 1$.

21.7. As in **G.22**, find the value of $(791/101)$.

21.8. Solve $x^2 \equiv 140 \bmod 221$.

21.9. Solve $x^2 \equiv 65 \bmod 280$.

21.10. Solve $x^2 \equiv 11 \bmod 101$ (no solutions!).

21.11. Solve $x^2 \equiv 33 \bmod 101$.

21.12. Show that for every prime $p > 3$ the *sum* of the quadratic residues mod p is divisible by p. (Hint: Use EX. **2.2**.)

The beautiful has its place in mathematics
for here are triumphs of the creative
imagination, beautiful theorems, proofs
and processes whose perfection of form
has made them classic. He must be a
"practical" man who can see no
poetry in mathematics.—W. F. WHITE

CHAPTER 22

The quadratic reciprocity law

22.1. Results leading to the quadratic reciprocity law

We now begin a chain of theorems and corollaries which culminate in the justly revered quadratic reciprocity law with whose aid the Legendre symbol can always be evaluated, and hence the solvability of every pure quadratic congruence and, indeed, of every quadratic congruence decided.

It is this reciprocity law which the master, Gauss, declared to be "the jewel of arithmetic."

It will greatly simplify the statement of all the theorems if it is always understood, as in the previous lesson, that p is an odd prime, that $(a, p) = 1$, and that q is an odd prime distinct from p; furthermore, that $s = (p - 1)/2$ and that $t = (q - 1)/2$.

G.23: If K is the number of least positive residues of the set $a, 2a, 3a, \ldots, sa$ which exceed $p/2$, then $(a/p) = (-1)^K$.

For example, to evaluate $(3/101)$ we may note that $3, 2\cdot3, \ldots, 16\cdot3 = 48$ are $< 101/2$; then $17\cdot3, \ldots, 33\cdot3 = 99$ are $> 101/2$; next, $34\cdot3 = 102 \equiv 1 < 101/2$, $35\cdot3 \equiv 1 + 3, \ldots, 50\cdot3 \equiv 1 + 16\cdot3 < 101/2$; hence $K = 33 - 16 = 17$; therefore $(3/101) = (-1)^{17} = -1$.

Proof: Suppose $R_i a \equiv r_i$, $S_j a \equiv s_j \bmod p$, $0 < r_i < p/2$, $p/2 < s_j < p$, with $j = 1, 2, \ldots, K$; $i = 1, 2, \ldots, H = s - K$. Then we claim that

146

$r_1, r_2, \ldots, r_H, p - s_1, p - s_2, \ldots, p - s_H$ represent $1, 2, 3, \ldots, s$ in some order. Certainly the numbers of this list are all positive, all less than $p/2$, and are s in number; that the numbers are distinct, which will complete the claim, may be seen as follows:

(1) If $r_i = r_m$, then $R_i a \equiv R_m a \bmod p$; since $(a, p) = 1$, it follows that $R_i \equiv R_m \bmod p$; hence $R_i = R_m$ for $0 < R_i, R_m \leqslant s < p$.

(2) Similarly, $p - s_j = p - s_m$ implies $S_j = S_m$.

(3) If $r_i = p - s_j$, then $r_i + s_j \equiv 0 \bmod p$ so that $(R_i + S_j)a \equiv 0 \bmod p$; since $(a, p) = 1$, it follows that $R_i + S_j \equiv 0 \bmod p$; but this is impossible since $0 < R_i, S_j \leqslant s$ so that $0 < R_i + S_j < 2s = p - 1 < p$.

Hence if we multiply together the numbers of the set $a, 2a, 3a, \ldots, sa$ we may write

$$s! \, a^s = (R_1 a) \ldots (R_H a)(S_1 a) \ldots (S_K a) \equiv r_1 \ldots r_H s_1 \ldots s_K$$
$$= (-1)^K r_1 \ldots r_H (p - s_1) \ldots (p - s_K) = (-1)^K s! \bmod p$$

Since p is a prime, it follows that $(s!, p) = 1$, so that we may apply **G.6** and arrive at $a^s \equiv (-1)^K \bmod p$.

Finally, because of **G.22.2** it follows that $(a/p) = (-1)^K$, the congruence replaced by equality because of the limited range of values of the two symbols appearing and because $p > 2$.

Before continuing with the next theorem let us make use of the notions introduced in the preceding proof to define

$$A = r_1 + r_2 + \cdots + r_H, \quad B = s_1 + s_2 + \cdots + s_K,$$
$$M = [a/p] + [2a/p] + \cdots + [sa/p]$$

where the brackets indicate the bracket function of Chapter 12.

G.24: $(a - 1)(p^2 - 1)/8 = (M - K)p + 2B$.

Proof: By the division algorithm we find

$$R_i a = p[R_i a/p] + r_i, \qquad S_j a = p[S_j a/p] + s_j.$$

By EX. **3.1** we know that $1 + 2 + 3 + \cdots + s = s(s + 1)/2 = (p^2 - 1)/8$. Hence we may write

(22.1) $a(p^2 - 1)/8 = a + 2a + \cdots + sa = Mp + A + B.$

Then using the preliminary claim in the *proof* of **G.23**, we may write

(22.2) $(p^2 - 1)/8 = 1 + 2 + \cdots + s = r_1 + \cdots + r_H + (p - s_1)$
$$+ \cdots + (p - s_K) = A + Kp - B.$$

By subtracting (22.2) from (22.1) we eliminate A and arrive at **G.24**.

G.24.1: $(2/p) = (-1)^{(p^2-1)/8}$.

Proof: When we take $a = 2$ in **G.24**, we must take $M = 0$, because $M = [2/p] + [4/p] + \cdots + [(p - 1)/p]$ contains only summands for which the bracket function is zero. Hence **G.24** shows that $(p^2 - 1)/8 = 2B - Kp \equiv -Kp \equiv -K \equiv +K \bmod 2$. Then from **G.23** we obtain **G.24.1**.

G.24.2: If $M = [q/p] + [2q/p] + \cdots + [sq/p]$, then $(q/p) = (-1)^M$.

Proof: Since q is odd, $(q - 1)$ is even and if we take $a = q$ in **G.24** we find since p also is odd that $M \equiv K \bmod 2$. By **G.23** it follows that $(q/p) = (-1)^M$.

G.24.3: If $N = [p/q] + [2p/q] + \cdots + [tp/q]$, then $(p/q) = (-1)^N$.

Proof: For this corollary we need but change the roles of p and q in the preceding **G.24.2**.

G.25: In the notation of **G.24.2** and **G.24.3**, $M + N = st$.

Proof: The proof is a geometric one, originated by Eisenstein, a pupil of Gauss. Consider a Cartesian coordinate system and define a lattice point to be a point (x, y) both of whose coordinates are integers.

On the one hand, since p and q are odd, the number of lattice points *inside* the rectangle whose vertices are $O: (0, 0)$, $A: (p/2, 0)$, $B: (p/2, q/2)$, $C: (0, q/2)$ is given by st.

On the other hand, there are no lattice points within the rectangle on the diagonal OB; and the numbers of lattice points *inside* triangles OAB and OBC are given by M and N, respectively.

The first of these assertions follows from the fact that the equation of OB is $py = qx$; then inasmuch as $(p, q) = 1$, it follows that a lattice point (x, y) satisfying this equation would have to have x a multiple of p (and y a multiple of q), but the x's under consideration range only from 1 to s.

The second assertion follows from the fact that $[kq/p]$ is the number of lattice points on the vertical line $x = k$ between OA and OB, because these lattice points must have y-coordinates satisfying $0 < y \leqslant [kq/p]$. Summing from $k = 1$ to $k = s$, we find M lattice points inside triangle OAB. In a similar manner $[up/q]$ is the number of lattice points on the horizontal line $y = u$ between OC and OB. Summing from $u = 1$ to $u = t$, we find N lattice points inside triangle OBC.

Equating the results of the two ways of counting the number of lattice points inside the rectangle, we have the desired relation $M + N = st$.

G.26:   The *quadratic reciprocity law:* $(q/p) = (p/q)(-1)^{st}$.

Proof: From **G.24.2**, **G.24.3**, and **G.25**, we find

$$(p/q)(q/p) = (-1)^M(-1)^N = (-1)^{M+N} = (-1)^{st}.$$

Finally, whether (p/q) is $+1$ or -1, we have $(p/q)^2 = +1$; hence if we multiply the last displayed equation by (p/q) we arrive at the law stated in **G.26**.

This law receives its name for obvious reasons. On the one hand it deals with symbols which concern "quadratic" residues or nonresidues. On the other hand, the symbols (q/p) and (p/q) which appear in the law are in a sense "reciprocal." The implications of this last statement are well used in the next section.

22.2.   The evaluation of Legendre's symbol

Given any A not a multiple of p, we may decide whether the congruence $x^2 \equiv A \bmod p$ has a solution by finding whether (A/p) is $+1$, or -1, respectively.

To evaluate (A/p) we may proceed as follows:

(1) If a is the absolutely least residue of $A \bmod p$, we may write $(A/p) = (a/p)$ by **G.22.1**.

(2) If a contains any perfect squares, say $a = m^2b$, where b is "square-free," we may write $(a/p) = (b/p)$ by **G.22.4**.

(3) The most complicated form for b is $b = (-1)2q_1q_2 \cdots q_k$ where the q's are distinct odd primes; by **G.22.3** we may write

$$(b/p) = (-1/p)(2/p)(q_1/p) \cdots (q_k/p).$$

(4) To evaluate $(-1/p)$ we use $(-1)^s$ as in **G.21**.

(5) To evaluate $(2/p)$ we use -1 with the exponent $(p^2 - 1)/8$ as in **G.24.1**.

(6) To evaluate each (q/p) we use the quadratic reciprocity law **G.26** for this leads us to a new problem with a smaller "denominator," since in (p/q) we have $q \leqslant |b| \leqslant |a| \leqslant s < p$. We may begin the above routine again for (p/q) and eventually arrive at Legendre symbols that can be evaluated directly.

(7) Collecting the results in (4), (5), and (6) and substituting carefully in (3) we find the value of (A/p).

As an example we consider the evaluation of $(231/997)$. Here the prime 997 is so large that a direct consideration of the congruence $x^2 \equiv 231 \bmod$

997 is not practical. After factoring $231 = 3 \cdot 7 \cdot 11$, we write $(231/997) = (3/997)(7/997)(11/997)$.

To find $(3/997)$ we use **G.26** to write

$$(3/997) = (997/3)(-1)^{498 \cdot 1} = (1/3) = +1.$$

Here we have used $s = (997 - 1)/2$, $t = (3 - 1)/2$, and $997 \equiv 1 \bmod 3$.

To find $(7/997)$ we use **G.26** twice to write

$$(7/997) = (997/7)(-1)^{498 \cdot 3} = (3/7) = (7/3)(-1)^{3 \cdot 1} = -(1/3) = -1.$$

To find $(11/997)$ we use **G.26** twice to write

$$(11/997) = (997/11)(-1)^{498 \cdot 5} = (7/11) = (11/7)(-1)^{5 \cdot 3} = -(4/7) = -1.$$

Combining these results we conclude that

$$(231/997) = (+1)(-1)(-1) = +1.$$

Hence 231 *is* a quadratic residue of 997.

As a further example let us consider the problem of finding all odd primes p for which 11 is a quadratic residue. Evidently we must determine p so that $(11/p) = +1$ and by **G.26** and **G.22.1** we may suppose $p \equiv p'$ mod 11 and write

$$(11/p) = +1 = (p'/11)(-1)^{5(p-1)/2}, \qquad 0 < p' < 11.$$

When $(p'/11) = +1$, i.e., when $p' = p_1$ is a quadratic residue mod 11, we must have $(p - 1)/2$ *even*, so $p \equiv 1 \bmod 4$. When $(p'/11) = -1$, i.e., when $p' = p_2$ is a quadratic nonresidue mod 11, we must have $(p - 1)/2$ *odd*, so $p \equiv 3 \bmod 4$. By the Chinese remainder theorem, we must have in the first case $p \equiv p_1 \bmod 11$, $p \equiv 1 \bmod 4$, or $p \equiv 33 + 12p_1 \bmod 44$; and in the second case, with $p \equiv p_2 \bmod 11$, $p \equiv 3 \bmod 4$, we must have $p \equiv 11 + 12p_2 \bmod 44$. Since $11 \equiv 3 \bmod 4$, it follows from **G.21** that $(-1/11) = -1$, hence we may pair off the numbers p_2 and p_1 by the relation $p_2 = 11 - p_1$. But also $11 \equiv -33 \bmod 44$, so the two cases in the above argument may be combined into one formula: $p \equiv \pm(33 + 12p_1) \bmod 44$. Specifically, since 1, 4, 9, 5, 3 are the quadratic residues mod 11, we find that 11 is a quadratic residue of an odd prime p if and only if p has the form

$$p = 44T \pm u$$

where $u = 1, 5, 7, 9, 19$, and where T is an arbitrary integer such that p is prime and $p > 0$.

Some examples are as follows:

$$p = 5, 7, 19, 37, 43, 53, 79, 83, 89, 97, 107, 113, 127, 131.$$

22.3.   Concluding remarks

Legendre's symbol and the quadratic reciprocity law afford an elegant solution of the problem of determining the *existence* of solutions of $x^2 \equiv a \bmod p$; but in those cases where solutions exist, and it is required that they be found, there remains considerable labor, especially in case of a large prime.

If we consider $x^2 \equiv a \bmod m$, where the modulus is composite, we may use the methods of Chapter 21 to solve the problem. In particular, by virtue of EXS. **21.3, 21.4, 21.5,** and the results of this lesson, we can decide whether the congruence has a solution without actually solving it. Some reduction in this last problem can be effected by the use of the Jacobi symbol, which is an interesting generalization of the Legendre symbol. Some properties of the Jacobi symbol are given in the following exercises.

EXERCISES

22.1.   Evaluate $(783/997)$ and $(127/997)$.

22.2.   Evaluate $(2/p)$ for $p = 8K + 1, 8K + 3, 8K + 5, 8K + 7$.

22.3.   Determine whether $x^2 \equiv 239 \bmod 2431$ has solutions. Note that $2431 = 11 \cdot 13 \cdot 17$.

22.4.   Find all primes p for which 7 is a quadratic residue.

22.5.   Find all primes p for which 13 is a quadratic residue.

22.6.   If p and q are distinct odd primes with $p \equiv 1 \bmod 4$, show that $(p/q) = +1$, if and only if q has the form

$$q \equiv p + a(p + 1) \bmod 2p$$

where $(a/p) = +1$.

22.7.   If p and q are distinct odd primes with $p \equiv 3 \bmod 4$, show that $(p/q) = +1$, if and only if q has the form

$$q \equiv \pm\{3p + a(p + 1)\} \bmod 4p$$

where $(a/p) = +1$.

22.8.   If $P = p_1 p_2 \ldots p_k$ where the p's are odd primes, not necessarily distinct, use induction on k to prove that

$$(P - 1)/2 \equiv (p_1 - 1)/2 + (p_2 - 1)/2 + \cdots + (p_k - 1)/2 \bmod 2.$$

22.9.   Using EX. **22.8** and assuming $(P, q) = 1$ where q is an odd prime, show that $(P/q) = (q/p_1) \ldots (q/p_k)(-1)^{(P-1)(q-1)/4}$.

22.10.   If $P = p_1 p_2 \ldots p_k$ where the p's are odd primes and if $(Q, P) = 1$ define the Jacobi symbol (Q/P) as follows

$$(Q/P) = (Q/p_1)(Q/p_2) \ldots (Q/p_k).$$

If $(Q/P) = -1$, show that $x^2 \equiv Q \bmod P$ has no solution.

If $(Q/P) = +1$, show that $x^2 \equiv Q \bmod P$ may *or* may not have solutions.

22.11. Use the preceding exercises to show if Q and P are odd with $(Q, P) = 1$, then

$$(P/Q) = (Q/P)(-1)^{(P-1)(Q-1)/4}.$$

22.12. Make a sketch to illustrate the proof of **G.25** when $p = 23$ and $q = 13$.

Arithmetical symbols are written
diagrams, and geometrical figures
are graphic formulas.—D. HILBERT

CHAPTER 2 3

Pythagorean triplets

23.1.   The Diophantine equation $x^2 + y^2 = z^2$

Since the preceding chapters have provided us with a rather thorough
discussion of quadratic and higher degree congruences, it is natural to turn
our attention to the subject of Diophantine equations of quadratic and
higher degree. We soon discover that in general this new subject is extremely difficult. But if we limit ourselves to certain well-known equations
we can obtain complete and interesting results.

As an introduction to the subject of quadratic Diophantine equations
it is natural to try to find the complete solution in integers of the Pythagorean equation $x^2 + y^2 = z^2$, for, as every student of geometry and
trigonometry knows, the variables x, y, z can be interpreted as the sides
and hypotenuse of a right triangle, and it is particularly convenient for
"nice" problems or for the drawing of a right angle to have a fund of
whole number solutions such as the well-known 3, 4, 5 and 5, 12, 13. But
our object here is a bit more profound—we wish to find formulas exhibiting
all integral solutions of the equation.

Theorem: Except for interchanging x and y, all solutions in positive
integers x, y, z of the Pythagorean equation $x^2 + y^2 = z^2$ are given,
without repetition, by

(23.1) $x = k2uv, \quad y = k(u^2 - v^2), \quad z = k(u^2 + v^2)$

153

where k, u, v are positive integral parameters with $(u, v) = 1, u \not\equiv v \bmod 2$, and $u > v$.

Proof: (A) For clarity in establishing (*23.1*) we shall show in numbered steps the plan of proof. The student reader may be able to justify these steps for himself; if not, he can read on through the details of the proof.

(*1*) To find all solutions it will suffice to find all primitive solutions, i.e., those for which $(x, y, z) = 1$.

(*2*) Primitive solutions must have $(x, y) = 1, (x, z) = 1, (y, z) = 1$.

(*3*) Primitive solutions must have $x \not\equiv y \bmod 2$ and $z \equiv 1 \bmod 2$. Assume $x \equiv 0$ and $y \equiv 1 \bmod 2$. Define X, r, s by $x = 2X, 2r = z + y$, $2s = z - y$.

(*4*) Primitive solutions must have $(r, s) = 1$ and $r \not\equiv s \bmod 2$.

(*5*) The equation $x^2 + y^2 = z^2$ may be replaced by $X^2 = rs$.

(*6*) To satisfy (*4*) and (*5*) we must have $r = u^2, s = v^2, X = uv$, where $(u, v) = 1$ and $u \not\equiv v \bmod 2$.

(*7*) Every primitive solution must have the form

$$x = 2uv, \quad y = u^2 - v^2, \quad z = u^2 + v^2, \quad (u, v) = 1,$$
$$u \not\equiv v \bmod 2, \quad u > v > 0.$$

(*8*) Every x, y, z of the form (*7*) is a solution of $x^2 + y^2 = z^2$.

(*9*) Every x, y, z of the form (*7*) has the property $(x, y, z) = 1$.

(*1*) Observe that if x, y, z is a solution in integers of $x^2 + y^2 = z^2$ and if $(x, y, z) = d, x = Xd, y = Yd, z = Zd$, then $X^2 + Y^2 = Z^2$ with $(X, Y, Z) = 1$. Conversely, if $(x, y, z) = 1$ and $x^2 + y^2 = z^2$, then for any integer k, the integers $X = xk, Y = yk, Z = zk$ satisfy the relation $X^2 + Y^2 = Z^2$. If we describe a solution for which $(x, y, z) = 1$ as a *primitive triplet* and a solution for which $(x, y, z) = d > 1$ as an *imprimitive triplet*, then the situation which we have just investigated may be described as follows:

Every primitive triplet generates a family of imprimitive triplets; and conversely, every imprimitive triplet may be obtained from a properly chosen primitive triplet. Hence to find *all* solutions in integers of the Pythagorean equation it will suffice to find *all primitive* solutions.

(*2*) If x, y, z is a primitive solution so that $(x, y, z) = 1$ we must also have $(x, y) = 1, (x, z) = 1, (y, z) = 1$. For example, suppose $(x, y) = d$. Then from $x^2 + y^2 = z^2$, it follows that d^2 divides z^2. If p is a prime factor of d, then by the fundamental lemma of **8.1**, p must divide z; but then p must divide $(x, y, z) = 1$ which is a contradiction; hence d must be without prime factors; in other words, $d = 1$. Similarly, $(x, z) = 1$ and $(y, z) = 1$.

(*3*) If $x \equiv y \equiv 0 \bmod 2$, there is a contradiction of $(x, y) = 1$. If $x \equiv y \equiv 1 \bmod 2$, then $z^2 \equiv x^2 + y^2 \equiv 2 \bmod 8$, but the only quadratic residues of 8 are 0, 1, and 4. Hence $x \not\equiv y$ mod 2. We may assume, say, $y \equiv 1$ and $x \equiv 0$ mod 2, and set $x = 2X$. Then $z^2 \equiv x^2 + y^2 \equiv 1$ mod 2, so that $z \equiv 1$ mod 2. Since $z + y \equiv 0$ mod 2 and $z - y \equiv 0$ mod 2, we may set $z + y = 2r$ and $z - y = 2s$ where r and s are integers.

(4) From (3) we have $y = r - s$ and $z = r + s$; hence if $(r, s) = d$ we see that d divides both y and z. But from (2) we have $(y, z) = 1$, hence $d = 1$. Since $y \equiv 1$ mod 2 we see that $r \not\equiv s$ mod 2.

(5) If we rewrite $x^2 + y^2 = z^2$ as $x^2 = z^2 - y^2 = (z + y)(z - y)$ we find $4X^2 = 4rs$ and $X^2 = rs$.

(6) Suppose $(r, X) = m$ with $r = um$, $X = vm$. Then $(u, v) = 1$ and $X^2 = rs$ becomes $v^2m = us$. By EX. **6.10** we know $(u, v) = 1$ implies $(u, v^2) = 1$. Hence by Theorem 2 in **6.4** we have $m = uw$, so that $s = v^2w$ and $r = u^2w$. But $(r, s) = 1$, so $w = 1$. Thus $r = u^2$, $s = v^2$, $X = uv$, with $(u, v) = 1$. Furthermore, $a^2 \equiv a$ mod 2 for every a, so that $r \not\equiv s$ mod 2 requires $u \not\equiv v$ mod 2.

(7) Summarizing the previous steps, all primitive solutions of $x^2 + y^2 = z^2$, *if there are any*, must have the form

$$x = 2X = 2uv, \quad y = r - s = u^2 - v^2, \quad z = r + s = u^2 + v^2$$

where $(u, v) = 1$ and $u \not\equiv v$ mod 2. Moreover, if we are to have $x > 0$, $y > 0$, we must have $uv > 0$ and $|u| > |v|$. To avoid repetitions we may use positive values of the parameters and insist that $u > v > 0$.

(8) We have tried to emphasize in (7) the possibility that there may be no solution of the original equation, but it is easy to check that every set of integers x, y, z defined in (7) *is* a solution, for by elementary algebra we find that

$$(2uv)^2 + (u^2 - v^2)^2 = u^4 + 2u^2v^2 + v^4 = (u^2 + v^2)^2.$$

(9) Suppose x, y, z are defined as in (7) and let $d = (2uv, u^2 - v^2, u^2 + v^2)$ with $d \geqslant 1$. Since $(u + v)^2 = (u^2 + v^2) + (2uv)$ and $(u - v)^2 = (u^2 + v^2) - (2uv)$, it follows that d divides both $(u + v)^2$ and $(u - v)^2$. If $d > 1$, let p be a prime factor of d. By the fundamental lemma it follows that p divides both $u + v$ and $u - v$. Hence p divides both $2u = (u + v) + (u - v)$ and $2v = (u + v) - (u - v)$. Therefore, p divides $(2u, 2v) = 2(u, v) = 2$, so that $p = 2$. However, this is impossible since p also divides $u^2 + v^2$ and $u^2 + v^2 \equiv 1$ mod 2 because $u \not\equiv v$ mod 2. Thus $d = 1$ and the x, y, z defined by (7) do form a primitive triplet.

Combining steps (1) through (9) we have established that every Pythagorean triplet has the form (23.1), and, conversely, every triplet of the form (23.1) is a Pythagorean triplet.

(B) To show that (23.1) gives solutions of $x^2 + y^2 = z^2$ without repetition let us assume that X, Y, Z are obtained from (23.1) by using the values K, U, V of the parameters with $(U, V) = 1$, $U \not\equiv V \bmod 2$, $U > V > 0$, and $K > 0$.

The situation $x = Y$, $y = X$, $z = Z$ cannot arise. For the parity conditions $u \not\equiv v \bmod 2$, $U \not\equiv V \bmod 2$ insure that x has a factor 4 not present in y, and X has a factor 4 not present in Y. Of course z and Z are the greatest members of the sets, so the only way for the solutions from (23.1) to agree is to have $x = X$, $y = Y$, and $z = Z$.

Let $(K, k) = d$ with $K = Td$, $k = td$, and $(T, t) = 1$. From $Z + Y = z + y$ and $Z - Y = z - y$ we have $2KU^2 = 2ku^2$ and $2KV^2 = 2kv^2$. Thus $TU^2 = tu^2$ and $TV^2 = tv^2$. But $(T, t) = 1$; hence T divides both u^2 and v^2. However, $(u, v) = 1$ implies $(u^2, v^2) = 1$; hence $T = \pm 1$. Similarly, t must divide both U^2 and V^2, so $t = \pm 1$. Hence $K = \pm k$; but $K > 0$, $k > 0$, so $K = k$. Then $U^2 = u^2$ shows $U = \pm u$; but $U > 0$, $u > 0$, so $U = u$. Similarly, $V = v$.

By ordering x and y (with x divisible by a higher power of 2) we have shown in (A) that every Pythagorean triplet must have the form (23.1), and we have shown in (B) that triplets of this form can arise from only one set of parameter values. This completes the proof of the theorem.

In computing or checking primitive triplets like those in the following table, it is helpful to note the formulas

$$(23.2) \qquad x = 2uv, \quad z = x + (u - v)^2, \quad y = z - 2v^2$$

for these involve squares smaller than u^2.

v	u	x	y	z	v	u	x	y	z
1	2	4	3	5	2	5	20	21	29
1	4	8	15	17	2	7	28	45	53
1	6	12	35	37	2	9	36	77	85
1	8	16	63	65	3	4	24	7	25
2	3	12	5	13	3	8	48	55	73

23.2. The inradius of Pythagorean triplets

Let us consider a Pythagorean triplet (x, y, z) of positive integers x, y, z such that $x^2 + y^2 = z^2$ and let r designate the radius of the inscribed circle of the corresponding right triangle as in Figure 7. Let us call r the "inradius" of the triplet.

R.1: Given the Pythagorean triplet x, y, z, then its inradius r is an integer.

Proof: There are two rather obvious ways to express the area A of the triangle leading to the following equations:

$$r(x + y + z) = 2A = xy.$$

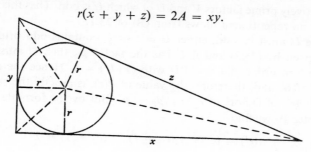

FIGURE 7.

By the discussion in **23.1** we know that all positive integer solutions of $x^2 + y^2 = z^2$ have the form

$$x = k2uv, \quad y = k(u^2 - v^2), \quad z = k(u^2 + v^2),$$

where k, u, v are positive integers with $(u, v) = 1$, with u and v of different parity, and with $u > v$. By substitution in the displayed equation we obtain the relation $2rk(u^2 + uv) = 2k^2uv(u^2 - v^2)$ which simplifies readily to $r = kv(u - v)$, thus proving r to be an integer.

With certain agreements we can write every positive integer r uniquely in the following form

$$(23.3) \qquad r = 2^a p_1{}^{a_1} p_2{}^{a_2} \dots p_n{}^{a_n}, \qquad a \geqslant 0, \quad n \geqslant 0,$$

where p_i is an odd prime, $a_i \geqslant 1$, and $2 < p_1 < p_2 < \cdots < p_n$. If $n = 0$, it is understood that $r = 2^a$. If $a = 0$, $2^0 = 1$.

We will let the number-theoretic function $P(r)$ represent the number of distinct positive primitive Pythagorean triplets having r as the corresponding inradius. (We consider triplets corresponding to congruent triangles to be the same: e.g., $x = 3$, $y = 4$, $z = 5$ is considered the same as $x = 4$, $y = 5$, $z = 5$.)

R.2:   If r is given by (23.3), then $P(r) = 2^n$.

Proof: The integers x, y, z as used in the proof of **R.1** will form a primitive triplet if and only if $k = 1$. Then the equation for r takes the form $r = v(u - v)$, where the second factor, $u - v$, must be odd, since u and v are of different parity. Furthermore, from $(u, v) = 1$ it follows that $(v, u - v) = 1$ as in EX. **6.11**. Conversely, if $r = VU$ where V and U are positive integers with U odd and with $(V, U) = 1$, then the equations $V = v$, $U = u - v$ may be solved for $u = U + V$, $v = V$ where u and v are positive integers such that $u > v$, $(u, v) = 1$, and u and v are of opposite parity. Hence all positive primitive Pythagorean triplets having r as inradius are found by factoring r in all possible ways as a product VU of two relatively prime factors V and U of which U is odd. That this procedure leads to no repetitions follows from (B) of **23.1**.

Since U must be odd, either $U = 1$ or U contains odd prime factors. If r is given by (23.3) and if U has the factor p_i, then U must have the factor $p_i^{a_i}$ in order that $r = VU$ with $(V, U) = 1$. Hence the number of choices of U, and, therefore, the value of $P(r)$, is exactly the same as the number $\tau(r')$ of factors of $r' = p_1 p_2 \ldots p_n$. But by the formula developed in Chapter 10 we find

$$\tau(r') = (e_1 + 1)(e_2 + 1) \ldots (e_n + 1) = 2^n$$

since each exponent e_i in r' has the value 1. Since $P(r) = \tau(r')$, this completes the proof of **R.2**.

In particular, we have shown that $P(r)$ is positive for every r and that the range of $P(r)$ consists exactly of all powers of 2, including $2^0 = 1$.

As an example, consider $r = 15$ for which $n = 2$ so that $P(15) = 4$. In tabular form the solutions are as follows:

V	U	u	v	x	y	z
15	1	16	15	480	31	481
5	3	8	5	80	39	89

V	U	u	v	x	y	z
3	5	8	3	48	55	73
1	15	16	1	32	255	257

Let $N(r)$ represent the total number of distinct positive Pythagorean triplets, *not necessarily primitive*, having r as the corresponding inradius.

R.3:   If r is given by (23.3), then

$$N(r) = (a + 1)(2a_1 + 1)(2a_2 + 1) \ldots (2a_n + 1).$$

Proof: From the formula $r = kv(u - v)$ in **R.1** we see that k must be a divisor of r. Then $d = r/k$ is the inradius of a primitive Pythagorean triplet. Conversely, if d is a divisor of r, say $r = kd$, then a Pythagorean triplet of inradius r can be found by magnifying a primitive Pythagorean triplet of inradius d by the factor of proportionality k. The Pythagorean triplets obtained for different values of d correspond to different values of k; hence by (B) of **23.1** they will be distinct. Therefore, the desired function $N(r)$ can be obtained as follows:

$$N(r) = \sum P(d)$$

where the summation is extended over all positive divisors d of r.

This is a perfect occasion to apply the theorem on multiplicative functions developed in **11.1**, for we can show $P(d)$ to be a multiplicative function. In fact by **R.2** we know $P(d) = 2^{\nu(d)}$ where $\nu(d)$ is the number of distinct odd prime factors of d. When $(a, b) = 1$, the integers a and b can have no odd prime factors in common, hence $\nu(ab) = \nu(a) + \nu(b)$. Therefore if $(a, b) = 1$, then

$$P(ab) = 2^{\nu(ab)} = 2^{\nu(a) + \nu(b)} = 2^{\nu(a)} 2^{\nu(b)} = P(a)P(b),$$

so that $P(d)$ is a multiplicative function.

It follows from **11.1** that $N(r) = \sum P(d)$ is also a multiplicative function, so to find the precise form for $N(r)$ we need only to investigate $N(p^a)$ for primes p.

When $p = 2$, the only even prime, we find

$$N(2^a) = P(1) + P(2) + P(2^2) + \cdots + P(2^a)$$
$$= 2^0 + 2^0 + 2^0 + \cdots + 2^0 = a + 1.$$

When p is odd, we find

$$N(p^a) = P(1) + P(p) + P(p^2) + \cdots + P(p^a)$$
$$= 2^0 + 2^1 + 2^1 + \cdots + 2^1 = 2a + 1.$$

Combining these results with the fact that $N(r)$ is multiplicative, we arrive at the formula displayed in **R.3**.

For a numerical example, we take $r = 15$. Here $a = 0, a_1 = 1, a_2 = 1$, hence $N(15) = (0 + 1)(2 + 1)(2 + 1) = 9$. Then we compute

$k = 15, d = 1, P(1) = 1$ with $(4, 3, 5)$ leading to $(60, 45, 75)$;
$k = 5, d = 3, P(3) = 2$ with $(8, 15, 17)$ leading to $(40, 75, 85)$,
    and with $(24, 7, 25)$ leading to $(120, 35, 125)$;
$k = 3, d = 5, P(5) = 2$ with $(12, 35, 37)$ leading to $(36, 105, 111)$,
    and with $(60, 11, 61)$ leading to $(180, 33, 183)$;
$k = 1, d = 15, P(15) = 4$ leading to the four primitive triplets
    given in the previous example.

EXERCISES

23.1.   Extend the table in **23.1** to find all 22 primitive Pythagorean triplets for which $0 < v < u \leqslant 10$.

23.2.   If $u > 1$, let $J(u)$ be the number of integers v such that $0 < v < u$, $(u, v) = 1$, $u \not\equiv v \bmod 2$. Show that

$$J(u) = \phi(u), \text{ if } u \equiv 0 \bmod 2; \quad J(u) = \tfrac{1}{2}\phi(u), \text{ if } u \equiv 1 \bmod 2.$$

23.3.   Find all primitive Pythagorean triplets having $x = 60$.

23.4.   Show that it is impossible to find a primitive Pythagorean triplet with side T where T is even but not a multiple of 4. Show that all other integers T can be the side of at least one primitive Pythagorean triplet.

23.5.   Let T be written in the form (23.3) and let $S(T)$ indicate the number of primitive Pythagorean triplets of side T. Show that $S(T) = 2^{n-1}, 0, 2^n$, according as $a = 0, a = 1, a > 1$. (E. Bahier.)

23.6.   Follow the method of **23.1** and obtain the complete solution of the Diophantine equation $x^2 + 2y^2 = z^2$, supplying the proofs of the following steps:

      (*1*)   To find all solutions it will suffice to find all primitive solutions for which $(x, y, z) = 1$.

      (*2*)   Primitive solutions must have $(x, y) = 1$, $(x, z) = 1$, $(y, z) = 1$.

      (*3*)   Both x and z must be odd and y even. Define $y = 2Y$, $z + x = 2r$, $z - x = 2s$.

      (*4*)   From $(x, z) = 1$ it follows that $(r, s) = 1$.

      (*5*) $x^2 + 2y^2 = z^2$ becomes $2Y^2 = rs$.

      (*6*)   Either (I) $r = 2R^2$, $s = S^2$, with $(2R, S) = 1$; or (II) $r = S^2$, $s = 2R^2$, with $(2R, S) = 1$.

      (*7*)   Every primitive solution must have the following form

$$x = \pm (2R^2 - S^2), \quad y = 2RS, \quad z = 2R^2 + S^2, \quad (2R, S) = 1.$$

      (*8*)   Every x, y, z of the form (*7*) is a *solution* of $x^2 + 2y^2 = z^2$.

      (*9*)   Every x, y, z of the form (*7*) is a *primitive* solution.

23.7.   Graph the function $P(r)$ in **R.2** of **23.2** for values of r from 1 through 30.

23.8.   Find the eight smallest solutions of $P(r) = 8$.

23.9.   Graph the function $N(r)$ in **R.3** of **23.2** for values of r from 1 through 30.

23.10.   Find the eight smallest solutions of $N(r) = 6$.

23.11.   Show that $N(r) = t$ has a solution r for every positive integer t, but that the solution is unique if and only if t is a power of 2, including $2^0 = 1$.

23.12.   Investigate the meaning and origin of the word "harpedonaptae."

23.13.   Let r_x, r_y, r_z designate the radii of the three escribed circles of the triangle corresponding to a Pythagorean triplet. Prove that r_x, r_y, r_z are all integers. If r is the inradius, show that $rr_z = r_x r_y$ and $r_z = r + r_y + r_z$.

23.14.   Prove that one side "x" of a Pythagorean triplet always has an extra factor 4 as compared with the other side "y." Let $N_x(r)$, $N_y(r)$, $N_z(r)$ indicate the total numbers of Pythagorean triplets such that $r = r_x$, $r = r_y$, $r = r_z$, respectively. Beginning with EX. **23.13**, prove that

$$N(r) = N_x(r) + N_y(r) + N_z(r) + 1,$$

where $N(r)$ is defined as in **23.2**.

23.15.   For a set of points in three dimensions let M be the property that the distance between each pair of points is an integer. For example, given three (or four) compatible positive integers, we can construct a triangle (or tetrahedron) whose vertices have property M.

      (*1*)   The "line": show that the infinite set of points with Cartesian coordinates (x, y, z) given by $(n, 0, 0)$ where n runs over all integers has property M.

         For the next parts of the exercise let a_i, b_i, c_i for $i = 1, 2, \ldots, m$ represent m *dissimilar* Pythagorean triplets with $a_i{}^2 + b_i{}^2 = c_i{}^2$.

Observe from (23.1) that m may be as large as desired. Define

$$A_m = a_1 a_2 \ldots a_m, \quad B_m = b_1 b_2 \ldots b_m, \quad C_m = c_1 c_2 \ldots c_m.$$

(2) The "rack": when $m = 2$, show that the nine points with coordinates $(0, 0, 0)$, $(\pm a_1 b_1, 0, 0)$, $(\pm a_2 b_2, 0, 0)$, $(0, \pm a_1 b_2, 0)$, $(0, \pm a_2 b_1, 0)$ have property M.

(3) The "diamonds": prove that the $4m + 3$ points with coordinates $(0, 0, 0)$, $(\pm A_m B_m, 0, 0)$, $(0, 0, \pm a_i A_m B_m / b_i)$, $(0, 0, \pm b_i A_m B_m / a_i)$ with $i = 1, 2, \ldots, m$, have property M.

(4) The "wheel": prove that the $4m + 3$ points with coordinates $(0, 0, 0)$, $(\pm C_m{}^2, 0, 0)$, $(\pm (2a_i{}^2 - c_i{}^2) C_m{}^2 / c_i{}^2, \pm 2a_i b_i C_m{}^2 / c_i{}^2, 0)$ with $i = 1, 2, \ldots, m$, have property M.

(5) The "wheel and axle": combine (3), magnified by a factor $C_m{}^2$, with (4), magnified by a factor $A_m B_m$, to produce a set of $8m + 3$ points with property M.

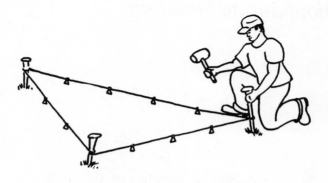

As we apply this projective geometry let
the spirit delight in the artistic balance
of this enchanted realm.—C. J. KEYSER

CHAPTER 24

Homogeneous quadratic
Diophantine equations

24.1   Concerning families of solutions

We recognize that the Pythagorean relation $x^2 + y^2 = z^2$ is a special instance of the general homogeneous quadratic Diophantine equation in three variables:

(24.1) $H(x, y, z) = Ax^2 + Bxy + Cy^2 + Dxz + Eyz + Fz^2 = 0,$

where A, B, C, D, E, F are given integers, not all zero, and the problem is to determine all solutions in integers x, y, z.

It is obvious that (24.1) always has the trivial solution $0, 0, 0$. We concern ourselves with finding all the nontrivial solutions, for which at least one of x, y, z is not zero; but we must realize that (24.1) may have no nontrivial solutions—see the later Examples 1 and 3.

To make our discussion easier we shall introduce a plan for dividing all ordered triples of integers x, y, z [which may or may not be solutions of (24.1)] into families of related triples. We understand that triples x_1, y_1, z_1 and x_2, y_2, z_2 are considered to be the same triple if and only if $x_1 = y_1$, $y_1 = y_2, z_1 = z_2$; and then we introduce the following definition.

162

Definition: The ordered triple of integers x_1, y_1, z_1 is said to be *related to* (or *in the family of*) the triple x_2, y_2, z_2, designated by $x_1, y_1, z_1 \sim x_2, y_2, z_2$, if and only if there exist nonzero integers u and v such that

$$(24.2) \qquad ux_1 = x_2 v, \quad uy_1 = y_2 v, \quad uz_1 = z_2 v, \quad u \neq 0, \quad v \neq 0.$$

For example, although the triples $12, 10, -6$ and $-18, -15, 9$ are not the same, we do have $12, 10, -6 \sim -18, -15, 9$ using $u = 3$ and $v = -2$. But we find that the triples $5, 0, -2$ and $40, 0, 8$ are not related, which we write $5, 0, -2 \nsim 40, 0, 8$, because the conditions $5u = 40v$ and $-2u = 8v$ require $5u = -10u$, which is impossible unless $u = 0$. Sometimes we say that related triples are *proportional*, but this use of fractions may be awkward if some of the integers in a triple are zero, so we prefer the definition (24.2), for it does not require discussion of special cases.

Theorem 1: "Being related" as defined in (24.2) is an equivalence relation (as defined in **13.2**) for the set of all ordered triples of integers.

Proof: (*1*) By definition the relation is determinative: just one of the situations $x_1, y_1, z_1 \sim x_2, y_2, z_2$ or $x_1, y_1, z_1 \nsim x_2, y_2, z_2$ will hold depending upon the existence or nonexistence of $u \neq 0$ and $v \neq 0$ which will satisfy (24.2). (*2*) The relation is reflexive: for a triple is related to itself by the simple choice $u = 1$ and $v = 1$. (*3*) The relation is symmetric: for if $x_1, y_1, z_1 \sim x_2, y_2, z_2$ using $u \neq 0$ and $v \neq 0$, then $x_2, y_2, z_2 \sim x_1, y_1, z_1$ using $u' = v$ and $v' = u$. (*4*) The relation is transitive: for if $x_1, y_1, z_1 \sim x_2, y_2, z_2$ using $u_1 \neq 0$ and $v_1 \neq 0$; and if $x_2, y_2, z_2 \sim x_3, y_3, z_3$ using $u_2 \neq 0$ and $v_2 \neq 0$; then $x_1, y_1, z_1 \sim x_3, y_3, z_3$ using $u_3 = u_2 u_1 \neq 0$ and $v_3 = v_2 v_1 \neq 0$; for by hypothesis $u_1 x_1 = x_2 v_1$ and $u_2 x_2 = x_3 v_2$, hence $u_3 x_1 = u_2 u_1 x_1 = u_2 x_2 v_1 = x_3 v_2 v_1 = x_3 v_3$, with similar equations for "y" and "z".

Every equivalence relation divides the set of objects over which it is defined exhaustively into mutually exclusive families of related objects; that is, because of (*2*) every object is in at least one family, and because of (*4*) these families do not overlap. In the present case we note that if, say, $x_1 = 0$, then every triple x_2, y_2, z_2 such that $x_2, y_2, z_2 \sim 0, y_1, z_1$ must have $x_2 = 0$. In particular, the triple $0, 0, 0$ is in a class by itself; whereas every other triple is a member of a family containing infinitely many triples. This follows because if $k \neq 0$ we may use $u = k$ and $v = 1$ to show $x, y, z \sim kx, ky, kz$; and if at least one of x, y, z is not zero, the triples kx, ky, kz and $k'x, k'y, k'z$, as k and k' run over all integers, are the same if and only if $k = k'$. With this result as motivation we describe $0, 0, 0$ as the *trivial* triple; and we say that x, y, z is a *nontrivial* triple if and only if at least one of x, y, z is not zero.

A nontrivial triple is called *primitive* if $(x, y, z) = 1$; and *imprimitive* if $(x, y, z) = d > 1$.

Theorem 2: In every family of nontrivial triples there are two and only two primitive triplets. If X, Y, Z is a primitive triplet, then every triple x, y, z in the same family has the form

$$(24.3) \qquad x = kX, \quad y = kY, \quad z = kZ, \quad k \neq 0$$

where k is an integer. The primitive members have $k = +1$ and $k = -1$.

Proof: (A) For every nontrivial triple x, y, z we know $(x, y, z) = d$ is uniquely defined, except for sign, and $x = Xd$, $y = Yd$, $z = Zd$ with $(X, Y, Z) = 1$. Using $u = 1$ and $v = d \neq 0$, we have $x, y, z \sim X, Y, Z$.

(B) Suppose $x, y, z \sim X, Y, Z$ where $(X, Y, Z) = 1$. From $ux = Xv$, $uy = Yv$, $uz = Zv$, with $u \neq 0$ and $v \neq 0$, by removing the factor (u, v) we obtain $u'x = Xv'$, $u'y = Yv'$, $u'z = Zv'$, where $u' \neq 0$ and $v' \neq 0$ and $(u', v') = 1$. Therefore, u' divides each of X, Y, Z; but $(X, Y, Z) = 1$, hence $u' = \pm 1$. Choosing $k = u'v'$, we have $x = kX$, $y = kY$, $z = kZ$, $k \neq 0$, as in (24.3). Furthermore, since $(kX, kY, kZ) = k(X, Y, Z) = k$, we see that x, y, z is primitive if and only if $k = +1$ or $k = -1$.

Theorem 3: If a nontrivial triple x_1, y_1, z_1 is a solution of (24.1), then every triple x_2, y_2, z_2 related to x_1, y_1, z_1 is also a solution of (24.1).

Proof: If x_1, y_1, z_1 solves (24.1), it is easy to check that vx_1, vy_1, vz_1 also solves (24.1), for the homogeneity of (24.1) allows multiplication by v^2 to be followed by simple rearrangement to complete the check. If $x_2, y_2, z_2 \sim x_1, y_1, z_1$ so that $ux_2 = vx_1$, $uy_2 = vy_1$, $uz_2 = vz_1$ with $u \neq 0$ and $v \neq 0$, it is clear by identity that ux_2, uy_2, uz_2 solves (24.1). Then because $u \neq 0$ and because of the homogeneity of (24.1) we may remove the nonzero factor u^2 to show that x_2, y_2, z_2 solves (24.1).

Combining Theorems 1, 2, 3 we see that the nontrivial solutions of (24.1)—*if there are any*—may be divided into disjoint families of solutions, each containing infinitely many triples but exactly two primitive triples; and (24.3) will allow us to describe all the solutions of (24.1) if we can find all primitive solutions. Even if we succeed only in describing some method of finding one and only one member of each family of solutions (perhaps not primitive), we can see that the problem is nearly solved—for in individual cases we can find $d = (x, y, z)$ and then convert to (24.3)—and this is what we shall do in the next section.

The ideas of dealing with whole families of solutions and of picking a representative for each family should not seem strange to the student if he will recall in the study of congruences the concepts of residue classes and complete residue systems.

Some equations of type (24.1) are of such simple nature that rather elementary arguments will produce all the solutions.

Example 1: $x^2 + y^2 + z^2 = 0$ has only the trivial solution.

Example 2: $x^2 - 2y^2 - 2xz + z^2 = 0$ has just one family of non-trivial solutions—namely, $x = k$, $y = 0$, $z = k$, $k \neq 0$—for the equation may be rewritten $(x - z)^2 = 2y^2$, and since 2 is not a square, the only solutions are those for which $x - z = 0$ and $y = 0$.

Example 3: $2x^2 + 3y^2 = z^2$ has only the trivial solution. The existence of solutions in integers requires $z^2 \equiv 2x^2 \bmod 3$. If $x \equiv \pm 1 \bmod 3$, then $z^2 \equiv 2 \bmod 3$; but this is impossible since 2 is not a quadratic residue mod 3. If $x \equiv 0 \bmod 3$, then $z \equiv 0 \bmod 3$. Let $x = 3X$, $z = 3Z$, then the equation reduces to $6X^2 + y^2 = 3Z^2$, which implies $y \equiv 0 \bmod 3$. Then every non-trivial solution—if there are any—has (x, y, z) divisible by 3. But this contradicts Theorems 2 and 3, for every nontrivial solution belongs to a family containing a primitive solution.

For the proof of our main theorem the following discussion will be helpful. A nontrivial triple x, y, z having $z = 0$ will be called *ideal*, but having $z \neq 0$ will be called *ordinary*.

Theorem 4: A nontrivial triple x, y, z is related to an ordinary triple x_0, y_0, z_0, having $z_0 \neq 0$, if and only if

(24.4) $\qquad\qquad xz_0 = x_0z, \quad yz_0 = y_0z.$

Proof: (A) If $x, y, z \sim x_0, y_0, z_0$ so that $ux = x_0v$, $uy = y_0v$, $uz = z_0v$ with $u \neq 0$ and $v \neq 0$; then $uxz_0v = x_0vuz$, but $uv \neq 0$, so $xz_0 = x_0z$. Similarly, $yz_0 = y_0z$.

(B) Conversely, if $xz_0 = x_0z$ and $yz_0 = y_0z$, we also have $zz_0 = z_0z$ and therefore $x, y, z \sim x_0, y_0, z_0$ using $u = z_0 \neq 0$ and $v = z$, providing we can show $z \neq 0$. But if $z = 0$, the assumed relations (24.4) require, since $z_0 \neq 0$, that $x = 0$, $y = 0$, contradicting the hypothesis that x, y, z is a nontrivial triple.

24.2. Method for solving
$$Ax^2 + Bxy + Cy^2 + Dxz + Eyz + Fz^2 = 0$$

In order that the following theorem shall apply without exception we need to think for a moment in terms of a larger number system (apologies) and suppose that our quadratic problem does not reduce to two linear problems because of $H(x, y, z)$ being expressible as the product of two linear factors of the form $L(x, y, z) = \alpha x + \beta y + \gamma z$, where α, β, γ are complex numbers However, at the close of the section we show that the hypothesis that

$H(x, y, z)$ is irreducible may be expressed entirely in terms of integers (so we can recall the apologies). If $H(x, y, z)$ is reducible the problem is readily solved for all of its possible integer solutions x, y, z by solving each of the linear problems $L(x, y, z) = 0$.

For instance, the theorem does not apply to Example 2 in **24.1** for in that case $H(x, y, z) = (x - z)^2 - 2y^2 = (x - z + \sqrt{2}y)(x - z - \sqrt{2}y)$.

We also suppose that $H(x, y, z) = 0$ has a nontrivial primitive ordinary solution x_0, y_0, z_0. If there is any nontrivial solution X_0, Y_0, Z_0 it is just a matter of notation to arrange that $Z_0 \neq 0$ and it is a matter of applying Theorems 2 and 3 to replace X_0, Y_0, Z_0 by x_0, y_0, z_0 where $(x_0, y_0, z_0) = 1$ and $z_0 \neq 0$.

But it is not always easy as in Examples 1 and 3 of **24.1** to decide whether $H(x, y, z) = 0$ has *any* nontrivial solution. In many problems a nontrivial solution can be found by inspection, perhaps by letting one variable be zero.

For instance, if $H(x, y, z) = bx^2 - 2axy + by^2 - bz^2$ we may use

$$x_0 = \pm 1, \; y_0 = 0, \; z_0 = \pm 1; \quad \text{or } x_0 = b, \; y_0 = 2a, \; z_0 = b \text{ if } (2a, b) = 1.$$

It will be obvious that the solutions obtained by the following theorem will have their simplest form, in general, when x_0, y_0, z_0 is in simplest form.

Theorem 5: If $H(x, y, z) = Ax^2 + Bxy + Cy^2 + Dxz + Eyz + Fz^2$ with integer coefficients A, B, C, D, E, F is such that

(H.1) $H(x, y, z)$ is irreducible (even using complex numbers); and

(H.2) there exists a nontrivial primitive triple of integers

$$x_0, y_0, z_0 \text{ with } z_0 \neq 0 \text{ such that } H(x_0, y_0, z_0) = 0;$$

then $H(x, y, z) = 0$ has infinitely many families of nontrivial solutions, and each such family contains one and only one member x', y', z' of the form

$$(24.5) \quad \begin{cases} x' = -(Ax_0 + By_0 + Dz_0)r^2 - (2Cy_0 + Ez_0)rs + Cx_0 s^2, \\ y' = Ay_0 r^2 - (2Ax_0 + Dz_0)rs - (Bx_0 + Cy_0 + Ez_0)s^2, \\ z' = z_0(Ar^2 + Brs + Cs^2), \end{cases}$$

where r and s are integers with $(r, s) = 1$ and $r \geqslant 0$.

(If $r = 0$ we agree to take $s = 1$, rather than $s = -1$.)

Proof: (A) Let X, Y, Z be any nontrivial triple of integers not related to x_0, y_0, z_0. By Theorem 4 the integers $Xz_0 - x_0 Z$, $Yz_0 - y_0 Z$ cannot both be zero. Hence $(Xz_0 - x_0 Z, Yz_0 - y_0 Z) = d$ is defined and $Xz_0 - x_0 Z = rd$, $Yz_0 - y_0 Z = sd$ with $(r, s) = 1$. If $r \neq 0$ we may assume

$r > 0$ by remembering that $-d$ is an alternate for d. If $r = 0$, then $s \neq 0$, and in fact $s = \pm 1$. In both cases we have

(24.6)
$$r(Yz_0 - y_0Z) = s(Xz_0 - x_0Z).$$

We wish to find necessary and sufficient conditions that $H(X, Y, Z) = 0$. From $(H.2)$ we have $H(x_0, y_0, z_0) = 0$ with $z_0 \neq 0$. Then elementary algebra shows us that

$$\begin{aligned}
z_0^2 H(X, Y, Z) &= z_0^2 H(X, Y, Z) - Z^2 H(x_0, y_0, z_0) \\
&= (A(Xz_0 + x_0Z) + BZy_0 + Dz_0Z)(Xz_0 - x_0Z) \\
&\quad + (BXz_0 + C(Yz_0 + y_0Z) + Ez_0Z)(Yz_0 - y_0Z).
\end{aligned}$$

If $r \neq 0$ we employ (24.6) to eliminate Y, and we use (24.5) to write

$$r^2 z_0^2 H(X, Y, Z) = (Xz_0 - x_0Z)(Xz' - x'Z).$$

Since $r^2 z_0^2 \neq 0$ and $Xz_0 - x_0Z = rd \neq 0$, we find that $H(X, Y, Z) = 0$ if and only if $Xz' = x'Z$. If this condition is satisfied, then (24.6) and (24.5) show that $Yz' = y'Z$.

Similarly, if $r = 0$ we have $s \neq 0$ and we can study $s^2 z_0^2 H(X, Y, Z)$ to show $H(X, Y, Z) = 0$ if and only if $Yz' = y'Z$; and if this condition is satisfied, then $Xz' = x'Z$.

In both cases we have shown that necessary and sufficient conditions for a nontrivial triple X, Y, Z which is not related to x_0, y_0, z_0 to be a solution of $H(x, y, z) = 0$ are that the x', y', z' of (24.5) determined by the specific r and s, $(r, s) = 1, r \geq 0$, which are associated with $(Xz_0 - x_0Z, Yz_0 - y_0Z) = d, Xz_0 - x_0Z = rd, Yz_0 - y_0Z = sd$, shall satisfy

(24.7)
$$Xz' = x'Z, \quad Yz' = y'Z.$$

(B) We shall show that x', y', z' defined by (24.5) for any r, s with $(r, s) = 1$ and $r \geq 0$, in the presence of $(H.1)$ and $(H.2)$ form a nontrivial triple. It will be convenient to define

$$J = -z_0((2Ax_0 + By_0 + Dz_0)r + (Bx_0 + 2Cy_0 + Ez_0)s)$$

for then it is easy to check that

(24.8)
$$x'z_0 - x_0z' = rJ, \quad y'z_0 - y_0z' = sJ.$$

Since r and s are not both zero, the hypothesis $x' = 0, y' = 0, z' = 0$ requires from (24.8) and $(H.2)$ that $J = 0$ and that $Ar^2 + Brs + Cs^2 = 0$. But this pair of conditions combined with $(H.2)$ are precisely the conditions for $H(x, y, z)$ to have the linear factor $r(yz_0 - y_0z) - s(xz_0 - x_0z)$ which contradicts $(H.1)$.

(C) First, the triple x', y', z' is related to x_0, y_0, z_0 if and only if $J = 0$; for this is the implication of Theorem 4 and (24.8).

Second, there is one and only one pair of integers r, s with $(r, s) = 1$ and $r \geqslant 0$ such that $J = 0$. Both of the integers $R = Bx_0 + 2Cy_0 + Ez_0$ and $S = -(2Ax_0 + By_0 + Dz_0)$ cannot be zero, since if it is assumed that they are both zero it will follow that

$$z_0{}^2 H(x, y, z) =$$
$$A(xz_0 - x_0 z)^2 + B(xz_0 - x_0 z)(yz_0 - y_0 z) + C(yz_0 - y_0 z)^2.$$

But the quadratic $Ax^2 + Bxy + Cy^2$ always has linear factors, if we are permitted to use complex numbers, so we have a contradiction of $(H.1)$. Hence $(R, S) = d_0$ is defined and $R = r_0 d_0$, $S = s_0 d_0$ with $(r_0, s_0) = 1$ and $r_0 \geqslant 0$. Then $J = 0$ requires $Rs = Sr$, and hence $r_0 s = s_0 r$.

If $r_0 = 0$, then $s_0 = \pm 1$, and $J = 0$ implies $r = 0$, so $s = \pm 1$. The natural agreement to take $s_0 > 0$ and $s > 0$ results in $s = s_0$.

If $r_0 \neq 0$ and $r = 0$, we have $s = 1$ and $J \neq 0$. In the remaining case $r_0 \neq 0$ and $r \neq 0$ with $r_0 s = s_0 r$ and $(r_0, s_0) = 1$ and $(r, s) = 1$, so we find that r divides r_0 and r_0 divides r, hence $r = \pm r_0$, but the agreements $r > 0, r_0 > 0$ require $r = r_0$; and consequently $s = s_0$.

(D) The triple x', y', z' in (24.5) is always a solution of $H(x, y, z) = 0$.

First, if $J = 0$, we have shown in (C) that the triple x_0', y_0', z_0' based on r_0, s_0 is related to x_0, y_0, z_0. Hence by Theorem 3 and $(H.2)$ it follows that x_0', y_0', z_0' is a solution of $H(x, y, z) = 0$.

Second, if $J \neq 0$, we have shown in (C) that x', y', z' is not related to x_0, y_0, z_0; we have shown in (B) that x', y', z' is a nontrivial triple; so we are in a position to apply to x', y', z' the test developed in (A). The test in (A) requires first that we determine "r" and "s" for x', y', z'; but (24.8) shows "d" $= J$ and "r" $= r$, "s" $= s$. Consequently, the test (24.7) takes the trivial form $x'z' = x'z'$, $y'z' = y'z'$.

(E) Every nontrivial solution X, Y, Z is related to one of the solutions x', y', z' given in (24.5).

In (C) we showed that x_0, y_0, z_0 is related to x_0', y_0', z_0' based on r_0, s_0. By Theorem 1, if $X, Y, Z \sim x_0, y_0, z_0$, then $X, Y, Z \sim x_0', y_0', z_0'$.

In (A) we showed for every nontrivial solution $X, Y, Z \nsim x_0, y_0, z_0$ how to determine r and s so that $Xz' = x'Z$, $Yz' = y'Z$ as in (24.7). Coupled with $Zz' = z'Z$, the conditions (24.7) will show $X, Y, Z \sim x', y', z'$ providing that $u = z' \neq 0$ and $v = Z \neq 0$.

It remains to dispose of the other possibilities. To have $z' = 0$, but $Z \neq 0$, implies in (24.7) that $x' = 0$ and $y' = 0$, but this contradicts the result in (B). To have $Z = 0$, but $z' \neq 0$, implies in (24.7) that $X = 0$ and $Y = 0$, whereas X, Y, Z is supposedly nontrivial.

To have both $Z = 0$ and $z' = 0$ is possible. But then (24.8) shows $x'z_0 = rJ$, $y'z_0 = sJ$, $z'z_0 = 0$; and the relations in (A) show $Xz_0 = rd$, $Yz_0 = sd$, $Zz_0 = 0$. Consequently, in this case $X, Y, Z \sim x', y', z'$ using $u = Jz_0 \neq 0$ and $v = Jd \neq 0$.

Commenting on this last case we mention that $z' = 0$ is possible for at most two families of solutions, for the requirements: $Ar^2 + Brs + Cs^2 = 0$, $(r, s) = 1$, $r \geqslant 0$, can be met in at most two ways, since the quadratic $Ax^2 + Bxy + Cy^2$ has at most two factors with integer coefficients. In other words, $H(x, y, z) = 0$ has at most two families of "ideal" solutions.

(F) We shall show that no family of solutions of (24.1) has more than one member in (24.5).

In (C) we showed there is just one pair of integers r_0, s_0 such that the corresponding triple x_0', y_0', z_0' is related to x_0, y_0, z_0, a situation characterized by $J_0 = 0$.

Let x_1', y_1', z_1' be defined by (24.5) and r_1, s_1 where $(r_1, s_1) = 1$, $r_1 \geqslant 0$, and either $r_1 \neq r_0$ or $s_1 \neq s_0$, so that the corresponding $J_1 \neq 0$. Let x_2', y_2', z_2' be defined by (24.5) and r_2, s_2 where $(r_2, s_2) = 1$, $r_2 \geqslant 0$. We shall show that x_2', y_2', $z_2' \sim x_1'$, y_1', z_1' implies $r_2 = r_1$, $s_2 = s_1$.

On the one hand, by hypothesis $ux_2' = vx_1'$, $uy_2' = vy_1'$, $uz_2' = vz_1'$ with $u \neq 0$ and $v \neq 0$. On the other hand, from (24.8) we have

$$x_1'z_0 - x_0z_1' = r_1J_1, \quad x_2'z_0 - x_0z_2' = r_2J_2,$$
$$y_1'z_0 - y_0z_1' = s_1J_1, \quad y_2'z_0 - y_0z_2' = s_2J_2.$$

Combining these facts we have $vr_1J_1 = ur_2J_2$ and $vs_1J_1 = us_2J_2$. These relations imply $s_2vr_1J_1 = s_2ur_2J_2 = r_2vs_1J_1$. Since $v \neq 0$ and $J_1 \neq 0$, we find $s_2r_1 = r_2s_1$. Then the same argument used in (C) shows that $r_2 = r_1$ and $s_2 = s_1$.

This completes the proof of the theorem, but we outline the scheme for clarity. Part (A) was a tool in proving (D) and (E). In (B) and (D) we showed that every triple defined in (24.5) is a nontrivial solution of (24.1). In (C) and (E) we showed that every family of nontrivial solutions of (24.1) has at least one member in (24.5). In (C) and (F) we showed that no family of solutions of (24.1) has more than one member in (24.5).

We repeat the caution that (24.5) need not provide a primitive triple, so that before applying (24.3) we must think of finding $d = (x', y', z')$ with $x' = Xd$, $y' = Yd$, $z' = Zd$ and $(X, Y, Z) = 1$.

For this purpose the system (24.5) may be rewritten—by Cramer's rule or other elimination devices—in the equivalent form:

(24.9)
$$\begin{cases} \Delta r^2 = A_{11}x' + A_{12}y' + A_{13}z', \\ \Delta rs = A_{21}x' + A_{22}y' + A_{23}z', \\ \Delta s^2 = A_{31}x' + A_{32}y' + A_{33}z', \end{cases}$$

where Δ and the A_{ij} are all integers.

In (24.9) we have $\Delta = z_0(AR^2 + BRS + CS^2)$, where R and S have been defined in (C). Using the argument at the close of (B) we find that $(H.1)$ and $(H.2)$ guarantee that $\Delta \neq 0$. Consequently, since $(r^2, s^2) = 1$, the relations (24.9) imply that $d = (x', y', z')$ must divide Δ. If d' is the greatest common divisor of the A_{ij} and Δ with $\Delta = d'\Delta'$, then the restriction on d may be increased to say that d must divide Δ'.

We find that Δ may also be expressed in the form

$$\Delta = z_0{}^3(AE^2 - BDE + CD^2 + B^2F - 4ACF).$$

Still assuming $(H.2)$ we may replace $(H.1)$ by the equivalent requirement

$(H.3)$ $\Delta'' = AE^2 - BDE + CD^2 + B^2F - 4ACF \neq 0.$

The necessity was explained above, in reference to the argument in (B).

The sufficiency can be checked (negatively) by assuming that $H(x, y, z)$ has linear factors, obtaining the relations between the coefficients and proving that $\Delta'' = 0$.

24.3.   Examples to illustrate the method

As a first example let us check the results of Theorem 5 against the results in **23.1**.

For $x^2 + y^2 = z^2$ it is easy to satisfy $(H.2)$ with $x_0 = -1$, $y_0 = 0$, $z_0 = 1$ and it is easy to verify $(H.3)$ since $\Delta'' = 4$. Then (24.5) gives as the representative solution

$$x' = r^2 - s^2, \quad y' = 2rs, \quad z' = r^2 + s^2, \quad (r, s) = 1, \quad r \geqslant 0.$$

Noting that $2r^2 = z' + x'$, $2s^2 = z' - x'$, we see that $d = (x', y', z')$ must divide $\Delta' = 2$. Thus two cases arise as $d = 1$ or $d = 2$.

If $d = 1$, we must have $r \not\equiv s \bmod 2$. The primitive triplets thus obtained seem in exact agreement with (23.1), except for interchanging x and y, for the extra hypotheses $r > s > 0$ (and $k > 0$) were imposed to restrict attention to positive solutions.

We find $d = 2$ if and only if $r \equiv s \equiv 1 \bmod 2$, for the case $r \equiv s \equiv 0$ mod 2 is ruled out by $(r, s) = 1$. Then the appropriate primitive member of the family is $x'' = (r^2 - s^2)/2$, $y'' = rs$, $z'' = (r^2 + s^2)/2$ with $r \equiv s \equiv 1 \bmod 2$ and $(r, s) = 1$.

If we note that $y'' = rs \equiv 1 \bmod 2$, while $x'' \equiv 0 \bmod 4$, whereas in the first case it was $x' \equiv 1 \bmod 2$, while $y' \equiv 0 \bmod 4$, then the suspicion dawns that one of these types of solutions must be those ignored in (23.1) by making the agreement to order x and y in a certain way. That this is indeed the case may be verified by observing that $r \equiv s \equiv 1 \bmod 2$ implies we can define integers u and v by $2u = r + s$, $2v = r - s$, then $r = u + v$, $s = u - v$ with $u \not\equiv v \bmod 2$ and $(u, v) = 1$. Furthermore, $x'' = (r^2 - s^2)/2 = 2uv$, $y'' = rs = u^2 - v^2$, $z'' = (r^2 + s^2)/2 = u^2 + v^2$ in exact agreement with the first case, except for interchanging x and y.

As a second example consider the problem of determining all triangles whose sides x, y, z are integers and in which the sides x and y include an angle θ such that $\cos \theta = a/c$ where a and c are integers with $(a, c) = 1$ and with $0 \leqslant |a| < c$. From the law of cosines we have

$$z^2 = x^2 + y^2 - 2xy \cos \theta,$$

so we arrive at the Diophantine equation

$$cx^2 - 2axy + cy^2 - cz^2 = 0$$

which is of type (24.1). After discovering the solution $x_0 = -1$, $y_0 = 0$, $z_0 = 1$ and checking that $\Delta'' = 4c(c^2 - a^2) \neq 0$, we apply (24.5) to find the representative solutions:

$$x' = c(r^2 - s^2), \quad y' = 2s(cr - as), \quad z' = cr^2 - 2ars + cs^2$$

with $(r, s) = 1$ and $r \geqslant 0$. To fit the geometric problem we may add conditions to make x', y', z' all positive; and then we can restate the result about exactly one member in each family of solutions of the Diophantine equation to say we are specifying exactly one member in each family of directly similar triangles. We can show that $d = (x', y', z')$ must divide $\Delta' = 2c(c^2 - a^2)$, but it is tedious, in general, to describe the primitive triples. We may note, however, that the case $a = 0$, $c = 1$, with $\Delta' = 2$, is exactly the Pythagorean problem with $\theta = 90°$ we have just previously analyzed.

When $a = 1$, $c = 2$, we have $\theta = 60°$, which is easily discussed. In this case, and whenever c is even, the equation and solutions should be simplified by removing the factor 2. We find

(24.10)
$$x'' = r^2 - s^2, \quad y'' = s(2r - s),$$
$$z'' = r^2 - rs + s^2, \quad (r, s) = 1, \quad r \geqslant 0$$

as the representative solutions. From the relations $x'' + y'' + 2z'' = 3r^2$ and $-2x'' + y'' + 2z'' = 3s^2$ we see that $d = (x'', y'', z'')$ must divide 3. Since we find

$$x'' \equiv (r - s)(r + s), \quad y'' \equiv 2s(r + s), \quad z'' \equiv (r + s)^2 \bmod 3,$$

the condition $r \equiv 2s \not\equiv 0 \bmod 3$ is necessary to make $d = 3$ and keep $(r, s) = 1$. Thus if we are to describe a primitive triplet in each family of solutions we have two cases:

(1) $d = 1: X = x'', \quad Y = y'', \quad Z = z'', \quad (r, s) = 1, \quad r \geq 0,$
$$r \not\equiv 2s \bmod 3;$$

(2) $d = 3: X = x''/3, \quad Y = y''/3, \quad Z = z''/3, \quad (r, s) = 1, \quad r \equiv 2s \bmod 3,$
$$r > 0.$$

For example: using the notation $(r, s):(X, Y, Z)$, we find

$(2, 1):(1, 1, 1);$ $(3, 1):(8, 5, 7);$ $(3, 2):(5, 8, 7);$
$(4, 1):(15, 7, 13);$ $(4, 3):(7, 15, 13);$ $(5, 1):(8, 3, 7);$
$(5, 2):(21, 16, 19);$ $(5, 3):(16, 21, 19);$ $(1, 2):(-1, 0, 1);$
$(1, 3):(-8, -3, 7);$ $(2, 3):(-5, 3, 7);$ $(3, -2):(5, -16, 19).$

For a final example, let us use Cartesian coordinates (α, β) to represent a point P, and ask for all points P with $\alpha = x/z$, $\beta = y/z$ where x, y, z are integers with $z \neq 0$, such that the sum of the squares of the distances of P from $P_1:(0, 0)$; $P_2:(1, 0)$; $P_3:(1, 2)$; $P_4:(0, 2)$ is 18.

The geometric problem

$$\alpha^2 + \beta^2 + (\alpha - 1)^2 + \beta^2 + (\alpha - 1)^2 + (\beta - 2)^2 + \alpha^2 + (\beta - 2)^2 = 18$$

becomes the Diophantine problem

$$x^2 + y^2 - xz - 2yz - 2z^2 = 0$$

with a search for all ordinary solutions x, y, z having $z \neq 0$.

As a particular solution we have $x_0 = 2$, $y_0 = 0$, $z_0 = 1$ and we find $\Delta'' = 13 \neq 0$, so we may apply (24.5) to obtain the representative solutions: $x' = 2s^2 + 2rs - r^2$, $y' = 2s^2 - 3rs$, $z' = s^2 + r^2$, $(r, s) = 1$ with $r \geqslant 0$. Since $3x' + 2y' + 3z' = 13s^2$, $-3x' - 2y' + 10z' = 13r^2$ we find that $d = (x', y', z')$ must divide 13. We find that

$$x' \equiv (s - 8r)(2s + 5r), \quad y' \equiv (s - 8r)2s, \quad z' \equiv (s - 8r)(s + 8r) \bmod 13.$$

Since 13 is a prime we find that $d = 13$ and $(r, s) = 1$ only if $s \equiv 8r \not\equiv 0$ mod 13. So a primitive solution in each family of solutions can be obtained by using

(1) $X = x'$, $Y = y'$, $Z = z'$, $s \not\equiv 8r \bmod 13$, $(r, s) = 1$, $r \geqslant 0$,
(2) $X = x'/13$, $Y = y'/13$, $Z = z'/13$, $s \equiv 8r \bmod 13$, $(r, s) = 1$, $r > 0$.

Then using (24.3) we know the complete solution. The form of z' shows that the requirement $z \neq 0$ is always satisfied.

For example: $r = 1$, $s = 7$ gives $X = 111$, $Y = 91$, $Z = 50$, so that $\alpha = 111/50$, $\beta = 91/50$; $r = 1$, $s = 8$ gives $X = 11$, $Y = 8$, $Z = 5$, so that $\alpha = 11/5$, $\beta = 8/5$.

EXERCISES

24.1.   For ordered triplets of integers define x_1, y_1, z_1 to be *directly* related to x_2, y_2, z_2 if and only if *positive* integers u and v exist so that $ux_1 = vx_2$, $uy_1 = vy_2$, $uz_1 = vz_2$, $u > 0$, $v > 0$. Prove that being directly related is an equivalence relation.

24.2. In EX. **24.1** if the word "positive" is replaced by "negative" (i.e., $u < 0$, $v < 0$), show that the relation so defined is *not* an equivalence relation.

24.3. Generalize Example 3 in **24.1**. If p is a prime and a is not a quadratic residue mod p, show that $ax^2 + py^2 = z^2$ has only the trivial solution.

24.4. Check that $x^2 + 4y^2 - 4yz + z^2 = 0$ has the particular solution $x_0 = 0$, $y_0 = 1$, $z_0 = 2$. Try the formulas (24.5) and show they fail to satisfy some of the conclusions of Theorem 5, therefore $(H.1)$ and $(H.3)$ must fail to be satisfied. Show that the equation has only one family of nontrivial solutions.

24.5. Repeat the steps of EX. **24.4** on the equation $x^2 - 4y^2 + 4yz - z^2 = 0$, but at the final step show that the equation has infinitely many families of nontrivial solutions.

24.6. Complete the proof of (B) in Theorem 5 concerning the reducibility of $H(x, y, z)$.

24.7. Complete the proof of (C) in Theorem 5 concerning the reducibility of $H(x, y, z)$.

24.8. Find all primitive solutions of the triangle problem in **24.3** when $\theta = 120°$, i.e., $\cos \theta = -1/2$.

24.9. Repeat EX. **24.8** when $\cos \theta = 1/3$.

24.10. Repeat EX. **24.8** when $\cos \theta = 3/5$.

24.11. Referring to the triangle problem in **24.3** show that if just one of x' or y' is negative there is a geometric interpretation in which θ is an exterior angle of the triangle.

24.12. In (24.10) what relation exists between r_1, s_1 and r_2, s_2 if (a) $X_2 = Y_1$, $Y_2 = X_1$; or (b) $X_2 = -X_1$, $Y_2 = -Y_1$?
(Answers: (a) $r_2 = r_1$, $s_2 = r_1 - s_1$; (b) $r_2 = r_1 - 2s_1$, $s_2 = 2r_1 - s_1$, except for sign.)

24.13. Find all points $P:(\alpha, \beta)$ with rational coordinates $\alpha = x/z$, $\beta = y/z$, $z \neq 0$ such that the sum of the *squares* of the distances of P from $P_1:(0, 0)$, $P_2:(5, 0)$, $P_3:(2, 3)$ is 30. (I.e., find all ordinary solutions of $3x^2 + 3y^2 - 14xz - 6yz + 8z^2 = 0$.)

24.14. Find all points $P:(\alpha, \beta)$ with rational coordinates such that the sum of the *distances* of P from $P_1:(0, 0)$ and $P_2:(5, 0)$ is 7. (I.e., find all ordinary solutions of $24x^2 + 49y^2 - 120xz - 144z^2 = 0$.)

24.15. Recall property M defined in EX. **23.15**. Let $\cos \theta = a/c$ where a and c are integers with $0 < a < c$ and $(a, c) = 1$. From **24.3** we know each of the following Diophantine equations has infinitely many nontrivial and not-related solutions in positive integers x_i, y_i, z_i:

$$(1)\ cx^2 - 2axy + cy^2 = cz^2; \quad (2)\ cx^2 + 2axy + cy^2 = cz^2.$$

Take any set of m of these triples, no two related, and define:

$$X_m = x_1 x_2 \ldots x_m, \quad Y_m = y_1 y_2 \ldots y_m, \quad Z_m = z_1 z_2 \ldots z_m.$$

(a) The "quarter-rack": when $m = 2$ and both triples solve (1) show that the 5 points with coordinates $(0, 0)$, $(x_1 x_2, 0)$, $(y_1 y_2, 0)$, $(x_1 y_2 \cos \theta, x_1 y_2 \sin \theta)$, $(x_2 y_1 \cos \theta, x_2 y_1 \sin \theta)$ have property M.

(b) The "half-diamonds": if all m triples solve (1), show that the

$4m + 3$ points with coordinates $(0, cX_mY_m \sin \theta)$, $(\pm aX_mY_m, 0)$, $(\pm(cy_i - ax_i)X_mY_m/x_i, 0)$, $(\pm(cx_i - ay_i)X_mY_m/y_i, 0)$ for $i = 1$, $2, \ldots, m$, have property M. (There may be only $4m + 2$ distinct points in this set if, say, $cx_i = ay_i$; but a solution of (1) with this property is possible if and only if a, b, c is a Pythagorean triplet.)

(c) The "circle": use P_1 and P_2 separated by a distance of Z_m; if x_i, y_i, z_i solves (1), locate Q_{1i} and Q_{2i} on one side of P_1P_2 (and all in the same plane) so that

$$P_1Q_{1i} = x_iZ_m/z_i = P_2Q_{2i}, \quad P_2Q_{1i} = y_iZ_m/z_i = P_1Q_{2i};$$

but if x_i, y_i, z_i solves (2), locate Q_{1i} and Q_{2i} on the other side of P_1P_2 by the same distance rules. Prove that the set of $2m + 2$ points: P_1, P_2, Q_{1i}, Q_{2i} for $i = 1, 2, \ldots, m$ has property M. (Hint: Use the Theorem of Ptolemy in the geometry of the circle.)

(d) As in EX. **23.15** we may combine (b) and (c) into a three-dimensional figure with property M.

Note that the figures obtained in (a), (b), (c), (d) are not similar, in general, to subsets of (1), (2), (5) in EX. **23.15**. Thus (a), (b), (c) cannot be extended by reflection, in general, without losing property M; in general, the origin cannot be adjoined to (b); and in general, the center cannot be adjoined to (c). The exceptions occur when a, b, c form a Pythagorean triplet.

Do there exist configurations with property M which are not similar to subsets of the figures described in EXS. **23.15** and **24.15**? Do there exist infinite configurations with property M which are not similar to subsets of the "line" in EX. **23.15**?

CHAPTER 25

Fermat's method of descent

25.1. Fermat's "last theorem"

On the margin of his copy of Diophantus, Fermat wrote that the
Diophantine equation

$$x^n + y^n = z^n$$

is impossible of solution in *positive* integers x, y, z for $n = 3, 4, 5, \ldots$,
that he had found a truly remarkable way of proving this statement, but
that, unfortunately, the margin was not large enough to permit his writing
out the proof. (The restriction "positive" is, of course, essential, for
otherwise $x = 0$, $y = z$ is a solution of the problem, but certainly a trivial
solution.)

This general problem is still unsolved and is known usually as Fermat's
last theorem. By special methods the problem has been solved as far as
$n = 616$. Despite its special and impractical nature, this problem has been
the source of some of the best new algebra and analysis, as efforts to solve
Fermat's problem brought forth new methods and exposed hidden pitfalls
of older methods.

It is easy to show that the problem will be completely solved if it can be
shown that Fermat's conjecture is true for every odd prime $n = p$ and for
$n = 4$. Suppose that n is composite of the form $n = kp$ where p is an odd
prime for which Fermat's proposed theorem is known to be true; then the

175

theorem is also true for n; for if we suppose the theorem not true for n, then there exist positive integers x, y, z such that $x^n + y^n = z^n$, but this is a contradiction of the assumption that the theorem is true for p, inasmuch as it shows $X = x^k$, $Y = y^k$, $Z = z^k$ to be positive integers for which

$$X^p + Y^p = Z^p.$$

Similarly, if the theorem is true for $n = 4$, then the theorem is true for $n = 2^k$, $k \geqslant 2$.

The easiest case in which we can prove the "last theorem" is the case of $n = 4$ where we can employ a method known as Fermat's *method of descent* which may possibly have been the "remarkable way" which he mentioned.

25.2.   Fermat's "method of descent"

Let us recall that version of mathematical induction, described as **L.3** in **2.4**, which we may express as follows: If a proposition $P(n)$ is true for some positive integers, then there is a least positive integer for which $P(n)$ is true. But suppose it can be shown that the assumed truth of $P(n)$ always implies the truth of $P(n')$ where n' is a positive integer less than n. Then a contradiction has been reached and the proposition $P(n)$ must be false. This method of proof, depending as it does on descending from the positive integer n to the smaller positive integer n', has long been given the name "method of descent."

Usually we employ this method to prove the falsity of a given proposition. But sometimes we can use the method in a positive way, showing that the "descent" is possible until we reach a certain type of integer; if for this special type of integer the proposition is true, then we can reverse the argument and "ascend" to all solutions of the proposition.

Both these uses of the "method of descent" will be illustrated in the next sections.

25.3.   The relation $x^4 + y^4 = z^2$ is impossible in positive integers

To prove the proposition used as the title of this section we shall use the method of descent.

Let us assume that the equation $x^4 + y^4 = z^2$ does have some solutions in positive integers and let x, y, z be a specific one of these solutions. If

$(x, y) = d$, then $x = Xd$, $y = Yd$, and $z = Zd^2$; and furthermore $X^4 + Y^4 = Z^2$. Hence if we describe the problem we are studying as $P(z)$ and if $d > 1$, then we have already shown that the truth of $P(z)$ implies the truth of $P(Z)$ where Z is a positive integer less than z. But if $d = 1$, more argument will be required. However, if $(x, y) = 1$ it follows that $(x^2, y^2, z) = 1$, hence x^2, y^2, z is a primitive Pythagorean triplet. Therefore by the results of **23.1** we know that we may write $x^2 = 2rs$, $y^2 = r^2 - s^2$, $z = r^2 + s^2$, with $(r, s) = 1$ and with r and s of different parity. But we must not choose r to be even for then s and y are odd and the relation $y^2 + s^2 = r^2$ is impossible since $1 + 1 \not\equiv 0 \bmod 4$. Hence we have $(r, 2s) = 1$. Then as in step (6) of **23.1** we argue from $(r, 2s) = 1$ and $x^2 = 2rs$ that $r = R^2$ and $s = 2S^2$. The relation $(2S^2)^2 + y^2 = (R^2)^2$ and the condition $(2S^2, y, R^2) = 1$ show that $2S^2, y, R^2$ is another primitive Pythagorean triplet, so again using **23.1** we write $2S^2 = 2uv$, $y = u^2 - v^2$, $R^2 = u^2 + v^2$, with $(u, v) = 1$ and u and v of opposite parity. Again as in step (6) of **23.1** we see from $(u, v) = 1$ and $S^2 = uv$ that $u = U^2$ and $v = V^2$. Therefore $R^2 = U^4 + V^4$ and we have arrived at another solution of the equation of this section; in other words the truth of $P(z)$ implies the truth of $P(R)$ and (what is of critical concern for the method) R is a positive integer less than z because

$$R < R^4 + 4S^4 = r^2 + s^2 = z.$$

Hence as explained in **25.2** we have successfully demonstrated the descent and are therefore caught in a contradiction; the only way out of the contradiction is in the decision that $x^4 + y^4 = z^2$ is *impossible* in positive integers.

Corollary: Fermat's "last theorem" is true for $n = 4$. For if $x^4 + y^4 = z^4$ in positive integers, we would have $x^4 + y^4 = (z^2)^2$ contradicting the principal result of this section.

25.4.   The relation $x^4 - 8y^4 = z^2$ is impossible in positive integers

To establish the proposition used as the title of this section we shall use an argument that is seen on closer inspection to be merely a rephrasing of the method of descent.

Let us assume that the equation $x^4 - 8y^4 = z^2$ does have some solutions in positive integers and that among all these x, y, z is a solution with a minimum value of x. If $(x, y) = d$, then $x = Xd$, $y = Yd$, and $z = Zd^2$ with X, Y, Z providing a solution with $X < x$, unless $d = 1$.

Hence we assume $(x, y) = 1$. But also $(x, 2y) = 1$; for if x were even, z^2 would be a multiple of 8 and z would be a multiple of 4; but this would require y to be even, contradicting $(x, y) = 1$. Hence $(z, 2y^2, x^2) = 1$ and if we write the given equation in the form $z^2 + 2(2y^2)^2 = (x^2)^2$, we find that $z, 2y^2, x^2$ is a primitive solution of the equation studied in EX. **23.6**. Therefore we may write $z = \pm(2R^2 - S^2)$, $2y^2 = 2RS$, $x^2 = 2R^2 + S^2$, $(2R, S) = 1$. Then since $(R, S) = 1$ and $y^2 = RS$ we may write $R = u^2$, $S = v^2$, with $(2u^2, v^2) = 1$. But then $x^2 = 2(u^2)^2 + (v^2)^2$ so that v^2, u^2, x is also a primitive solution of the equation studied in EX. **23.6**. Therefore we may write $v^2 = \pm(2M^2 - N^2)$, $u^2 = 2MN$, $x = 2M^2 + N^2$, $(2M, N) = 1$. From $(2M, N) = 1$ and $u^2 = 2MN$ we may write $M = 2Y^2$, $N = X^2$, $(2Y, X) = 1$. Since v and N are odd, it follows since $1 \not\equiv -1$ mod 8 that $v^2 = 2M^2 - N^2 = 8Y^4 - N^2$ is impossible, and it is the second case $v^2 = N^2 - 2M^2 = X^4 - 8Y^4$ which must hold. But this is an equation of the same type with which we started, and it has a solution in which $X \leqslant X^2 = N < N^2 + 2M^2 = x$. Hence we have reached a contradiction of the minimal property supposedly enjoyed by x. The only resolution of this contradiction is in the theorem that the equation $x^4 - 8y^4 = z^2$ has no solution in positive integers.

Corollary: The relation $x^4 + 2y^4 = z^2$ is impossible in positive integers.

Proof: If we suppose that there exist positive integers x, y, z such that $x^4 + 2y^4 = z^2$, then we may write

$$(x^4 - 2y^4)^2 = (x^4 + 2y^4)^2 - 8x^4y^4 = z^4 - 8x^4y^4,$$

and inasmuch as we can show that $x^4 - 2y^4 \neq 0$, it follows that one of the triplets $z, xy, \pm(z^4 - 2y^4)$ provides a solution in positive integers that contradicts the principal theorem of this section.

The missing detail may be treated as follows: suppose there exist positive integers x and y such that $x^4 - 2y^4 = 0$ or $x^4 = 2y^4$. If $(x, y) = d$, then $x = Xd$, $y = Yd$, $(X, Y) = 1$, and $X^4 = 2Y^4$. Hence X must be even, say $X = 2S$ and $Y^4 = 8S^4$; but then Y must be even, which contradicts $(X, Y) = 1$.

25.5.　Chains of solutions of $x^4 - 2y^4 = z^2$

In contrast to the preceding result about the equation $x^4 + 2y^4 = z^2$, it appears that the equation $x^4 - 2y^4 = z^2$ does have some solutions in positive integers; for example, we find by inspection that $x = 3$, $y = 2$, $z = 7$ is a primitive solution, and from a primitive solution as many other solutions as desired can be obtained by taking $X = kx$, $Y = ky$, $Z = k^2z$ where k is any integer. Conversely, any solution of the equation is a kind of multiple of a primitive solution: for if x, y, z is a solution and $(x, y) = d$, then $x = Xd$, $y = Yd$, $z = Zd^2$, $(X, Y) = 1$, and $X^4 - 2Y^4 = Z^2$, with $(X, Y, Z) = 1$. Let us, therefore, seek all primitive solutions.

If $(x, y, z) = 1$ and $x^4 - 2y^4 = z^2$, then $(z, y^2, x^2) = 1$ and $z^2 + 2(y^2)^2 = (x^2)^2$ so that z, y^2, x^2 is a primitive solution of the equation studied in EX. **23.6**, and we can write

$$z = \pm(2R^2 - S^2), \quad y^2 = 2RS, \quad x^2 = 2R^2 + S^2, \quad (2R, S) = 1.$$

It follows from $(2R, S) = 1$ and $y^2 = 2RS$ that $R = 2u^2$, $S = v^2$, $(2u, v) = 1$. Then $(v^2, 2u^2, x) = 1$ and $(v^2)^2 + 2(2u^2)^2 = x^2$ so that v^2, $2u^2$, x is another primitive solution of the equation in EX. **23.6** and we can write

$$v^2 = \pm(2P^2 - Q^2), \quad 2u^2 = 2PQ, \quad x = 2P^2 + Q^2, \quad (2P, Q) = 1.$$

From $(2P, Q) = 1$ and $u^2 = PQ$ it follows that $P = a^2$, $Q = b^2$, $(2a, b) = 1$. We note that both v and b are odd and then proceed to consider the two cases for v^2.

Case 1: $v^2 = b^4 - 2a^4$. Since v and b are odd, this case is possible only if a is even; but then $y = 2uv = 2abv$, so that y is a multiple of 4. Since $a \leqslant ab = u < 2uv = y$, it is possible in this case to descend to a solution of the original equation with smaller "y" value. If this were the only kind of descent, then we would have a proof, just as in **25.3** and **25.4**, that the given equation has no solution. But we note that this kind of descent will fail as soon as we reach a "y" which is not a multiple of 4. We must turn our attention, therefore, to the other case for v^2.

Case 2: $v^2 = 2a^4 - b^4$. Since v and b are odd, this case is possible only if a is odd; but then $y = 2uv = 2abv$ is a multiple of 2, but not a multiple of 4.

Thus every solution of $x^4 - 2y^4 = z^2$ is a member of a chain of solutions of this same equation, descending with respect to "y," and ending at a primitive solution of an equation $2a^4 - b^4 = v^2$ whose complete solution we will now attempt, hoping to build backward from the solutions of this latter equation to solutions of the given problem.

Considerations mod 2 and mod 4 show that a primitive solution of $2a^4 - b^4 = v^2$ must have a, b, v all odd and $(b, v) = 1$. If we set $b^2 + v = 2T$ and $b^2 - v = 2U$, then $b^2 = T + U$ and $v = T - U$ and it follows that $(T, U) = 1$. Our equation takes the new form

$$2a^4 = b^4 + v^2 = (T + U)^2 + (T - U)^2 = 2T^2 + 2U^2, \quad a^4 = T^2 + U^2.$$

Hence T, U, a^2 form a primitive Pythagorean triplet, although not necessarily a triplet of positive integers for U may be negative or 0 (however, this last case occurs only when $T = v = b = 1$.) With this understanding we may write

$$T = m^2 - n^2, \quad U = 2mn, \quad a^2 = m^2 + n^2, \quad (m, n) = 1,$$

with m and n of opposite parity, but n not necessarily positive (in particular, we shall be interested in the case $n = 0$ and $m = 1$ corresponding to a minimum positive value of a). Since $b^2 = T + U = m^2 - n^2 + 2mn$ and b is odd, it follows that m must be odd, rather than n, so we have $(m, 2n) = 1$. Since $(m, n, a) = 1$ and $m^2 + n^2 = a^2$ we see that m, n, a is a primitive Pythagorean triplet so we set

$$m = g^2 - h^2, \quad n = 2gh, \quad a = g^2 + h^2, \quad (g, h) = 1,$$

with g and h of opposite parity. But we also have $(b, n, m + n) = 1$ and $b^2 + 2n^2 = (m + n)^2$ so that $b, n, m + n$ is a primitive solution of the equation in EX. **23.6**, hence we set

$$b = \pm(2A^2 - B^2), \quad n = 2AB, \quad m + n = 2A^2 + B^2, \quad (2A, B) = 1.$$

By comparison we have $gh = AB$ and $g^2 - h^2 = 2A^2 + B^2 - 2AB$ and these equations give us the clue as to how to proceed.

Let $(g, B) = D$ with $g = Da_1$, $B = Db_1$, and $(a_1, b_1) = 1$. Then from $gh = AB$ we have $a_1h = Ab_1$ and since $(a_1, b_1) = 1$ we find $h = Eb_1$, $A = Ea_1$. Since $(g, h) = 1$ it follows that $(D, E) = 1$. From $g^2 - h^2 = 2A^2 + B^2 - 2AB$ we find by substitution and rearrangement $E^2(2a_1^2 + b_1^2) - 2EDa_1b_1 = D^2(a_1^2 - b_1^2)$. If we multiply both sides of this equation by $2a_1^2 + b_1^2$ and then add to each side the term $D^2a_1^2b_1^2$ we find that

$$\{E(2a_1^2 + b_1^2) - Da_1b_1\}^2 = D^2(2a_1^4 - b_1^4).$$

Hence it follows (see EX. **25.1**) that $2a_1^4 - b_1^4$ must be a perfect square, say $2a_1^4 - b_1^4 = v_1^2$.

Ordinarily $a_1 \leqslant Da_1 = g < g^2 + h^2 = a$, so that it is usually possible to descend from a solution with a given "a" to a solution with a smaller "a." The one exception is the case $g = 1, h = 0$, when we find $a_1 = a = 1$. Thus a descent from any primitive solution of $2a^4 - b^4 = v^2$ to the basic solution $a = 1, b = 1, v = 1$ is always possible.

It remains to show the method of ascent, starting from 1, 1, 1 or any known solution a_1, b_1, v_1. From the last displayed equation we find, upon taking square roots, that

$$E(2a_1^2 + b_1^2) = D(a_1b_1 \pm v_1).$$

Since we must have $(D, E) = 1$, we find $K_1 = (2a_1^2 + b_1^2, a_1b_1 + v_1)$ and $K_2 = (2a_1^2 + b_1^2, a_1b_1 - v_1)$, and then in the first case we take $D = (2a_1^2 + b_1^2)/K_1$, $E = (a_1b_1 + v_1)/K_1$ and in the second case,

$D = (2a_1{}^2 + b_1{}^2)/K_2$, $E = (a_1 b_1 - v_1)/K_2$. Then we compute, for whichever case we desire, the values of $g = Da_1$, $h = Eb_1$, $A = Ea_1$, $B = Db_1$. Finally we compute

$$a = g^2 + h^2, \quad b = \pm(2A^2 - B^2), \quad v = (g^2 - h^2 - 2gh)^2 - 8(gh)^2.$$

For example, after 1, 1, 1 the next solution is $a = 13$, $b = 1$, $v = 239$, there being only one case in this first step of ascent.

Perhaps the following symbols will help indicate the sense in which the preceding formulas represent the complete set of primitive solutions of $2a^4 - b^4 = v^2$. Set $A(0) = (1, 1, 1)$ and $A(1) = (13, 1, 239)$; then let $A(n; i_2, i_3, \ldots, i_n)$ for $n \geqslant 2$, with each $i_j = 1$ or 2, indicate a solution a, b, v which is a member of the "nth generation" with the following "geneology"—that according as $i_j = 1$ or 2, the member (when $j = n$) or its "ancestor" of the jth generation (when $2 \leqslant j \leqslant n - 1$) was a "male" (K_1) or "female" (K_2) "offspring" of $A(j - 1; i_2, \ldots, i_{j-1})$.

Using this terminology we find in the second generation

$$A(2; 1) = (2165017, 2372159, 3503833734241),$$
$$A(2; 2) = (1525, 1343, 2750257).$$

In the third generation there would be four members: $A(3; 1, 1)$, $A(3; 1, 2)$, $A(3; 2, 1)$, $A(3; 2, 2)$; but we shall not bother to compute the values of a, b, v for these, because we are worn out with computing and checking the values of a, b, v for the second generation!

Of course this *recursive* complete solution is a very different article from an *explicit* complete solution like that for primitive Pythagorean triplets; but since every primitive solution of $2a^4 - b^4 = v^2$ occupies a definite place $A(n; i_2, \ldots, i_n)$ in the "family tree," the description of our formulas as providing a *complete* solution seems justified.

Now let us return to complete the solution of the original problem $x^4 - 2y^4 = z^2$.

It follows from the discussion preceding *Case 1* and *Case 2* that we can start from any primitive solution of $2a^4 - b^4 = v^2$ (whose complete solution has just been described) and can find a primitive solution of $x^4 - 2y^4 = z^2$; or we can continue from any primitive solution, say x', y', z' of the latter equation to find another primitive solution by exactly the same formulas, providing we set $b = x'$, $a = y'$, $v = z'$; the necessary formulas are as follows:

$$x = 2a^4 + b^4, \quad y = 2abv, \quad z = \pm(8a^4b^4 - v^4).$$

For example, from 1, 1, 1 solving $2a^4 - b^4 = v^2$ we find 3, 2, 7 solving $x^4 - 2y^4 = z^2$; then with $b = 3$, $a = 2$, $v = 7$, we ascend to the solution $x = 113$, $y = 84$, $z = 7967$; and so on, as far as we care to go in this particular chain.

The complete set of solutions of $x^4 - 2y^4 = z^2$ can be described as follows: use the symbols $S(0; t, k)$, $S(1; t, k)$ and $S(n; i_2, i_3, \ldots, i_n; t, k)$ with $n \geqslant 2$ and $i_j = 1$ or 2, and with $t \geqslant 1$ and $k \geqslant 1$. Here the 0, the 1, and the $n; i_2, i_3, \ldots, i_n$ refer to the solution $A(0)$, $A(1)$, and $A(n; i_2, i_3, \ldots, i_n)$, respectively, of $2a^4 - b^4 = v^2$ from which the chain of solutions of $x^4 - 2y^4 = z^2$ originates; the t indicates the "generation" of x, y, z in the chain of primitive solutions of $x^4 - 2y^4 = z^2$; and the k indicates a solution of x', y', z' obtained from a primitive solution x, y, z by setting $x' = kx$, $y' = ky$, $z' = k^2z$.

For example:

$$S(0; 1, 1) = (3, 2, 7), \quad S(0; 1, 2) = (6, 4, 28),$$
$$S(0; 1, 3) = (9, 6, 63); \quad S(0; 2, 1) = (113, 84, 7967);$$
$$S(1; 1, 1) = (57123, 6214, 3262580153).$$

EXERCISES

25.1. If m, n, k are given integers with $(m, n) = 1$, $mn \neq 0$, and $k \geqslant 2$, show that there exist nonzero integers x and y such that $mx^k = ny^k$ if and only if there are integers M and N such that $m = M^k$ and $n = N^k$.

25.2. If there exist nonzero relatively prime integers x and y such that

$$0 = a_0x^n + a_1x^{n-1}y + \cdots + a_rx^{n-r}y^r + \cdots + a_{n-1}xy^{n-1} + a_ny^n,$$

where the a_i are integers with $a_0a_n \neq 0$, show that x must divide a_n and that y must divide a_0.

25.3. Apply EX. **25.1** or EX. **25.2** to show that the Diophantine equations $x^2 = 2y^2$, $x^3 = 2y^3$, $x^4 = 2y^4$ are impossible of solution in nonzero integers x and y.

25.4. Use Fermat's method of descent to show that $x^4 + 4y^4 = z^2$ is impossible of solution in positive integers.

25.5. As a corollary to EX. **25.4** show that $x^4 - y^4 = z^2$ is impossible in positive integers.

25.6. As a corollary to EX. **25.5** show that the area of the right triangle corresponding to a Pythagorean triplet cannot be a perfect square.

25.7. Make a diagram showing the interrelated family trees for the 56 solutions A and S described in **25.5** for $n = 0, 1, 2, 3; t = 1, 2; k = 1, 2, 3$.

25.8. Solve $x^2 + 3y^2 = z^2$ [perhaps by (24.5)] and then find chains of solutions for $x^4 + 3y^4 = z^2$.

> The majority of ideas we deal with were
> conceived by others, often centuries ago.
> In a great measure, it is really
> the intelligence of other people
> that confronts us in science.—D. MACH

CHAPTER 26

Sum of four squares

26.1. Introduction to additive arithmetic

The principal problem of the additive theory of numbers may be phrased as follows: given a set A of integers $a_1, a_2, a_3, \ldots$, consider the representation of an integer n in the form $n = a_{i_1} + a_{i_2} + \cdots + a_{i_s}$, where s may or may not be fixed, where the a's may or may not be different, and where the order of the a's may or may not be relevant. Let $A(n)$ be the number of representations of n in this form. The simpler problem is to determine whether $A(n)$ is positive; the harder problem is to find the exact value of $A(n)$; a related problem would be to find the greatest restrictions on s under which $A(n)$ will remain positive.

As an example, let A be the set 1, 2, 3; let s be unrestricted, repetitions allowed and order disregarded. Then $A(n)$ is exactly the number of solutions in nonnegative integers of the equation $x + 2y + 3z = n$, where x, y, z are the number of repetitions of 1, 2, 3, respectively, and $s = x + y + z \geqslant 1$. When $n > 0$, it is clear that $A(n) > 0$, since $x = n$, $y = 0$, $z = 0$ is a solution. By the same method as in EX. **15.15** it is possible to show $A(n) = 1 + [n(n + 6)/12]$. (If s is restricted, say $s \leqslant k$, then the maximum value of $x + 2y + 3z$ is $3k$; hence the corresponding $A(n, k) = 0$ when $n > 3k$.)

A problem amusingly related to the preceding one is provided by letting A^* contain all nonnegative integers, requiring s^* to be 3, allowing

183

repetition, and disregarding order. For we may show $A^*(n) = A(n)$ when $n > 0$.

On the one hand, if $n = u + 2v + 3w$, with u, v, w nonnegative, then we may write $n = a + b + c$, where $a = u + v + w$, $b = v + w$, $c = w$ are nonnegative, and such that $a \geqslant b \geqslant c$. Conversely, if $n = a + b + c$, with a, b, c nonnegative and arranged in the order $a \geqslant b \geqslant c$, then $n = u + 2v + 3w$, where $u = a - b$, $v = b - c$, $w = c$ are nonnegative.

Thus when $n = 6$, we have $A(6) = 7$ cases, as follows:

$$6 = 0\cdot1 + 0\cdot2 + 2\cdot3 = 1\cdot1 + 1\cdot2 + 1\cdot3 = 3\cdot1 + 0\cdot2 + 1\cdot3 = 0\cdot1 + 3\cdot2 + 0\cdot3$$
$$= 2\cdot1 + 2\cdot2 + 0\cdot3 = 4\cdot1 + 1\cdot2 + 0\cdot3 = 6\cdot1 + 0\cdot2 + 0\cdot3;$$

and the corresponding cases, as described above, showing $A^*(6) = 7$, are as follows:

$$6 = 2 + 2 + 2 = 3 + 2 + 1 = 4 + 1 + 1 = 3 + 3 + 0$$
$$= 4 + 2 + 0 = 5 + 1 + 0 = 6 + 0 + 0.$$

26.2. Waring's problem

In terms of additive arithmetic we may describe one of the most famous problems of the theory of numbers, usually known as *Waring's problem* although it seems that there was probably no case of his problem for which Waring could give a demonstration.

Let k be a fixed integer, $k \geqslant 2$, and let A be the set of kth powers of nonnegative integers: $0^k, 1^k, 2^k, \ldots$; then Waring's problem is to determine whether there exists an integer $s = s(k)$, depending on k but *independent* of n, such that if we allow repetitions, we have $A(n) > 0$ for all n.

In other words, for a given k we seek an $s = s(k)$, such that every n can be written in at least one way as

$$n = a_1{}^k + a_2{}^k + \cdots + a_s{}^k,$$

where $a_1, a_2, \ldots, a_s$ are nonnegative integers, not necessarily distinct.

It was a triumph, more for analysis than number theory, that Waring's problem was answered in the affirmative, for all k, by Hilbert, one hundred years after Waring. But the proof is an existential one, and the attempt to give an explicit value for s, for all k, is not yet quite successful. Knowing that s exists, we can see that any greater integer has the same property. Hence it is natural to define $g(k)$ to be the *least* value of s, such that every n is representable as the sum of g kth powers, but there is *at least one* n which cannot be represented by fewer than g kth powers. For example, it has been shown that $g(3) = 9$, meaning that every integer may be represented as the sum of 9 cubes of nonnegative integers, and that there is at least one integer which actually requires 9 cubes in this kind of representation. However, it turns out in this case that there are *only two* integers n requiring the full complement of 9 cubes; for this, and other reasons, it is natural to define $G(k)$ to be such that all but a finite number of integers n can be represented as the sum of G kth powers, and *infinitely many* integers n cannot be represented as the sum of fewer than G kth powers. For example, the value of $G(3)$ is still in doubt, but is restricted to the range $4 \leqslant G(3) < 9$, by the facts given above and the additional fact that there are known to be infinitely many integers requiring 4 cubes in their representation.

The only case of Waring's problem sufficiently simple for these lessons is the case when $k = 2$; and later in this chapter we will show that $g(2) = G(2) = 4$. In other words, every integer n can be written in at least one way as the sum of 4 squares of integers, and there are infinitely many integers which cannot be written as the sum of fewer than 4 squares. For a discussion of the recent status of the $g(k)$ and $G(k)$ problems, for other values of k, the reader may refer to Hardy and Wright.

26.3. Polygonal numbers

Let t be a fixed integer, $t \geqslant 3$. Let A_t be the set of all *polygonal numbers of order* t, defined for $i = 0, 1, \ldots$, by $a(i, t) = i\{2 + (t - 2)(i - 1)\}/2$. Let $s(t) = t$, let repetitions be allowed and order disregarded. Then the Cauchy-Fermat result is that $A_t(n) > 0$ for every positive integer n. Thus every n is the sum of three triangular numbers, four square numbers, five pentagonal numbers, etc.

The numbers receive their geometric description because, with the exception of 0 and 1, which occur in every set, they can be described, for a given t, as a nest of regular polygons, each of t sides, homothetic with respect to a common vertex, and having, successively, $i = 2, 3, \ldots$ points on a side. For if we count the number of points in the polygon at the stage where there are i points on a side, we obtain the polygonal number $a(i, t)$, inasmuch as the sum of the terms of the arithmetic progression

$$1, 1 + (t - 2), 1 + 2(t - 2), \ldots, 1 + (i - 1)(t - 2)$$

is precisely $a(i, t)$.

For example, the triangular numbers $a(i, 3) = i(i + 1)/2$ are 0, 1, 3, 6, 10, 15, 21, . . . ; and examples of the Cauchy-Fermat theorem are as follows:

$$18 = 15 + 3 + 0 = 6 + 6 + 6, \quad 19 = 15 + 3 + 1 = 10 + 6 + 3, \quad 20 = 10 + 10 + 0.$$

Since it turns out that the square numbers $a(i, 4) = i^2$ are, indeed, the squares of integers, this particular case of the Cauchy-Fermat theorem is the same as the Waring problem for $k = 2$, so the proofs of the next two sections are applicable. A modern discussion of the Cauchy-Fermat theorem, for all values of t, can be found in Dickson's "*Modern Elementary Theory of Numbers.*"

26.4.   Four lemmas

In this section and the next we shall present a proof, essentially due to Euler, that every positive integer is the sum of four squares of integers; i.e., in the language of **26.2**, we will solve Waring's problem, when $k = 2$, with the very precise result that $g(2) = G(2) = 4$. To this end the following lemmas will be useful.

L.1:   It is true that $g(2) \geqslant G(2) \geqslant 4$.

Proof: Consider the following table:

If
$$x \equiv 0, 1, 2, 3, 4, 5, 6, 7 \bmod 8,$$
then
$$x^2 \equiv 0, 1, 4, 1, 0, 1, 4, 1 \bmod 8, \text{ respectively.}$$

Consequently, a study of the various cases shows that if x, y, z are any three given integers, then
$$x^2 + y^2 + z^2 \equiv 0, 1, 2, 3, 4, 5, \text{ or } 6 \bmod 8.$$

Therefore there are infinitely many positive integers of the form $8m + 7$ which are not representable as the sum of three squares of integers. In the language of **26.2**, this is **L.1**.

L.2:   If every prime is the sum of four squares, then every composite integer is the sum of four squares.

Proof: It is a matter of patience to verify the following remarkable identity found by Euler:

$$(26.1) \begin{cases} (a^2 + b^2 + c^2 + d^2)(a_1{}^2 + b_1{}^2 + c_1{}^2 + d_1{}^2) = A^2 + B^2 + C^2 + D^2 \\ A = aa_1 + bb_1 + cc_1 + dd_1, \quad B = ab_1 - ba_1 + cd_1 - dc_1, \\ C = ac_1 - bd_1 - ca_1 + db_1, \quad D = ad_1 + bc_1 - cb_1 - da_1. \end{cases}$$

From this identity **L.2** is an immediate consequence, for every composite integer n is the product of primes and by application of (26.1), an appropriate number of times, a representation of n as the sum of four squares can be obtained if representations are known for each of the prime factors of n.

L.3: If p is an odd prime, there exists a solution in integers x, y, z, m of $x^2 + y^2 + z^2 = mp$ with $0 < m < p$.

Proof: First we show by contradiction that there is a solution x, y, z of the congruence $x^2 + y^2 + z^2 \equiv 0 \bmod p$, other than the trivial solution $x \equiv y \equiv z \equiv 0 \bmod p$. For if we suppose there is no solution of the given congruence, except the trivial solution, then (using the Legendre symbol of Chapter 21) we must have $(-1/p) = -1$. Otherwise, we would be able to find y so that $y^2 \equiv -1 \bmod p$, and we would have $1^2 + y^2 + 0^2 \equiv 0$ $\bmod p$ and a nontrivial solution. Again, if for any integer $a \not\equiv 0$ or -1, $\bmod p$, we assume $(a/p) = 1$, we must have $(-(a + 1)/p) = -1$. Otherwise we would be able to find x, y, z with $x^2 \equiv 1$, $y^2 \equiv a$, $z^2 \equiv -(a + 1)$ $\bmod p$ and would have a nontrivial solution of $x^2 + y^2 + z^2 \equiv 0 \bmod p$. Combining these observations and using **G.22.3** in Chapter 21, we find that if $(a/p) = 1$, for an $a \not\equiv 0$ or -1, $\bmod p$, then $((a + 1)/p) = (-1/p)(-(a + 1)/p) = (-1)(-1) = +1$. Beginning with the case $a = 1$, where $(1/p) = 1$, this would imply by induction that *every* nonzero residue class $\bmod p$ is a quadratic residue $\bmod p$ which would be an obvious contradiction of **G.20**.

Having shown the existence of a nontrivial solution x, y, z of the congruence, we may suppose this solution replaced by X, Y, Z where $X \equiv \pm x$, $Y \equiv \pm y$, $Z \equiv \pm z \bmod p$ with the signs so chosen that $|X| < p/2$, $|Y| < p/2$, $|Z| < p/2$. Then X, Y, Z is also a nontrivial solution of the congruence so that

$$0 < mp = X^2 + Y^2 + Z^2 < 3p^2/4 < p^2, \qquad \text{hence } 0 < m < p.$$

L.4: If p is an odd prime and if $x^2 + y^2 + z^2 + w^2 = mp$ with $1 < m < p$, then there exist integers x_1, y_1, z_1, w_1, and M such that $x_1^2 + y_1^2 + z_1^2 + w_1^2 = Mp$ with $1 \leqslant M < m$.

Proof: The proof is divided into two cases according as m is *even* or *odd*.

When m is *even*, then x, y, z, w are all even; or all are odd; or two are even and two are odd, say x and y. With this agreement we may use the hypothesis to write

$$((x + y)/2)^2 + ((x - y)/2)^2 + ((z + w)/2)^2 + ((z - w)/2)^2 = (m/2)p.$$

Hence $x_1 = (x + y)/2$, $y_1 = (x - y)/2$, $z_1 = (z + w)/2$, $w_1 = (z - w)/2$, and $M = m/2$ are integers satisfying the conclusions of **L.4**.

When m is *odd*, we may use the modified division algorithm for least absolute value remainder to write

$$x = am + a_1, \quad y = bm + b_1, \quad z = cm + c_1, \quad w = dm + d_1,$$

where

$$|a_1| < m/2, \quad |b_1| < m/2, \quad |c_1| < m/2, \quad |d_1| < m/2.$$

Substituting these expressions into the given equation and making use of the symbols introduced in (26.1) we find

$$(26.2) \quad a_1{}^2 + b_1{}^2 + c_1{}^2 + d_1{}^2 + 2Am + (a^2 + b^2 + c^2 + d^2)m^2 = mp.$$

Hence there exists a nonnegative integer M such that

$$(26.3) \qquad\qquad a_1{}^2 + b_1{}^2 + c_1{}^2 + d_1{}^2 = Mm.$$

Furthermore we cannot have $M = 0$ for this would imply that $a_1 = b_1 = c_1 = d_1 = 0$; then m^2 would divide $x^2 + y^2 + z^2 + w^2 = mp$, and m would divide p; but $1 < m < p$ and p is a prime, so this case cannot occur. Since we know $a_1{}^2 + b_1{}^2 + c_1{}^2 + d_1{}^2 < 4(m^2/4) = m^2$, it follows that M in (26.3) satisfies $M < m$. Putting these results together we have $1 \leqslant M < m$. Finally, from the relations (26.2) and (26.3) we find on dividing by m that

$$M + 2A + (a^2 + b^2 + c^2 + d^2)m = p.$$

If we multiply this last equation by M and employ (26.3) and (26.1) we obtain

$$M^2 + 2AM + A^2 + B^2 + C^2 + D^2 = Mp,$$
$$(M + A)^2 + B^2 + C^2 + D^2 = Mp.$$

Thus $x_1 = M + A$, $y_1 = B$, $z_1 = C$, $w_1 = D$, and M are integers satisfying the conclusions of **L.4**.

26.5. Representation by four squares

The preceding lemmas allow a precise disposition of Waring's problem when $k = 2$.

Theorem: For representation as a sum of squares $G(2) = g(2) = 4$.

Proof: For every odd prime p, **L.3** guarantees the existence of a solution of $x^2 + y^2 + z^2 + w^2 = mp$ with $1 \leqslant m < p$. If $m > 1$, then

L.4 allows a descent in a finite number of steps (say with $p > m > M = M_1 > M_2 > \cdots > M_k = 1$) to the situation

$$x_k^2 + y_k^2 + z_k^2 + w_k^2 = p.$$

In other words, this shows that every odd prime may be represented as the sum of four squares. The only even prime 2 may be represented in the form $2 = 1^2 + 1^2 + 0^2 + 0^2$. Since every prime can be represented as the sum of four squares, **L.2** guarantees that every composite number may be represented as the sum of four squares. For the unit 1 we have $1 = 1^2 + 0^2 + 0^2 + 0^2$. Thus we have shown that every positive integer may be represented as the sum of four squares. In other words, $g(2) \leqslant 4$.

If we now apply **L.1**, we have $4 \leqslant G(2) \leqslant g(2) \leqslant 4$. Therefore, we conclude that $G(2) = g(2) = 4$.

According to W. W. R. Ball, the mental calculator Jacques Inaudi could express numbers less than $(10)^5$ as a sum of four squares in a minute or two. Such ability is certainly unusual and either depended on unusual memory or on the application of some trick process, certainly not on following through the processes indicated by the above proof, for in the case of large primes it is not so easy to produce a solution of the type whose existence is guaranteed by **L.3**.

If $n = u^2 N$, it is clear that a representation for N, say

$$N = x^2 + y^2 + z^2 + w^2,$$

leads to a representation for n, say

$$n = X^2 + Y^2 + Z^2 + W^2,$$

with $X = ux$, $Y = uy$, $Z = uz$, $W = uw$. Thus if the problem is merely that of finding one representation, it suffices to deal with an N that is square-free.

For example, if $n = 351 = 9 \cdot 39$, we can write

$$N = 39 = 6^2 + 1^2 + 1^2 + 1^2$$

and then we can easily obtain $351 = (18)^2 + 3^2 + 3^2 + 3^2$. But we can also write $27 = 5^2 + 1^2 + 1^2 + 0^2$ and $13 = 3^2 + 2^2 + 0^2 + 0^2$, and apply (26.1) to obtain

$$A = 15 + 2 + 0 + 0 = 17, \quad B = 10 - 3 + 0 - 0 = 7,$$
$$C = 0 - 0 - 3 + 0 = -3, \quad D = 0 + 0 - 2 - 0 = -2,$$

so that $351 = (17)^2 + 7^2 + 3^2 + 2^2$.

The question of the total number of representations has received its neatest answer in the case in which the set A is described as including the squares of all integers, counting $(-x)^2$ as different from $(+x)^2$ except, of course, when $x = 0$, requiring $s = 4$, allowing repetitions and considering order. In this form of the problem Jacobi has shown that

$A(n) = 8\sigma(n)$, when n is odd;
$A(n) = 24\sigma(m)$, when m is odd and $n = 2^a m$ with $a \geqslant 1$.

Here $\sigma(n)$ is the number-theoretic function of Chapter 8 denoting the sum of the positive divisors of n.

For example, to explain $A(1) = 8$, we need to realize that the representations involving $(1, 0, 0, 0)$, $(-1, 0, 0, 0)$, $(0, 1, 0, 0)$, $(0, -1, 0, 0)$, $(0, 0, 1, 0)$, $(0, 0, -1, 0)$, $(0, 0, 0, 1)$, $(0, 0, 0, -1)$ as (x, y, z, w) are being counted as distinct. From this point of view, we find that 351 has $A(351) = 8 \cdot 40 \cdot 14 = 4480$ representations. From the point of view where negative solutions are not used and order is disregarded, there are just 14 representations of 351, as follows:

$(18, 3, 3, 3)$, $(18, 5, 1, 1)$, $(17, 7, 3, 2)$, $(17, 6, 5, 1)$, $(15, 11, 2, 1)$,
$(15, 10, 5, 1)$, $(15, 9, 6, 3)$, $(14, 11, 5, 3)$, $(14, 9, 7, 5)$, $(13, 13, 3, 2)$,
$(13, 11, 6, 5)$, $(13, 10, 9, 1)$, $(11, 11, 10, 3)$, $(11, 10, 9, 7)$.

It is easily found that ten of these solutions, under choice of sign and permutations, each lead to $16 \cdot 24 = 384$ of the solutions considered by Jacobi; there are three of these solutions which each lead to $16 \cdot 12 = 192$ of Jacobi's; and one solution which gives $16 \cdot 4 = 64$ of Jacobi's. The grand total of $3840 + 576 + 64 = 4480$ is in agreement with Jacobi's formula.

For discussion of Jacobi's enumeration formula, the reader may refer to Dickson's books, or Uspensky and Heaslet.

EXERCISES

26.1. If A contains 1 and k, if s is unrestricted, if repetitions are allowed and order disregarded, show that $A(n) = [n/k] + 1$ in two ways:
  (*1*) by direct enumeration;
  (*2*) by considering $A^*(n)$, where A^* consists of all nonnegative integers, $s^* = 2$, repetitions allowed and order disregarded.

26.2. If A contains 2 and 3 with s unrestricted, repetitions allowed and order disregarded, show that $A(n) = [n/6]$, or $[n/6] + 1$ according as $n \equiv 1$ or $n \not\equiv 1$, mod 6.

26.3. If A contains $a_1, a_2, \ldots, a_k$ where $0 < a_1 < a_2 < \cdots < a_k$, if s is unrestricted, if repetitions are allowed and if order *is* considered, show that by defining $A(0) = 1$ and noting that $A(n) = 0$ for $n = 1, 2, \ldots$, $a_1 - 1$, then all other $A(n)$ may be computed by the following recursion formulas:

$$A(n) = A(n - a_1) + A(n - a_2) + \cdots + A(n - a_i), \quad a_i \leqslant n < a_{i+1},$$
$$i = 1, 2, \ldots, k - 1;$$

$$A(n) = A(n - a_1) + A(n - a_2) + \cdots + A(n - a_k), \qquad a_k \leqslant n.$$

(Hint: Arrange the representations of n in lexicographic order.)

26.4. In the special case of EX. **26.3** where A contains only 1 and 2, compute some of the $A(n)$—these are the *Fibonacci numbers*.

26.5. If $(a_1, a_2, \ldots, a_k) = d$ and $a_i = A_i d$, let A^* contain $A_1, A_2, \ldots, A_k$; then under the conditions of EX. **26.3** compare $A(n)$ and $A^*(n)$, making appropriate use of **15.1**.

26.6. With $a(i, t)$ as defined in **26.3** and illustrated in the tailpiece, show (*1*) geometrically and (*2*) algebraically:

(a) $4a(i, 3) + (i + 1) = a(i + 1, 6)$,
(b) $(t - 2)a(i, 3) + (i + 1) = a(i + 1, t)$;
(a) $a(i, 5) + a(i - 1, 3) = a(i, 6)$,
(b) $a(i, t) + a(i - 1, 3) = a(i, t + 1)$;
(a) $a(i, 6) + 1 = 2a(i, 3) + a(i - 1, 4)$,
(b) $a(i, 2t) + 1 = 2a(i, t) + a(i - 1, 4)$.

26.7. Verify Euler's identity (*26.1*).

26.8. Show that no integer of the form $4^k(8m + 7)$, $k \geqslant 0$, can be a sum of three squares. (Hint: If $k > 0$, make an argument by descent to the case $k - 1$; for $k = 0$, use **L.1**.)

26.9. Note $p = 151 \equiv 7 \bmod 8$. Illustrate the proof of **L.4**, starting with $(20)^2 + 7^2 + 2^2 = 3 \cdot 151$.

26.10. Find all representations of 408 as the sum of four squares.

26.11. If $x_1 \geqslant x_2 \geqslant x_3 \geqslant x_4$, show that

$$6(x_1^2 + x_2^2 + x_3^2 + x_4^2)^2 = \sum ((x_i + x_j)^4 + (x_i - x_j)^4)$$

summed over the six cases where $i < j$.

26.12. Write $n = 6m + r$, $0 \leqslant r < 6$; $m = a_1^2 + a_2^2 + a_3^2 + a_4^2$; $a_k = x_{1k}^2 + x_{2k}^2 + x_{3k}^2 + x_{4k}^2$, $k = 1, 2, 3, 4$; $r = r \cdot 1^4$. Then apply $g(2) = 4$ and EX. **26.11** to show $15 < g(4) \leqslant 53$.

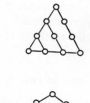

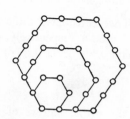

I do not know what I may appear to the world, but to myself I seem to have been only a boy playing on the seashore, and diverting myself in now and then finding a smoother pebble or a prettier shell than ordinary, whilst the great ocean of truth lay all undiscovered before me.—I. NEWTON

CHAPTER 27

Sum of two squares

27.1. Four lemmas and a theorem

From the preceding chapter it is clear that not every integer may be represented as the sum of two squares, so the object of the present lesson is to establish just which integers may be so represented. The lemmas which follow and their proofs are almost parallel to those of Chapter 26.

L.1: No integer of the form $4m + 3$ is a sum of two squares.

Proof: If we consider a table in which $x \equiv 0, 1, 2, 3 \bmod 4$ implies $x^2 \equiv 0, 1, 0, 1 \bmod 4$, respectively, it is clear that for given integers x and y, we must have $x^2 + y^2 \equiv 0, 1,$ or $2 \bmod 4$; whence **L.1** is an immediate consequence.

L.2: If the prime factors of a composite number n may each be written as the sum of two squares, then n is the sum of two squares.

Proof: It is easy to verify the following identity:

$$(27.1) \quad (a^2 + b^2)(a_1^2 + b_1^2) = A^2 + B^2, \quad A = aa_1 + bb_1, \quad B = ab_1 - ba_1.$$

192

From (27.1), applied several times if necessary, it follows that **L.2** is correct.

L.3: If p is a prime of the form $4K + 1$, there exists a solution in integers x, y, m of $x^2 + y^2 = mp$ with $0 < m < p$.

Proof: In EX. **21.6** we have shown that $(-1/p) = +1$ if $p = 4K + 1$, hence there exists an integer y such that $1 + y^2 \equiv 0 \bmod p$. We may find $Y \equiv \pm y \bmod p$ and such that $|Y| < p/2$, then

$$0 < mp = 1 + Y^2 < 1 + p^2/4 < p^2, \text{ so } 0 < m < p.$$

Thus the integers 1, Y, and m satisfy the conclusions of **L.3**.

L.4: If p is a prime of the form $4K + 1$ and if $x^2 + y^2 = mp$ with $1 < m < p$, then there exist integers x_1, y_1 and M such that $x_1{}^2 + y_1{}^2 = Mp$ with $1 \leqslant M < m$.

Proof: If m is *even*, we must have $x \equiv y \bmod 2$ and we may rewrite the equation of the hypothesis in the form

$$((x + y)/2)^2 + ((x - y)/2)^2 = (m/2)p$$

to see that $x_1 = (x + y)/2$, $y_1 = (x - y)/2$, $M = m/2$ satisfy the conclusions of **L.4**.

If m is *odd*, we can use a modified division algorithm to write

$$x = am + a_1, \quad |a_1| < m/2; \quad y = bm + b_1, \quad |b_1| < m/2.$$

If these expressions are substituted in the given equation, we find, using the symbols of (27.1), that

$$a_1{}^2 + b_1{}^2 + 2Am + (a^2 + b^2)m^2 = mp.$$

Hence it follows that there is a nonnegative integer M such that $a_1{}^2 + b_1{}^2 = Mm$, and we may write

$$M + 2A + (a^2 + b^2)m = p,$$
$$M^2 + 2AM + (a^2 + b^2)(a_1{}^2 + b_1{}^2) = (M + A)^2 + B^2 = Mp.$$

If $M = 0$, we would have $a_1 = b_1 = 0$, so that m^2 would divide $x^2 + y^2 = mp$ and m would divide p. Since p is a prime and $1 < m < p$, this is a contradiction. Hence we have $1 \leqslant M$. But also $Mm = a_1{}^2 + b_1{}^2 < m^2/2 < m^2$, so $M < m$. Thus $x_1 = M + A$, $y_1 = B$, and M are integers satisfying the conclusions of **L.4**.

Theorem: Every prime of the form $4K + 1$ can be represented as the sum of two squares.

Proof: By **L.3** we may find integers x, y so that $x^2 + y^2 = mp$, $1 \leqslant m < p$. In case $m > 1$, we may apply **L.4** a finite number of times (say with $m > M = M_1 > M_2 > \cdots > M_k = 1$) to "descend" to the situation where $x_k^2 + y_k^2 = p$.

27.2.   Representation as a sum of two squares

In the preceding section **L.1** shows that no prime of the form $4K + 3$ is the sum of two squares. But since, for example, the product n of two such primes, say $n = (4K + 3)(4K_1 + 3)$, is of the form $4T + 1$, further investigation is required to see if such an n is representable as the sum of two squares. The answer, for this example, turns out to be yes, if $K = K_1$; and no, if $K \neq K_1$. The general case is discussed in what follows.

Let us say that n has a *proper* representation as the sum of two squares if and only if there exist relatively prime integers x and y such that $n = x^2 + y^2$.

Theorem 1: If n is divisible by a prime p of the form $4K + 3$, then n has no proper representation as the sum of two squares.

Proof: The proof is by contradiction. Suppose there is a proper representation $n = x^2 + y^2$, $(x, y) = 1$. Then we must have $(x, p) = 1$. Otherwise, we would have p dividing x and n, and hence y, thus denying $(x, y) = 1$. But with $(x, p) = 1$ we can solve $xu \equiv y \bmod p$ for u as in **G.7** of **14.4**. Then $n \equiv 0 \bmod p$ shows $x^2 + y^2 \equiv x^2(1 + u^2) \equiv 0 \bmod p$. Since $(x, p) = 1$, the cancellation law applies to show $1 + u^2 \equiv 0 \bmod p$. But this is a contradiction, for in EX. **21.6**, we have shown $(-1/p) = -1$ for primes of the form $p = 4K + 3$.

Theorem 2: If $n = p^c m$, where p is a prime of the form $4K + 3$, where c is *odd* and $(p, m) = 1$, then n has no representation as the sum of two squares.

Proof: The proof is by contradiction. Suppose there is a representation $n = x^2 + y^2$. Let $(x, y) = d, x = Xd, y = Yd$. Then $(X, Y) = 1$ and $n = Nd^2$. Since p^c divides n and c is *odd*, it follows that p divides N. But $N = X^2 + Y^2$ with $(X, Y) = 1$, and to have N with such a proper representation, yet divisible by a prime p of the form $4K + 3$, is a contradiction of preceding *Theorem 1*.

Theorem 3: A positive integer is representable as the sum of two squares if and only if each of its prime factors of the form $4K + 3$ appears to an even power.

Proof: (A) For the unit 1, we have $1 = 1^2 + 0^2$. For the only even prime 2, we have $2 = 1^2 + 1^2$. For every prime of the form $4K + 1$ a representation as the sum of two squares exists by the theorem of **27.1**. An even power p^{2s} of a prime of the form $p = 4K + 3$ is a sum of two squares since $p^{2s} = (p^s)^2 + 0^2$. Then by **L.2** of **27.1**, every composite number n in which prime factors of the form $4K + 3$ appear only to even powers is representable as a sum of two squares. This includes the case where such prime factors are *absent*, if we interpret $p^0 = 1$ with the zero exponent as an even power.

(B) If even one prime of the form $4K + 3$ appears to an odd power, and not to a higher power, as a factor of n, then n is not representable as the sum of two squares; for this is the content of the preceding *Theorem 2*.

For example, in our previous examination of $n = 351$ no representation as the sum of two squares was found. This could have been predicted since $351 = 3^3 13$ with the prime 3 appearing to an odd power. On the other hand, we have examples like $117 = 3^2 13 = 9^2 + 6^2$ (where only improper representations are available, see *Theorem 1*) and $65 = 5 \cdot 13 = (1^2 + 2^2)(2^2 + 3^2) = 8^2 + 1^2$ (to illustrate **L.2**).

An elegant result, due to Jacobi and discussed in Uspensky and Heaslet, shows how to enumerate the representations of n as the sum of two squares, distinguishing $(-x)^2$ from $(+x)^2$ and considering order. Jacobi considered the positive divisors of n separated into four classes according to their residues 1, 2, 3, 4 mod 4 and indicated the number of divisors in each of these classes by $\tau_1(n)$, $\tau_2(n)$, $\tau_3(n)$, $\tau_4(n)$, respectively. [In this notation the $\tau(n)$ of Chapter 10 would be given by $\tau(n) = \tau_1(n) + \tau_2(n) + \tau_3(n) + \tau_4(n)$.] Jacobi showed that there are $A(n) = 4(\tau_1(n) - \tau_3(n))$ representations of n as a sum of two squares.

For example, if $n = 351 = 3^3 13$, we find $\tau_1(n) = 4$ and $\tau_3(n) = 4$, corresponding to the sets of divisors 1, 9, 13, 117 and 3, 27, 39, 351, respectively; so $A(n) = 0$ and there are no representations. If $n = 72 = 2^3 3^2$, we have $\tau_1(n) = 2$ and $\tau_3(n) = 1$, corresponding to the sets of divisors 1, 9 and 3, respectively; so $A(n) = 4$, the appropriate representations being $(\pm 6)^2 + (\pm 6)^2$. If $n = 65 = 5 \cdot 13$, then $\tau_1(n) = \tau(n) = 4$; so $A(n) = 16$, the appropriate representations being $(\pm 8)^2 + (\pm 1)^2$, $(\pm 1)^2 + (\pm 8)^2$, $(\pm 7)^2 + (\pm 4)^2$, $(\pm 4)^2 + (\pm 7)^2$.

It is more difficult to discuss in entirety the result concerning representation as the sum of three squares, although EX. **26.8** establishes the easier part of the proof. The correct theorem is that a positive integer n is the sum of three squares of integers if and only if n is not of the form

$4^k(8m + 7)$, $k \geqslant 0$. Expositions of this result can be found in the books of Dickson or in Uspensky and Heaslet.

27.3.   Representation as the difference of two squares

We shall let $Q(n)$ indicate the number of solutions of the Diophantine equation $x^2 - y^2 = n$, where n is a given positive integer and we require x and y to be positive integers.

Theorem: (a) If $n \equiv 2 \bmod 4$, then $Q(n) = 0$.

                 (b) If $n \equiv 1$ or $n \equiv 3 \bmod 4$, then $Q(n) = [\tau(n)/2]$.

                 (c) If $n \equiv 0 \bmod 4$, then $Q(n) = [\tau(n/4)/2]$.

Proof: (a) We note that according as $x \equiv 0, 1, 2, 3 \bmod 4$, we have $x^2 \equiv 0, 1, 0, 1 \bmod 4$. Hence for any given integers x and y, we must have $x^2 - y^2 \equiv 0, 1$, or $3 \bmod 4$; but we cannot have $x^2 - y^2 \equiv 2 \bmod 4$. Therefore $Q(n) = 0$ when $n \equiv 2 \bmod 4$.

A solution $x > 0$, $y > 0$ of $n = x^2 - y^2 = (x + y)(x - y)$ implies a factorization of n in the form $n = dd'$ where $d = x + y$ and $d' = x - y$ so that $d + d' = 2x$ and $d - d' = 2y$. It follows that $d > d' > 0$ and $d \equiv d' \bmod 2$. Conversely, for every factorization $n = dd'$ with $d > d' > 0$ and $d \equiv d' \bmod 2$, there is a solution $x = (d + d')/2$ and $y = (d - d')/2$ of the Diophantine equation with $x > 0$ and $y > 0$.

(b) If $n \equiv 1$ or if $n \equiv 3 \bmod 4$, then n is odd and both d and d' must be odd so $d \equiv d' \bmod 2$ is satisfied. If n is not a square, every factorization $n = dd'$ has $d \neq d'$. There are $\tau(n)$ choices for d, where $\tau(n)$ is even (EX. **10.3**); and exactly $\tau(n)/2$ choices of d with $d > d' > 0$. Hence as explained above, there are the same number of solutions in positive integers of the Diophantine equation; so $Q(n) = \tau(n)/2$. If n is a square, there is one, but only one, factorization $n = dd'$ in which $d = d'$, which would *not* lead to a suitable solution with $y > 0$. In this case $\tau(n)$ is odd, so the number of suitable factorizations of $n = dd'$ with $d > d' > 0$, each leading to a solution of the Diophantine equations and all solutions so obtainable, is given by $Q(n) = (\tau(n) - 1)/2$. The two cases are readily combined by writing $Q(n) = [\tau(n)/2]$.

(c) If $n \equiv 0 \bmod 4$, then n is even and if $n = dd'$, then one, at least, of d and d' must be even; then in order to satisfy $d \equiv d' \bmod 2$, both d and d' must be even, say $d = 2D$, $d' = 2D'$. Then the number of solutions of the Diophantine equation depends exactly on the number of factorizations $n = 4K = (2D)(2D')$, or $n/4 = K = DD'$, $D > D' > 0$. As in part (b), if K is not a square, we find $Q(n) = \tau(K)/2$; but if K is a square, $Q(n) = (\tau(K) - 1)/2$. Both cases are correctly described by $Q(n) = [\tau(n/4)/2]$.

For example, with $n = 351 = 3^3 13 \equiv 3 \bmod 4$, since $\tau(n) = 8$, we find $Q(n) = 4$ solutions. Corresponding to the factorizations $351 \cdot 1$, $117 \cdot 3$, $39 \cdot 9$, $27 \cdot 13$, the solutions x, y are 176, 175; 60, 57; 24, 15; 20, 7.

EXERCISES

27.1. Show that (27.1) is a special case of (26.1).

27.2. Find all representations as a sum of two squares for (a) 209, (b) 221, (c) 1225.

27.3. Find all representations as a difference of two squares for (a) 426, (b) 427, (c) 428, (d) 429.

27.4. If a is a given positive integer and positive integers b, c are required so that

$$b^2 - a^2 = c(c + 1),$$

prove that the number $N(a)$ of solutions b, c is given by

$$N(a) = \frac{\tau(4a^2 - 1)}{2} - 1.$$

27.5. Find the number of Pythagorean triplets of a given *side*.

CHAPTER 28

Egyptian fractions

28.1. Egyptian fractions

For reasons of their own, which we can only "guesstimate," the early Egyptians believed that it was best to replace a fraction such as 3/7 by a sum of distinct unit fractions, i.e., fractions of the form $1/x$ where x is a positive integer; thus they might have used, in this instance,

$$1/4 + 1/7 + 1/28.$$

We see, of course, that a problem of the form $a/b = 1/x + 1/y + 1/z$ can be rewritten as $axyz = b(xy + yz + zx)$ and then treated as a Diophantine equation where a and b are given integers and x, y, z are integers to be determined; but the problem is so much easier to phrase in terms of fractions that we will depart from our usual habit of avoiding them.

Extending the idea of additive arithmetic to embrace fractions we may state the general "Egyptian fraction problem" as follows:

Given the set A of all unit fractions: $1, 1/2, 1/3, \ldots$; let s be unrestricted, but *finite*; let repetitions *not* be allowed; and let order be disregarded; discuss $A(a/b)$ for any given positive rational number a/b; i.e., discuss the determination of a set of s integers $x_1, x_2, \ldots, x_s$ with $1 \leqslant x_1 < x_2 < \cdots < x_s$ such that

(28.1)
$$\frac{a}{b} = \frac{1}{x_1} + \frac{1}{x_2} + \cdots + \frac{1}{x_s}.$$

198

28.2. Algorithm for proper fractions

An amusing variant of the Euclidean algorithm, involving nonpositive remainders, allows us to solve the problem *(28.1)* when a/b is a proper fraction.

Theorem 1: If $1 \leqslant a < b$, then a/b has a representation in the form *(28.1)* with $s \leqslant a$.

Proof: The following construction will be shown adequate by an induction argument on the numerator a.

(I) Obviously if $a = 1$, *(28.1)* is satisfied with $s = 1$ and $x_1 = b$.

(II) Assume that *(28.1)* is solved for all cases a'/b' where $1 \leqslant a' < a$ with $s' \leqslant a'$. Consider the division algorithm $b = qa + r$, $0 \leqslant r < a$.

If $r = 0$, then $b = qa$ may be rewritten $a/b = 1/q$, because the hypothesis $a < b$ guarantees $1 \leqslant q$, so *(28.1)* is solved with $s = 1 < a$.

If $0 < r < a$, then $b = (q + 1)a - (a - r) = xa - a'$, where $x = q + 1 \geqslant 2$ and $a' = a - r$ satisfies the conditions $1 \leqslant a' < a$. Then $a/b = 1/x + a'/bx$ and by hypothesis a'/bx has a representation in terms of s' distinct unit fractions with $s' \leqslant a'$. If $0 < x' \leqslant x$, then since $x < bx/a'$, we would have $1/x' > a'/bx$; hence all of the unit fractions $1/x'$ used in representing a'/bx have the property $x' > x$. Hence a representation in terms of $s = s' + 1$ *distinct* unit fractions is available for a/b; and since $s' \leqslant a' < a$, we have $s \leqslant a$.

By (I), (II), and induction we have established Theorem 1.

For example, by the method suggested here, we have for $3/7$ the algorithm: $7 = 3 \cdot 3 - 2$, $21 = 11 \cdot 2 - 1$ which is equivalent to

$$\frac{3}{7} = \frac{1}{3} + \frac{2}{21}, \quad \frac{2}{21} = \frac{1}{11} + \frac{1}{231} \quad \text{leading to} \quad \frac{3}{7} = \frac{1}{3} + \frac{1}{11} + \frac{1}{231}.$$

If we recall that another solution to this problem was given in **28.1**, we will be interested to see if the representation *(28.1)* is ever unique. But an immediate answer "No!" is obtained as soon as we notice the curious identity

(28.2)
$$\frac{1}{x} = \frac{1}{x + 1} + \frac{1}{x(x + 1)},$$

where the fractions on the right are distinct when $x > 1$. For we see the possibility of obtaining from any known representation *(28.1)* a new representation with more summands by simply applying *(28.2)* with $x = x_s$. (In case $x = 1$, two applications yield $1 = \frac{1}{2} + \frac{1}{3} + \frac{1}{6}$.)

Thus $\frac{3}{7} = \frac{1}{4} + \frac{1}{7} + \frac{1}{28} = \frac{1}{4} + \frac{1}{7} + \frac{1}{29} + \frac{1}{832}$. Of course, if we are careful about not introducing duplications, we may apply (28.2) in other ways: thus $\frac{3}{7} = \frac{1}{5} + \frac{1}{7} + \frac{1}{20} + \frac{1}{28}$. In fact, it seems reasonable to use (28.2) as a tool for solving the general Egyptian fraction problem. Why not treat the last $a - 1$ fractions of $\frac{a}{b} = \frac{1}{b} + \frac{1}{b} + \cdots + \frac{1}{b}$ with (28.2) and if duplications appear remove them by further use of (28.2)? For example,

$$\frac{3}{7} = \frac{1}{7} + \frac{1}{7} + \frac{1}{7} = \frac{1}{7} + \frac{1}{8} + \frac{1}{56} + \frac{1}{8} + \frac{1}{56}$$

$$= \frac{1}{7} + \frac{1}{8} + \frac{1}{56} + \frac{1}{9} + \frac{1}{72} + \frac{1}{57} + \frac{1}{3192}.$$

The difficulty with this approach is in devising some simple argument to guarantee that duplications will be removed in a *finite* number of steps.

For now we mention for the first time that it is conceivable to have an infinite representation based on the form (28.1). For example, the reader probably will have studied geometric series and understand the definitions and argument which allow us to write

$$\frac{2}{3} = \frac{1}{2} + \frac{1}{8} + \frac{1}{32} + \cdots + \left(\frac{1}{2}\right)^{2k-1} + \cdots.$$

This reminder about infinite series leads us naturally to the next section.

28.3. The harmonic series and the general problem

It is doubtful that the Egyptian scholar worried about a representation of the type (28.1) for an improper fraction $a/b \geq 1$. Probably he would have removed the largest integer and contented himself with applying his tricks or algorithm to the remaining proper part. But for our own satisfaction we consider the general problem and show that there is always a solution [and from (28.2) many solutions].

For $n \geq 1$ let us define $S_n = 1 + \frac{1}{2} + \frac{1}{3} + \cdots + \frac{1}{n}$. Then it is a rather simple matter to show that for any positive integer M there exists a corresponding integer N such that $S_n \geq M$ when $n \geq N$. This result is usually described by saying "The harmonic series is divergent."

Note first that $S_{n+1} = S_n + 1/(n + 1) > S_n$ so the sequence S_n increases as n increases. Note secondly that $2^k = 2^{k-1} + 2^{k-1}$ and that

$$\frac{1}{2^{k-1} + t} \geq \frac{1}{2^k} \text{ when } 1 \leq t \leq 2^{k-1} \text{ so that for } k \geq 1,$$

$$S_{2^k} - S_{2^{k-1}} = \frac{1}{2^{k-1} + 1} + \frac{1}{2^{k-1} + 2} + \cdots + \frac{1}{2^{k-1} + 2^{k-1}} \geq \frac{2^{k-1}}{2^k} = \frac{1}{2}.$$

Hence

$$S_{2^k} = (S_{2^k} - S_{2^{k-1}}) + (S_{2^{k-1}} - S_{2^{k-2}}) + \cdots + (S_2 - S_1) + S_1$$

$$\geqslant \frac{1}{2} + \frac{1}{2} + \cdots + \frac{1}{2} + 1 = \frac{k+2}{2}, \qquad k \geqslant 0.$$

Consequently, if we are given the positive integer M, we may take $N = 2^{2M-2}$, to prove the divergence. For if $n \geqslant N$, we have

$$S_n \geqslant S_N \geqslant \frac{2M - 2 + 2}{2} = M.$$

Theorem 2: For every positive rational number there exists a representation of the type (28.1).

Proof: (A) If a/b is proper, $0 < a/b < 1$, we may use Theorem 1.

(B) If a/b is improper, $1 \leqslant a/b$, we may use the divergence of the harmonic series to find $n \geqslant 1$ so that $S_n \leqslant a/b < S_{n+1}$.

Let $A/B = a/b - S_n$. Then $0 \leqslant A/B < S_{n+1} - S_n = 1/(n+1)$. If $A/B = 0$, we have $a/b = S_n$, a representation of type (28.1). If $0 < A/B < 1/(n+1)$, $n \geqslant 1$, we have a proper fraction A/B to which we can apply Theorem 1 to obtain a representation. Moreover, fractions $1/x'$ used in representing A/B must have $x' > n + 1$ since $A/B < 1/(n+1)$. Hence the combined representation for $a/b = S_n + A/B$ will not involve duplications.

For example, if $a/b = 11/4$, we find $S_8 < 11/4 < S_9$ and $A/B = 9/280$. As in Theorem 1 we find $280 = 32 \cdot 9 - 8$, and since 8 divides 32, our work is over, and we have

$$\frac{11}{4} = 1 + \frac{1}{2} + \frac{1}{3} + \frac{1}{4} + \frac{1}{5} + \frac{1}{6} + \frac{1}{7} + \frac{1}{8} + \frac{1}{32} + \frac{1}{1120}.$$

28.4. Representation with $s = 2$

When $s = 2$ we may rephrase the representation problem (28.1) as indicated in the following theorem.

Theorem 3: The Diophantine equation $a/b = 1/x + 1/y$ where a and b are given positive, relatively prime integers is solvable for distinct positive integers x and y if and only if distinct, positive, relatively prime integers P and Q exist such that P and Q divide b and $P + Q \equiv 0 \bmod a$.

Proof: (A) If the conditions are satisfied, then $P + Q = ka$, $k > 0$, $b = PP' = QQ'$, and

$$\frac{a}{b} = \frac{ka}{kb} = \frac{P + Q}{kb} = \frac{1}{kP'} + \frac{1}{kQ'},$$

so we may take $x = kP'$ and $y = kQ'$ as a solution. The assumption $P \neq Q$ implies $x \neq y$. The hypothesis $(P, Q) = 1$ is not required.

(B) Suppose a solution x, y exists, then $axy = b(x + y)$. Let $(x, y) = d$, then $x = Xd$, $y = Yd$, with $(X, Y) = 1$. We have $aXYd = b(X + Y)$. From $(X, Y) = 1$ we know $(X, X + Y) = 1$; hence X divides b. Similarly, Y divides b. Since $(a, b) = 1$, we see that a divides $X + Y$, so $X + Y \equiv 0 \bmod a$. Thus we may take $P = X$, $Q = Y$ to satisfy the conditions in Theorem 3. The assumption $x \neq y$ implies $P \neq Q$, and the condition $(X, Y) = 1$ shows $(P, Q) = 1$.

For example, 19/280 may be represented with $s = 2$, for among the divisors of 280 we have $P = 56$ and $Q = 1$, such that $P + Q = 3 \cdot 19$. Therefore

$$\frac{19}{280} = \frac{3 \cdot 19}{3 \cdot 280} = \frac{56 + 1}{3 \cdot 280} = \frac{1}{15} + \frac{1}{840}.$$

For another example, if $p = 6K + 1$ is a prime, then $3/p$ cannot be represented with $s = 2$. For the only possible values of P and Q are $P = 6K + 1$ and $Q = 1$ and $P + Q = 6K + 2 \equiv 2 \not\equiv 0 \bmod 3$.

Corollary 3.1: It is possible to decide in a finite number of steps whether a/b has a representation of the form (28.1) with $s = 3$.

Proof: The representation $\dfrac{a}{b} = \dfrac{1}{x} + \dfrac{1}{y} + \dfrac{1}{z}$ with $1 \leqslant x < y < z$ requires $\dfrac{1}{x} < \dfrac{a}{b} < \dfrac{3}{x}$ hence $\dfrac{b}{a} < x < \dfrac{3b}{a}$, so there are only a finite number of values of x to be considered. For each such value of x we have a new problem: "Can $\dfrac{a}{b} - \dfrac{1}{x}$ be represented in the form $\dfrac{1}{y} + \dfrac{1}{z}$?" But this is exactly the situation for which Theorem 3 provides a complete and finite test.

For example, consider 8/17. Here $17/8 < x < 51/8$ limits x to the values 3, 4, 5, 6. When $x = 3$, we have $8/17 - 1/3 = 7/51$, but none of the combinations $1 + 3$, $1 + 17$, $1 + 51$, $3 + 17$ (see EX. **28.8** for a check that no combination of distinct relatively prime divisors has been overlooked) has the required property of being a multiple of 7. When $x = 4$, we have $8/17 - 1/4 = 15/68$, but none of the combinations $1 + 2$, $1 + 4$, $1 + 17$, $1 + 34$, $1 + 68$, $2 + 17$, $4 + 17$ is a multiple of 15. When $x = 5$, we have $8/17 - 1/5 = 23/85$, but none of $1 + 5$, $1 + 17$, $1 + 85$, $5 + 17$ is a multiple of 23. Finally, when $x = 6$, we have $8/17 - 1/6 = 31/102$, but none of $1 + 2$, $1 + 3$, $1 + 6$, $1 + 17$, $1 + 34$, $1 + 51$, $1 + 102$, $2 + 3$, $2 + 17$, $2 + 51$, $3 + 17$, $3 + 34$, $6 + 17$ is a multiple of 31. Thus $8/17$ has no representation with $s = 3$.

28.5.   The Erdös and Sierpinski conjectures

It was Erdös who first conjectured that every fraction of the form $4/n$ has a representation of the form (28.1) with $s = 3$ when $n \geqslant 3$. If the conjecture is true, it would be something of a surprise, for the best that Theorem 1 will guarantee is that $s \leqslant 4$. Perhaps even more surprising is the conjecture of Sierpinski that every fraction of the form $5/n$ has a representation of the form (28.1) with $s = 3$ when $n \geqslant 3$. These and other authors have studied these problems and deduced considerable evidence to support the conjectures. We shall use our own method centered around Theorem 3 and pursue the problem involving $5/n$ somewhat further than seems to have been done previously.

Theorem 4:   If there are any integers $n \geqslant 3$ such that a representation for $5/n$ in the form (28.1) requires $s > 3$, then n must have the form $n = 278460K + 1$.

Proof: (A) We begin by establishing a result of Palamà which shows that the only possible exceptions have the form $n = 1260E + 1$. To save space we shall arrange the results in tabular form. After selecting x we compute $A/nx = 5/n - 1/x$ with $A = 5x - n$. To the fraction A/nx we apply Theorem 3 by indicating a choice of P and Q which are divisors of nx and are such that $P + Q \equiv 0 \bmod A$. The corresponding solutions y and z will satisfy $x < y < z$ if we always understand $n \geqslant 3$. The argument proceeds by considerations modulo 5, 4, 3, 3, and 7; so we insert lines in the table to show the stage reached and the next modulus to be used.

Since the results of (B) and (C) show there can be no exceptions except possibly when $E \equiv 0 \bmod 13$ and when $E \equiv 0 \bmod 17$, i.e., when $E \equiv 0 \bmod 221$, we set $E = 221K$ and assert that the only possible exceptions are those for which $n = 1260 \cdot 221K + 1$, which is the $n = 278460K + 1$ in Theorem 4.

Our original hope was to produce an endless list of primes, like 13 and 17, for which all the residue classes of $E \bmod p$, except $E \equiv 0 \bmod p$, would have a representation with $s = 3$ for $5/(1260E + 1)$. For if this hope were realized, then Sierpinski's conjecture would be established.

k	x	A	P	Q

Let $n = 5U + k$. Assume $n \geqslant 3$.

k	x	A	P	Q
0	U	0	Use (28.2).	
2	$U + 1$	3	n	x
3	$U + 1$	2	n	x
4	$U + 1$	1	Use (28.2).	

Leaves $n = 5U + 1$. Let $U = 4V + k$.

k	x	A	P	Q
1	$4V + 2$	4	x	2
2	$4V + 3$	4	x	1
3	$4V + 4$	4	n	x

Leaves $n = 20V + 1$. Let $V = 3W + k$.

k	x	A	P	Q
1	$12W + 6$	9	6	3
2	$12W + 9$	4	3	1

Leaves $n = 60W + 1$. Let $W = 3D + k$.

k	x	A	P	Q
1	$36D + 14$	9	n	2
2	$36D + 26$	9	x	1

Leaves $n = 180D + 1$. Let $D = 7E + k$.

k	x	A	P	Q
1	$252E + 39$	14	$x/3$	1
2	$252E + 75$	14	$x/3$	3
3	$252E + 111$	14	x	1
4	$252E + 147$	14	x	7
5	$252E + 183$	14	$nx/3$	3
6	$252E + 219$	14	nx	1

Leaves $n = 1260E + 1$.

(B) Similarly, we study $n = 1260E + 1$ with $E = 13F + k$.

k	x	A	P	Q
1	$52(63F + 5)$	39	26	13
2	$39(84F + 13)$	14	13	1
3	$4(819F + 191)$	39	$x/4$	4
4	$78(42F + 13)$	29	26	3
5	$468(7F + 4)$	3059	$234n$	$x/468$
6	$4(819F + 380)$	39	x	1
7	$52(63F + 34)$	19	$13n$	$x/26$
8	$4(819F + 506)$	39	x	1
9	$91(36F + 25)$	34	$13n$	$x/91$
10	$26(126F + 97)$	9	26	1
11	$26(126F + 107)$	49	$26n$	$x/13$
12	$234(14F + 13)$	89	$13n$	$x/26$

(C) Similarly we study $n = 1260E + 1$ with $E = 17G + k$.

k	x	A	P	Q
1	$51(84G + 5)$	14	$x/51$	51
2	$102(42G + 5)$	29	$17n$	$x/102$
3	$204(21G + 4)$	299	$102n$	$x/102$
4	$204(21G + 5)$	59	$17n$	$x/34$
5	$12(357G + 107)$	119	$x/12$	12
6	$7(612G + 217)$	34	$nx/7$	1
7	$68(63G + 26)$	19	17	2
8	$119(36G + 17)$	34	119	17
9	$34(126G + 67)$	49	$17n$	$x/34$
10	$7(612G + 361)$	34	$nx/7$	1
11	$102(42G + 29)$	929	$51n$	$x/51$
12	$34(126G + 89)$	9	17	1
13	$7(612G + 469)$	34	$x/7$	7
14	$7(612G + 505)$	34	x	1
15	$12(357G + 317)$	119	$x/4$	1
16	$7(612G + 577)$	34	$x/7$	1

However, we have not been able to find even one more such p, although 19 and 23 are nearly complete. Using such results (expressed in terms of K rather than E) and observations such as EX. **28.2**, we can establish the following corollary.

Corollary 4.1: Sierpinski's conjecture is correct for every n in the range $3 \leqslant n \leqslant 1,057,438,801$.

Proof: We shall merely outline the method of proof. When $p = 23$ only the five classes $K \equiv 0, 12, 18, 20, 22$ resist the method of Theorem 3. When $p = 5$, only the classes $K \equiv 0, 2, 3$ remain. When $p = 11$, only the classes $K \equiv 0, 4, 5, 6, 7, 8$ remain. Thus mod 1265 only 90 classes require further investigation. But when $p = 19$ only $K \equiv 0, 2, 3, 7, 8, 12, 14$ remain; and when $p = 29$ only $K \equiv 0, 2, 5, 7, 10, 12, 15, 16, 17, 18, 23, 25$ are in doubt. This is enough information to reduce drastically the 270 cases which would seem to need investigation when $1 \leqslant K \leqslant 3 \cdot 1265$. The few cases remaining may be studied on an individual basis and each has a solution with $s = 3$. We stop this number chase arbitrarily at $K = 3795$ and find the strange looking, but we hope impressively large, n in the statement of the corollary.

We have presented this material as an example of the tantalizing nature of some number theory problems. Theorem 4 and Corollary 4.1 certainly substantiate Sierpinski's conjecture, yet they by no means provide a proof. Perhaps some of our student readers can suggest just what subtle twist or fresh viewpoint will allow us to settle the matter one way or the other.

There are many interesting and challenging variations of the Egyptian fraction problems. The exercises will suggest a few and current literature will show others.

EXERCISES

28.1. Use the algorithm in Theorem 1 to obtain Egyptian fraction representations for (a) 8/13, (b) 8/17, (c) 8/23, (d) 8/29.

28.2. For the problem of representing a/b in the form (28.1) prove that it suffices to consider the cases where $b = 1$ and where b is a prime. [Hint: If $b = BB'$, then $a/b = (a/B)(1/B')$.]

28.3. Rephrase the algorithm of Theorem 1 in terms of the bracket function.

28.4. Why might (28.2) be called (a) an *optic* formula? (b) a *resistance* formula?

28.5. Establish the following formula:

$$\frac{1}{B} = \frac{1}{2B + 1} + \frac{1}{3B + 2} + \frac{1}{3(2B + 1)} + \frac{1}{B(2B + 1)}$$
$$+ \frac{1}{3(2B + 1)(3B + 2)}.$$

If B is an odd integer, show that every denominator in the formula is an odd integer, and that they are, in general, distinct.

28.6. Repeat EX. **28.5** for the formula:

$$\frac{1}{B} = \frac{1}{B+2} + \frac{1}{B(B+2)}$$
$$+ \frac{1}{B^2 + 2B + 2}$$
$$+ \frac{1}{B(B+2)(B^2 + 2B + 3)/2}$$
$$+ \frac{1}{B(B+2)(B^2 + 2B + 2)(B^2 + 2B + 3)/2}.$$

28.7. Prove Theorem 1 using the binary system of representation. (*1*) If $b = 2^k$, express a in binary form and consider a/b. (2) If $2^k < b < 2^{k+1}$ and $a2^k = qb + r$, $0 \leqslant r < b$, express q and r in binary form and consider $a/b = a2^k/b2^k$. Be sure to clarify the matter of distinct unit fractions.

28.8. For the application of Theorem 3, let $U(n)$ be the number of pairs of divisors of n, say P and Q, with $P > Q \geqslant 1$ and $(P, Q) = 1$. If $n = p_1^{a_1} \ldots p_k^{a_k}$ is in standard form, show that $U(n) = [S(n) - 1]/2$ where $S(n) = (2a_1 + 1) \ldots (2a_k + 1)$. [Hint: Begin by showing that $S(n)$, which counts the number of ordered pairs of divisors of n with $(P, Q) = 1$, is multiplicative.]

28.9. List the divisors of 280 and apply Theorem 3 and EX. **28.8** to find all solutions of (*28.1*) with $s = 2$ for (a) 9/280, (b) 19/280, (c) 29/280, (d) 39/280, (e) 49/280, (f) 59/280.

28.10. Show that the number of representations of $1/n$ in the form (*28.1*) with $s = 2$ is given by $U(n)$ in EX. **28.8**.

28.11. Show that the number of representations of $2/n$ in the form (*28.1*) with $s = 2$ is given by $U(n)$ if $n \equiv 1 \mod 2$, and by $U(n/2)$ if $n \equiv 0 \mod 2$.

28.12. Show that 11/37 cannot be represented by (*28.1*) with $s = 3$.

28.13. Verify some of the assertions in (*B*) of Theorem 4.

28.14. Apply the method of Theorem 4 to Erdös' conjecture. (a) Show that if there are any $n \geqslant 3$ for which a representation of $4/n$ in the form (*28.1*) requires $s > 3$, then n must have the form $n = 120T + 1$ or $n = 120T + 49$. (b) Extend the previous result to show that the only possible exceptions are $n = 840S + k$ where $k = 1, 121, 361, 169, 289, 529$. (c) Apply EX. **28.2** to conclude that Erdös' conjecture is true for $3 \leqslant n \leqslant 1128$.

PART II

An axiomatic approach
to number theory

CHAPTER 29

Mathematical systems
and introduction to group theory

29.1. Concerning mathematical systems

The reader has probably become acquainted with the postulational method
in mathematics by a study of plane geometry, but if he has had only the
traditional courses in algebra he may never have realized that algebra too is
susceptible of such a postulational treatment. Historically, this is understandable, for geometry has been regarded abstractly for over twenty
centuries, while algebra has been so viewed for scarcely one century. But
there was a revolution in attitude toward the axiomatic basis of geometry
at the beginning of the nineteenth century; and the revolution spread out
to cause a study of the foundations of all branches of mathematics.

In order to describe how the postulational method touches the theory
of numbers, it will be convenient at the outset to have a definition of a
general mathematical system. All such definitions have their faults, being
criticized as either too general or too restrictive, but the following one
seems quite useful.

A mathematical system is the resultant of the application of a system
of logic to a set of elements, relations, and operations whose properties
are described by a consistent set of postulates. If the elements, relations,

211

erations are left *undefined*, except that they are *assumed* to satisfy
stulates, then the system may be described as a *pure* or *abstract*
natical system. If the elements, relations, and operations are *defined*
s of previously studied concepts and the postulates are *proved* to
hold, then the system may be described as an *applied* mathematical system
or as a *concrete example*.

A student with some mathematical experience will sense that in the
development of a mathematical system both the abstract and the concrete
approaches are worthwhile. From a concrete example one obtains suggestions about theorems that may hold in the abstract system; but if the
theorem can be proved in the abstract form (and such a proof is sometimes easier, being free of distracting special details found in the example),
then it holds for *all* the concrete examples without any further special
investigations.

It may be helpful to discuss in detail some of the terms used in the
above definition.

By the word "resultant" we imply that not only the elements, relations,
operations, and postulates shall be thought of as part of the system, but
also all propositions that can be derived as a formal logical consequence
from the postulates. One natural way in which such a study of *all* propositions may be limited is suggested in a later paragraph. We should
speak of derived propositions as being *valid*, rather than true, to remind
ourselves that they can be no more "true" than the originally assumed
postulates or the previously studied systems.

In ordinary mathematics we use the Aristotelian system of logic with
the following basic laws:

(*1*) Law of the identity: A is A, a thing is itself.

(*2*) Law of the excluded middle: either A or not-A, a proposition is
valid or is not-valid, there being no other value that can be assigned to it.

(*3*) Law of contradiction: not both A and not-A, a proposition is not
both valid and not-valid.

But in our definition we have used the phrase, "a" system of logic,
because today there is study of systems of logic in which there are more
than two "truth values" to be considered for each proposition, and the
mathematical systems developed with such systems of logic may be
considered a part of mathematics.

In any definition, to avoid circular reasoning, certain basic ideas must
be left undefined. For example, the ideas of an *element*, a *set* of elements,
and of an element *belonging to* a set of elements are of this fundamental
nature.

An important example of a relation in a mathematical system is an
equivalence relation, a concept which we have already described at length
in **13.2**. If we consider the properties required for an equivalence relation

as postulates, then we already have at hand a simple type of mathematical system.

A possible synonym for the word operation is the word function. For example, a rule which determines for each element a of a set S a corresponding element $b = f(a)$ of S is an example of a *unary* operation. A rule which determines for each ordered pair of elements a, b of S a corresponding element $c = f(a, b)$ of S is an example of a *binary* operation. In similar manner, we may define functions of three or more variables. Operations are usually required to be closed and well defined: thus a binary operation $f(a, b)$ is said to be closed if $f(a, b)$ is in S for every a and b in S and is said to be well defined (with respect to a specified equivalence relation) if $a = a'$ and $b = b'$ imply $f(a, b) = f(a', b')$ for all a, b in S. Similar definitions apply when unary, ternary, and other operations are being considered. Some of these ideas have already been well illustrated in **13.3**.

The mathematical systems studied in modern algebra may be characterized, at least roughly, as those in which are present operations resembling some of the familiar operations of addition, multiplication, subtraction, and division.

The set of postulates in a mathematical system is, of course, man-made, sometimes suggested by external situations, sometimes pure invention; but in such a selection complete arbitrariness is not allowed, for the set of postulates is always required to be *consistent*. This term means that in the propositions derived from the postulates there must never appear a violation of the law of contradiction, i.e., it must never happen that a proposition is both valid and not-valid. The only known test for the consistency of a set of postulates is the exhibition of at least one example satisfying all the postulates.

It is desirable, although not absolutely necessary, that a set of postulates be such that no postulate can be derived as a theorem from the other postulates; a set of postulates with this property is said to be *independent*. The test for independence of a set of postulates is the exhibition of as many examples as there are postulates, one for each postulate, with the property that the example does not satisfy that particular postulate but does satisfy all the other postulates, hence the postulate in question could not possibly be derived as a theorem from the other postulates.

To describe one further property of a set of postulates it is first necessary to explain just when two examples satisfying a set of postulates shall be considered distinct. It is reasonably clear that if the elements $a_1, b_1, \ldots$ of example S_1 in which there is, say, a binary operation $f_1(a_1, b_1)$, may be paired off in a "one-to-one" manner (see below) with the elements $a_2, b_2, \ldots$ of a second example S_2 in which there is a corresponding operation $f_2(a_2, b_2)$, and the pairing off is of such a nature that whenever a_1 and

a_2, b_1 and b_2 are corresponding elements, it then follows that $f_1(a_1, b_1)$ and $f_2(a_2, b_2)$ are corresponding elements, then the examples S_1 and S_2, although distinct in the sense that their elements and operations have different names, are "abstractly the same" or, to use technical terms (see below), they are "*isomorphic* with respect to the operations f_1 and f_2."

An important goal in the study of a mathematical system is the characterization of all the nonisomorphic examples satisfying the abstractly defined system. The theorems which may lead to such a goal are described as the *structure theory* of the system. It is this aiming of effort toward structure theory we had in mind when we mentioned earlier some natural limitation on the set of theorems to be derived from the postulates.

If it happens that all the possible examples are isomorphic, then the set of postulates is described as *categorical*. For some systems, especially those which are in some sense fundamental to the understanding or construction of others, it is important to prove that they are categorical. On the other hand some systems acquire their importance from being not-categorical so that there is a certain wealth of really different examples embraced by the abstract system.

29.2.   Mappings

To make the notion of isomorphism more precise let us consider the general matter of mapping one system S_1 with elements $x_1, y_1, \ldots$ and equivalence relation $x_1 \mathbf{E}_1 y_1$, or $x_1 \mathbf{E}_1 y_1$ into a second system S_2 with elements $x_2, y_2, \ldots$ and equivalence relation $x_2 \mathbf{E}_2 y_2$, or $x_2 \mathbf{E}_2 y_2$. Note that S_2 may be the system S_1 itself and that $\mathbf{E}_2$ may be the same as $\mathbf{E}_1$.

Let us consider a correspondence F by which an element x_1 of S_1 is made to correspond to an element x_2 of S_2, indicated by $x_2 \mathbf{E}_2 x_1 F$, to be read "x_2 is the image of x_1 under the correspondence F." Let us list and name four properties which the correspondence F may or may not possess.

F.1:   If x_1 is in S_1 implies $x_1 F$ is in S_2, then F is "complete over S_1."

F.2:   If $x_1 \mathbf{E}_1 y_1$ in S_1 implies $x_1 F \mathbf{E}_2 y_1 F$ in S_2, then F is "well defined."

F.3:   If x_2 in S_2 implies there exists an x_1 in S_1 such that $x_2 \mathbf{E}_2 x_1 F$, then F is "onto S_2."

F.4:   If $x_1 F \mathbf{E}_2 y_1 F$ in S_2 implies $x_1 \mathbf{E}_1 y_1$ in S_1, then F has "unique antecedents."

If F has properties **F.1** and **F.2**, then F will be called a "many-to-one mapping of S_1 into S_2."

If F has properties **F.1**, **F.2**, and **F.3**, then F will be called a "many-to-one mapping of S_1 onto S_2."

If F has properties **F.1**, **F.2**, **F.3**, and **F.4**, then F will be called a "one-to-one mapping between S_1 and S_2."

Note the converse nature of the pair of conditions **F.1** and **F.3**, one involving completeness over S_1; the other, completeness over S_2. Similarly, **F.2** and **F.4** form a converse pair, one involving unique images, the other, unique antecedents. Observe that this latter pair of conditions can be phrased: $x_1 F \mathbf{E}_2 y_1 F$ if and only if $x_1 \mathbf{E}_1 y_1$.

For example, let S_1 and S_2 be the set of all nonzero integers and let E_1 and E_2 be ordinary equality. Then the correspondence $x^2 = xF$ is a "many-to-one mapping of S_1 into itself." **F.1** and **F.2** are satisfied since the square of a nonzero integer is a uniquely determined nonzero integer; but **F.3** is not satisfied because there are integers, such as 2, in the set S_2 which are not squares of integers in S_1; and **F.4** is not satisfied, since $(-1)^2 = (+1)^2$ in S_2, but $-1 \neq +1$ in S_1. More precisely, the correspondence F is a "two-to-one mapping," for there are exactly two elements of S_1 having the same image in S_2. If we change S_1 and S_2 to include all integers, this last remark must be modified. If we change S_2 to be the set of all positive squares of integers, we can satisfy **F.3**, but not **F.4**, and so produce an example of a "many-to-one mapping of S_1 onto S_2" which is not "one-to-one."

If there is a one-to-one mapping of S_1 onto S_2, then S_1 and S_2 are said to be *equivalent* sets. Equivalence of sets is an equivalence relation, and if we note the separation into mutually exclusive classes produced by any equivalence relation, then we may appreciate the following definition due to B. Russell: the set of all sets equivalent to a given set shall be called the *cardinal number* of the set.

A *subset* T of a set S is a set of elements all of which belong to S. A *proper subset* T of a set S is a subset such that there exists at least one element of S not belonging to T. A set S is said to have a *finite* cardinal number if S is not equivalent to any of its proper subsets; but if S is equivalent to a proper subset of itself, then S is said to have an *infinite* cardinal number.

For example, the set S of all positive integers has an infinite cardinal number, for S has as a proper subset the set T of all even positive integers, and the correspondence $2x = xF$ is a one-to-one mapping between S and T, for it is easy to check properties **F.1**, **F.2**, **F.3**, and **F.4**.

If there is in the system S_1 an operation, say $f_1(x_1, y_1)$, and in the system S_2 an operation on the same number of elements, say $f_2(x_2, y_2)$, then the correspondence F may or may not possess the following property:

F.5: If x_1 and y_1 in S_1 implies $f_1(x_1, y_1)F \mathbf{E}_2 f_2(x_1F, y_1F)$, then F is "operation-preserving with respect to f_1 and f_2."

If F has properties **F.1**, **F.2**, **F.3**, **F.4**, and **F.5**, then F is called an "isomorphism of S_1 and S_2 with respect to f_1 and f_2."

Since an isomorphism is a one-to-one mapping that is operation-preserving, we can sense that the name is well chosen, for if we think of "iso-" meaning "same" and "morphism" meaning "form," the idea of two examples having the same form (i.e., differing only in the names given to the elements and operations) is exactly what we are trying to describe.

For example, let S_1 be the set of all positive integers and let S_2 be the set of all positive powers of 2, with ordinary equality as the equivalence relation in both cases. Let $f_1(x_1, y_1) = x_1 + y_1$ be the operation of addition; and let $f_2(x_2, y_2) = x_2 y_2$ be the operation of multiplication. Then the correspondence $2^x = xF$ is an "isomorphism of S_1 and S_2 with respect to addition in S_1 and multiplication in S_2." Properties **F.1** and **F.3** are obvious; properties **F.2** and **F.4** follow from $2^x = 2^y$ if and only if $x = y$; and property **F.5** follows from

$$(x_1 + y_1)F = 2^{x_1 + y_1} = 2^{x_1} 2^{y_1} = (x_1 F)(y_1 F)$$

using a well-known rule of exponents.

29.3.   Groups

As our first example of a mathematical system, treated in an axiomatic manner, let us define an "abstract group," for this kind of system is simple in the sense of involving just one operation, and yet is rich and important in the sense that examples occur in almost all branches of mathematics.

Definition: A group is a mathematical system consisting of a set G of elements $a, b, \ldots$ with an equivalence relation $a = b$, or $a \neq b$, and an ordered binary operation, written ab, which satisfies the following postulates:

H.1:   The group operation is closed and well defined: if a and b are in G, then ab is in G; if $a = a'$ and $b = b'$, then $ab = a'b'$.

H.2:   The group operation has a left-identity: there exists an element e in G such that if a is in G, then $a = ea$.

H.3:   The group operation possesses left-inverses: if a is in G, there exists a^{-1} in G such that $a^{-1}a = e$.

H.4:   The group operation is associative: if a, b, c are in G, then $(ab)c = a(bc)$.

It is not required that the group operation be commutative. However, it is convenient to be able to distinguish groups according to whether they satisfy the additional hypothesis:

H.5: The group operation is called *commutative* if a and b in G implies $ab = ba$.

For the reader who is just getting acquainted with such postulational statements, it may be well to add that each postulate is supposedly so worded that every possible element, or pair or triple of elements, in G is included. In the statement of **H.4** all the combinations involved are supposed to be in G. When a postulate statement involves two or three elements, it is not assumed that they are necessarily distinct.

As an illustration of the study of a proposed mathematical system and of the important relations that may exist between such a system and the theory of numbers, with each throwing light on the other, let us proceed at once to show that this set of postulates is consistent (i.e., from previous experience we construct an example satisfying all the postulates) and not-categorical (i.e., we produce at least two examples which are not isomorphic).

Example 1: The set of all integers under ordinary equality and the operation of addition $a + b$ forms an infinite commutative group with 0 as the identity (since $0 + a = a$ for every integer a) and with $-a$ as the inverse of a [since $(-a) + a = 0$]. Of course the reader must adjust himself to the convention of writing the operation of the abstract group in the form ab, while writing the operation of a concrete example in whatever form is most familiar.

Corollary 1: The group postulates are consistent.

Proof: Use Example 1.

Example 2: For every positive integer m there exists at least one commutative group with m elements.

Proof: Consider the system $G(m)$ whose elements are residue classes of integers mod m; whose equivalence relation is congruence mod m; and whose operation is addition of residue classes. In **G.2** we showed that congruence mod m is an equivalence relation. We defined (a-class) + (b-class) = $(a + b)$-class so that we have *closure*, and in **G.3** we proved that this addition of residue classes is *well defined*. It is easy to check that the 0-class serves as the *identity*, for we have (0-class) + (a-class) = $(0 + a)$-class = a-class. We may use the $(-a)$-class as the *inverse* of the a-class, for we have $((-a)$-class) + (a-class) = $((-a) + a)$-class = 0-class.

Since ordinary addition of integers is associative, it follows that addition of residue classes is *associative*. Since ordinary addition of integers is commutative, the addition of residue classes is *commutative*.

Corollary 2:   The group postulates are not-categorical.

Proof: If $m_1 \neq m_2$, then $G(m_1)$ is not-isomorphic to $G(m_2)$, because there are m_1 elements in one system and m_2 in the other; so it is not possible to find a one-to-one mapping between them, and hence impossible to find an isomorphism.

The next step in studying the abstract group might be to show that the postulates are independent, but this is an optional matter and we shall leave it as an exercise except for the comment that the independence of **H.4** from **H.1**, **H.2**, and **H.3** requires an example with at least six elements. Similarly, the independence of **H.5** from **H.1**, **H.2**, **H.3**, and **H.4** requires an example with at least six elements; and this question of the existence of noncommutative groups will be answered in the next chapter.

Instead we turn our attention to the notion of developing theorems true for the abstract group and hence true for every concrete example. In the proofs we shall adopt the habit of writing under each equality sign the name of the definition, postulate, hypothesis, or previously proved theorem which justifies the equality. If it is at all convenient we shall try to arrange a chain of equalities such that the first and last members, being equal by the extended transitive property of the equivalence relation, establish the proposition in the theorem.

Theorem 1:   In a group the left-identity is also a right-identity; and a left-inverse is also a right-inverse.

Proof: (A) By **H.3** if a is in G, then a^{-1} exists so that $a^{-1}a = e$; and since a^{-1} is in G, $x = (a^{-1})^{-1}$ exists so that $xa^{-1} = e$. Then

$$a \underset{\text{H.2}}{=} ea \underset{\text{H.3,H.1}}{=} (xa^{-1})a \underset{\text{H.4}}{=} x(a^{-1}a) \underset{\text{H.3,H.1}}{=} xe \underset{\text{H.2,H.1}}{=} x(ee) \underset{\text{H.4}}{=} (xe)e \underset{\text{H.1}}{=} ae,$$

where the last step is justified by the $a = xe$ occurring in the chain.

(B) In the proof of (A) we have $a = xe$, so by (A) itself we have $a = xe = x$. From the definition of x we find $e = xa^{-1} = aa^{-1}$.

Theorem 2:   In a group the equation $xa = b$ has a unique solution $x = ba^{-1}$; and the equation $ay = b$ has a unique solution $y = a^{-1}b$.

Proof: We shall establish only the first part of Theorem 2, for the second part may be proved in a similar manner.

(A) We find that $x = ba^{-1}$ is a solution of $xa = b$, for

$$xa \underset{\textbf{H.1}}{=} (ba^{-1})a \underset{\textbf{H.4}}{=} b(a^{-1}a) \underset{\textbf{H.3}}{=} be \underset{\textbf{T.1}}{=} b,$$

where **T.1** refers to Theorem 1 above.

(B) Suppose both x and y are solutions, so that $xa = b = ya$, then

$$x \underset{\textbf{T.1}}{=} xe \underset{\textbf{T.1}}{=} x(aa^{-1}) \underset{\textbf{H.4}}{=} (xa)a^{-1} \underset{\textbf{H}}{=} (ya)a^{-1} \underset{\textbf{H.4}}{=} y(aa^{-1}) \underset{\textbf{T.1}}{=} ye \underset{\textbf{T.1}}{=} y,$$

where **H** refers to the initial hypothesis of (B) and we have tired of inserting
H.1, although the notion that the group operation is well defined certainly
is used when, for example, we replace e by aa^{-1}.

Corollary 2.1:   The identity e and the inverse a^{-1} are unique.

Proof: By hypothesis e solves $xa = a$; by **T.2**, e is unique. By
hypothesis a^{-1} solves $xa = e$; by **T.2**, a^{-1} is unique.

Corollary 2.2:   The inverse of the inverse of a is a.

Proof: From (B) of Theorem 1 we know a solves $xa^{-1} = e$; and by
T.2 we know the solution is unique. Hence by the definition implied in
H.3 we have $(a^{-1})^{-1} = a$.

A group with a finite number of elements, say m, is described as a
group of *order m*. To describe a group of order m completely we may
show an m-by-m "group table" where the ordered product ab appears in
the a-row and the b-column of the table.

Corollary 2.3:   In a group table each element appears once and only
once in each row and column.

Proof: The element c occurs once and only once in the a-row, for by
T.2 there is exactly one element y such that $ay = c$. Similarly, c occurs
once and only once in the b-column, since by **T.2** there is exactly one
element x such that $xb = c$.

Theorem 3:   If the groups G_1 and G_2 are isomorphic under the mapping
F and if e is the identity of G_1, then eF must be the identity of G_2. If a^{-1}
is the inverse of a in G_1, then $a^{-1}F$ must be the inverse of aF in G_2.

Proof: By hypothesis, F is an isomorphism, so the operation-preserving property **F.5** holds for the operations in the two groups, i.e.,

$$\text{if } a \text{ and } b \text{ are in } G_1, \text{ then } (ab)F = (aF)(bF).$$

Of course the first juxtaposition ab indicates the group operation in G_1 and the second juxtaposition $(aF)(bF)$ indicates the (perhaps very different) group operation in G_2. If a is in G_1, this requires

$$aF \underset{\text{H.2,F.2}}{=} (ea)F \underset{\text{F.5}}{=} (eF)(aF).$$

But the mapping F is one-to-one, so by property **F.3** it follows that aF represents every element of G_2. Then by Corollary 2.1 it follows that eF must be the uniquely determined identity of G_2.

We also have

$$eF \underset{\text{H.3,F.2}}{=} (a^{-1}a)F \underset{\text{F.5}}{=} (a^{-1}F)(aF).$$

Since we have just shown that eF is the identity of G_2 and that aF represents every element of G_2, it follows from Corollary 2.1 that $a^{-1}F$ is the uniquely determined inverse of aF in G_2.

We have said that a typical goal in studying a mathematical system is to discover enough theorems to be able to characterize all nonisomorphic examples. An elementary and instructive illustration of partial progress toward this goal is now available.

Corollary 3.1: In the sense of isomorphism there are exactly two groups of order 4.

Proof: (A) The residue classes mod 4 under addition constitute a group G_1 of order 4 (see Example 2 above). The reduced residue classes mod 8 under multiplication constitute a group G_2 of order 4 (see EX. **29.8**). Although there are $4! = 24$ one-to-one mappings F between G_1 and G_2, not one of these is an isomorphism. For G_1 has only *two* self-inverse elements: $0 + 0 \equiv 0$, $2 + 2 \equiv 0 \bmod 4$; but for G_2 there are *four* self-inverse elements: $1 \cdot 1 \equiv 1$, $3 \cdot 3 \equiv 1$, $5 \cdot 5 \equiv 1$, $7 \cdot 7 \equiv 1$, $\bmod 8$; and according to Theorem 3 an isomorphism must map inverse elements into inverse elements, and therefore must map self-inverse elements into self-inverse elements.

(B) *In the sense of isomorphism* there are no other groups of order 4. For we may consider the possible ways of completing a group table when G contains the abstract elements a, b, c, e where e is the two-sided identity guaranteed by Theorem 1. According to Corollary 2.2 the inverse elements of G must occur in pairs or be self-inverse. Since e is self-inverse and G has an even number of elements, it follows that G must contain at least one other self-inverse element, say a. Then there are only two possibilities remaining—either $b^{-1} = c$, or $b^{-1} = b$.

G'	e	a	b	c
e	e	a	b	c
a	a	e		
b	b			e
c	c		e	

G''	e	a	b	c
e	e	a	b	c
a	a	e		
b	b		e	
c	c			e

The rest of the group table is determined in each case by Corollary 2.3.

G'	e	a	b	c
e	e	a	b	c
a	a	e	c	b
b	b	c	a	e
c	c	b	e	a

G''	e	a	b	c
e	e	a	b	c
a	a	e	c	b
b	b	c	e	a
c	c	b	a	e

That the table so completed is a group table with property **H.4** must be checked, but here the check is easy. In the first case a group G' is obtained isomorphic to G_1 of (A); in the second case a group G'' is obtained isomorphic to G_2 of (A) (see EX. **29.12**).

EXERCISES

29.1. Classify the following mappings of the set of all integers into itself, according as they do or do not possess properties **F.1, F.2, F.3, F.4**:

$$xU = x + 3, \quad xV = 2x + 3, \quad xW = -x + 2, \quad xF = [x/3].$$

29.2. Classify the following mappings of residue classes of integers modulo 11:

$$xU \equiv x + 3, \quad xV \equiv 2x + 3, \quad xS \equiv x^2.$$

29.3. Show that the mapping $xF = (x\text{-class})$ is a many-to-one mapping of integers onto residue classes mod m (**F.1, F.2, F.3**) which is operation-preserving (**F.5**) with respect both to addition in the two systems and to multiplication in the two systems.

29.4. If m is composite use the multiplication of residue classes mod m to demonstrate the independence of postulate **H.3**.

29.5. Define the a-class mod m to be "even" if a is even. Show that this concept is well defined if and only if m is even.

29.6. Referring to EX. **29.5** use the even classes mod $2m$ under multiplication of residue classes to demonstrate the independence of **H.2**. (Note how **H.3** depends upon **H.2**.)

29.7. Establish Theorem 1 about groups in another way:
(a) Start from $e = x^{-1}x$ and show that the left-inverse e is the only solution of $xx = x$.
(b) Show that $(aa^{-1})(aa^{-1}) = aa^{-1}$ and apply (a) to show $aa^{-1} = e$.
(c) Use (b) to show $ae = a$.

29.8.   Show that the classes of a reduced residue system mod m form a commutative group of order $\phi(m)$ under multiplication of residue classes.

29.9.   Write out the group tables corresponding to EX. **29.8** when $m = 8$, $m = 10$, $m = 12$ and compare these groups in the sense of isomorphism.

29.10. Determine whether the groups of EX. **29.8** for $m = 13$ and $m = 21$ are isomorphic.

29.11. If t is the smallest positive exponent such that in the group G we have $a^t = e$, we say that a has period t. Show that under an isomorphism between G and G' the image of a must have period t.

29.12. Complete the proof of (B) in Corollary 3.1. Show there are exactly two isomorphic mappings between G' and G_1 and exactly six isomorphic mappings between G'' and G_2.

Now this establishment
of correspondence between two aggregates
and investigation of the propositions
that are carried over by the correspondence
may be called the central idea
of modern mathematics.—W. K. CLIFFORD

CHAPTER 30

Transformation groups

30.1. Transformations

Using the language of **29.2** we define a *transformation* T of a set S to be a many-to-one mapping T of S into itself, where it is understood not only that S_1 and S_2 are the same set S, but also that $\mathbf{E}_1$ and $\mathbf{E}_2$ are the same relation $\mathbf{E}$. We define a *one-to-one* transformation T of S to be a transformation T of S with the additional properties **F.3** and **F.4**.

We define two transformations T and T_1 of S to be *equal*:

(30.1) $T = T_1$ if and only if $xT \, \mathbf{E} \, xT_1$ for every x in S.

It is easy to check that this newly defined equality of transformations of S is an equivalence relation.

We define the *product* TU of two transformations T and U of S to be that transformation of S determined by

(30.2) $x(TU) \, \mathbf{E} \, (xT)U$ for every x in S.

Since T is assumed to be a transformation of S, xT is a uniquely determined element of S; and then since U is a transformation of S and xT is in S, we see that $(xT)U$ is a uniquely determined element of S for every x of S, so TU as defined by *(30.2)* is indeed a transformation of S. Furthermore,

223

it is easy to check that the operation of forming TU is well defined with respect to the equality $T = T_1$, $U = U_1$ which is defined in (30.1).

The product TU is so defined in (30.2) that TU is found by first applying T, then U. To obtain this natural arrangement is the reason for using the notation xT instead of the notation $T(x)$, for if the latter functional notation is used, the product will appear as $U(T(x))$ and the reversal of order of the symbols as compared to the order of application of the mappings is a useless complication.

For an example of finding TU, let S be the set of all integers, let E be ordinary equality, and let T and U be defined by $x^2 = xT$ and $x + 3 = xU$. By (30.2) we find $x(TU) = (xT)U = (x^2)U = x^2 + 3$; however, since $x(UT) = (xU)T = (x + 3)T = (x + 3)^2 = x^2 + 6x + 9$, we find that $x(TU) = x(UT)$ only for $x = -1$, *not for all* x of S and therefore $TU \neq UT$.

The example just given illustrates that the operation of forming the product of two transformations of a set S is *not, in general, a commutative* operation. This negative observation lends more interest to the following positive result.

Q.1: The operation of forming the product of transformations is associative: thus if U, V, W are any transformations of a set S, then $(UV)W = U(VW)$.

Proof: The proof stems directly from the definition of the equality of two transformations and several applications, indicated by appropriate parentheses, of the definition (30.2):

$$x((UV)W) \text{ E } (x(UV))W \text{ E } ((xU)V)W \text{ E } (xU)(VW) \text{ E } x(U(VW)).$$

This holds for every x of S, hence $(UV)W = U(VW)$.

The most obvious transformation of all is the one which transforms each element of S into itself; it is indicated by the letter I and called the *identity* transformation; its defining property is that $x \text{ E } xI$ for every x of S.

Q.2: For every transformation T of S, $IT = T = TI$.

Proof: By the defining property of I and by (30.2) we find $x(IT) \text{ E } (xI)T \text{ E } xT \text{ E } (xT)I \text{ E } x(TI)$, for every x of S, hence $IT = T = TI$.

A transformation T of S will be said to *have an inverse* U if and only if there exists a transformation U of S such that $TU = UT = I$.

For example, if S is the set of all integers, if E is ordinary equality and k is a fixed integer, then the transformation T defined by $x + k = xT$ has

an inverse U defined by $x - k = xU$; for by (30.2) we find $x(TU) = (xT)U$
$= (x + k)U = (x + k) - k = x = xI$ for every x in S, hence $TU = I$.
Similarly, we may show $UT = I$.

Q.3: If a transformation T of S has an inverse U, then U is unique.

Proof: Suppose T has two inverses U and V, so that $TU = UT = I = TV = VT$. Then by **Q.1** and **Q.2** we find that $U = UI = U(TV) = (UT)V = IV = V$.

Q.4: If T is a transformation of S, then T has an inverse if and only if T is one-to-one.

Proof: (A) If T is one-to-one, we may define U by saying that $x'U \mathbf{E} x$ if and only if $x' \mathbf{E} xT$; then U *is* a transformation of S, for T is one-to-one, so by properties **F.3** and **F.4** of T we know there is a unique x in S for every x' in S, but this means that U has properties **F.1** and **F.2**. Furthermore we have both $x(TU) \mathbf{E} (xT)U \mathbf{E} (x')U \mathbf{E} x \mathbf{E} xI$ for every x in S, hence $TU = I$; and $x'(UT) \mathbf{E} (x'U)T \mathbf{E} xT \mathbf{E} x' \mathbf{E} x'I$ for every x' in S, hence $UT = I$. Thus U is an inverse of T, and by **Q.3**, U is *the* inverse of T.

(B) If T has an inverse U so that $TU = UT = I$, then for any x' of S, we find $x \mathbf{E} x'U$ is *a* solution of $x' \mathbf{E} xT$, since $xT \mathbf{E} (x'U)T \mathbf{E} x'(UT) \mathbf{E} x'I \mathbf{E} x'$; so T has property **F.3**. There is *only one* solution, for if $xT \mathbf{E} yT$, then we find

$$x \mathbf{E} xI \mathbf{E} x(TU) \mathbf{E} (xT)U \mathbf{E} (yT)U \mathbf{E} y(TU) \mathbf{E} yI \mathbf{E} y;$$

so T has property **F.4**. Hence T is one-to-one. This completes the proof of **Q.4**.

30.2. Transformation groups

When we compare the developments in **30.1** with the requirements in **29.3** that a system be a group, we see that many of the necessary details are already in evidence. As possible elements of a group we may take transformations $T, U, \ldots$ of a set S; as an equivalence relation we may use (30.1); as the group operation we may try (30.2). Because of **Q.1** we shall not have to concern ourselves with **H.4**, but because of **Q.4** we shall have to limit our attention to one-to-one transformations; otherwise if we use **Q.2** and **Q.3** to satisfy **H.2**, we shall have no chance of satisfying **H.3**.

Theorem 4:   A set G of one-to-one transformations of a set S, with (30.1) as an equivalence relation and (30.2) as an operation, will form a group, called a *transformation group*, if G has the following properties:

(1) if T and U are in G, then TU is in G;
(2) I is in G;
(3) if T is in G, then the inverse of T is in G.

Proof: Since the product rule for transformations is well defined and **Q.2** and **Q.4** have been established, it is clear that (1), (2), (3) correspond, respectively, to **H.1**, **H.2**, **H.3**. Since **Q.1** takes the place of **H.4**, the proof is complete.

There will be no confusion if we henceforth refer to (1), (2), (3) as equivalent to **H.1**, **H.2**, **H.3**, respectively. For example, let S be the set of all integers, let **E** be ordinary equality, and let G be the set of *all* transformations of the type T_k defined by $x + k = xT_k$ where k is a fixed integer; then we can show that G is a group by demonstrating each of the properties **H.1**, **H.2**, **H.3**. But first we should check that the transformations T_k are one-to-one; however, T_k is precisely the example given in **30.1** of a transformation with an inverse, and hence by **Q.4**, T_k is one-to-one. Moreover, the inverse of T_k was shown to be T_{-k} and since G contains all transformations of this type, it follows that G contains T_{-k} for every integer k, and hence **H.3** is satisfied. **H.1** is satisfied for if T_k and T_m are in G, we can show that $T_k T_m$ is in G; for

$$x(T_k T_m) = (xT_k)T_m = (x + k)T_m = (x + k) + m$$
$$= x + (k + m) = xT_{k+m}$$

for every x in S, and hence $T_k T_m = T_{k+m}$; since G contains all transformations of this type, it follows that G contains $T_k T_m = T_{k+m}$ for all integers k and m. Finally, **H.2** is satisfied, for $I = T_0$ since $xI = x = x + 0 = xT_0$ for every x in S; and since G contains all transformations of this type, G contains $I = T_0$. Thus G is a group, known as the *group of all translations* of S or as the *additive group* of S.

Corollary 4.1:   If S is a set of elements with an equivalence relation **E**, then the set $G(S)$ of *all* one-to-one transformations of S forms a group under the equality and product rules for transformations.

Proof: By Theorem 4 we need to show only that $G(S)$ has properties (1), (2), and (3). Using **Q.4** we have an easy test for deciding whether certain transformations are one-to-one. For example, I is one-to-one because I is self-inverse; so $G(S)$ contains I and has property (2). If T is in $G(S)$, then T is one-to-one and has an inverse U such that $UT = I = TU$; but this implies that U has the inverse T; hence U is one-to-one and must be in $G(S)$ because $G(S)$ contains all the one-to-one transformations of S; thus $G(S)$ has property (3). If T_1 and T_2 are in $G(S)$ we know U_1 and U_2 exist so that $U_1 T_1 = I = T_1 U_1$ and $U_2 T_2 = I = T_2 U_2$. Therefore

$$(T_1 T_2)(U_2 U_1) \underset{\text{Q.1}}{=} T_1(T_2(U_2 U_1)) \underset{\text{Q.1}}{=} T_1((T_2 U_2)U_1) \underset{\text{H}}{=} T_1(IU_1) \underset{\text{Q.2}}{=} T_1 U_1 \underset{\text{H}}{=} I.$$

Similarly, $(U_2 U_1)(T_1 T_2) = I$. Since $T_1 T_2$ has the inverse $U_2 U_1$, it follows from **Q.4** that $T_1 T_2$ is one-to-one. Therefore, $G(S)$ contains $T_1 T_2$ and has property (1). This completes the proof of the corollary.

Corollary 4.2:   There exist noncommutative groups.

Proof: Consider any set S with at least three elements distinct under the relation **E**; then the corresponding group $G(S)$ provided by Corollary 4.1 is noncommutative. For we may select three distinct elements of S, say x_1, x_2, x_3, and among the one-to-one transformations of S there exists V_1 defined by $x_1 V_1 \mathbf{E} x_1$, $x_2 V_1 \mathbf{E} x_3$, $x_3 V_1 \mathbf{E} x_2$, and $x V_1 \mathbf{E} x$ for all other x in S; and there exists V_2 defined by $x_1 V_2 \mathbf{E} x_3$, $x_2 V_2 \mathbf{E} x_2$, $x_3 V_2 \mathbf{E} x_1$, and $x V_2 \mathbf{E} x$ for all other x in S. We note that $x_3(V_1 V_2) \mathbf{E} (x_3 V_1)V_2 \mathbf{E} x_2 V_2 \mathbf{E} x_2$, but that $x_3(V_2 V_1) \mathbf{E} (x_3 V_2)V_1 \mathbf{E} x_1 V_1 \mathbf{E} x_1$. According to (30.1), since $x_2 \mathbf{E} x_1$, we have $V_1 V_2 \neq V_2 V_1$; hence the group $G(S)$ fails to satisfy **H.5** and is noncommutative.

For example, let us indicate the complete group table for $G(S)$ if S contains exactly three elements—say 1, 2, 3—and has simple identity as its equivalence relation. For brevity we shall write the set and its corresponding images under a transformation T as ordered triples: $(1, 2, 3)T = (1T, 2T, 3T)$. In this case $G(S)$ is of order 6 with

$(1, 2, 3)I = (1, 2, 3);$ $(1, 2, 3)R_1 = (2, 3, 1);$ $(1, 2, 3)R_2 = (3, 1, 2);$
$(1, 2, 3)V_1 = (1, 3, 2);$ $(1, 2, 3)V_2 = (3, 2, 1);$ $(1, 2, 3)V_3 = (2, 1, 3).$

Then the group table appears as follows:

	I	R_1	R_2	V_1	V_2	V_3
I	I	R_1	R_2	V_1	V_2	V_3
R_1	R_1	R_2	I	V_2	V_3	V_1
R_2	R_2	I	R_1	V_3	V_1	V_2
V_1	V_1	V_3	V_2	I	R_2	R_1
V_2	V_2	V_1	V_3	R_1	I	R_2
V_3	V_3	V_2	V_1	R_2	R_1	I

Corollary 4.3:   For every even integer $n = 2m$ with $n \geqslant 6$ there exists at least one noncommutative group of order n.

Proof: Let S be the set of all integers; let **E** be congruence mod m where m is a fixed integer, $m \geqslant 3$. Consider the set G of all correspondences $T(u, i)$ mapping S into itself of the form $xT(u, i) \equiv ux + i \bmod m$, where $u \equiv +1$ or $u \equiv -1$, and i is chosen from a complete residue system mod m. We showed in **G.3** of **13.3** that addition and multiplication mod m are closed and well-defined operations; so the proposed correspondences are indeed transformations of S.

Since there are two choices for u and m choices for i, there are at most $n = 2m$ transformations of the type $T(u, i)$. From the rule (30.1) we find that $T(u, i) = T(v, j)$ if and only if $ux + i \equiv vx + j \bmod m$ for every x in S. If $x \equiv 0$ this requires $i \equiv j \bmod m$; but i and j belong to a complete residue system mod m so $i = j$. The test condition reduces to $ux \equiv vx$ mod m, and if $x \equiv 1$ this requires $u \equiv v \bmod m$; but u and v are restricted to the values $+1$ and -1 and $m > 2$, so the only choice is $u = v$. Hence there are exactly $n = 2m$ transformations of the type $T(u, i)$.

From the product rule (30.2) we find that if x is in S, then

$$x(T(u, i)T(v, j)) \equiv (xT(u, i))T(v, j) \equiv (ux + i)T(v, j) \equiv v(ux + i) + j$$
$$\equiv (uv)x + (iv + j) \equiv xT(uv, iv + j) \bmod m.$$

Hence from the equality rule (30.1) we have

$$(30.3) \qquad\qquad T(u, i)T(v, j) = T(uv, iv + j).$$

Because of the restricted range of u and v we find that $w = uv = \pm 1$. From **G.3** we know that $iv + j \equiv k \bmod m$, where k is a uniquely determined member of the complete residue system mod m. Thus $T(uv, iv + j) = T(w, k)$ is a uniquely determined transformation belonging to G, so that G has property (1).

It is easy to see that $I = T(1, 0)$ which belongs to G, so G has property (2).

We can check that $T(u, -ui)$ is the inverse of $T(u, i)$ for by (30.3) we have $T(u, -ui)T(u, i) = T(uu, -uui + i) = T(1, 0) = I$, and we have $T(u, i)T(u, -ui) = T(uu, ui - ui) = T(1, 0) = I$. But $-ui$ is congruent to a uniquely determined member of the complete residue system mod m, so $T(u, -ui)$ belongs to G and G has property (3).

Finally, we show that G is not commutative by using (30.3) to compute $T(v, j)T(u, i) = T(vu, ju + i)$. Then $T(u, i)T(v, j) = T(v, j)T(u, i)$ if and only if $iv + j \equiv ju + i \bmod m$. But this condition is satisfied when $i = j$ if and only if $v = u$.

This completes the proof of Corollary 4.3. The exercises will suggest some interesting geometric groups which are isomorphic to those described in this corollary. In particular, when $m = 3$ and $n = 6$, we obtain a group isomorphic to the group whose table follows Corollary 4.2.

30.3. Cayley's theorem

As we review the concept of a transformation group we sense that it is the fact that the product rule of transformations is to be used, rather than some abstract rule, which distinguishes this special type of group. But the real surprise comes in the following theorem, for it turns out that transformation groups are not really "special," but truly representative of every possible abstract group.

Theorem 5: Cayley's theorem: An abstract group G is isomorphic to a properly chosen transformation group G'.

Proof: Given the abstract group G, consider the elements of G as forming a set. If a is in G, consider a correspondence T_a, mapping G into itself, defined by $xT_a = xa$, where xa is the group product in G.

We pause to check that T_a is a one-to-one transformation of G: for **F.1** and **F.2** are satisfied, since property **H.1** of G guarantees not only that xa is in G, but also that if $x = y$, then $xa = ya$; and **F.3** and **F.4** are satisfied, because Theorem 2 holds for G and guarantees that if x' is in G, then there is a unique x in G such that $x' = xa$.

Let G' be the set of all one-to-one transformations of G of the form T_a and let the equality and product rules of transformations convert G' into a mathematical system.

Consider the correspondence F between G and G' defined by $aF = T_a$. We shall show that F is an isomorphism between G and G' with respect to the group operation ab in G and the product rule (30.2) for T_aT_b in G'. **F.1** and **F.3** are satisfied by the definition of T_a and G'; **F.2** and **F.4** are satisfied since $T_a = T_b$ in G', according to (30.1), if and only if $xT_a = xT_b$ for every x in G, but Theorem 2 holds in G, so $xa = xb$ if and only if $a = b$ in G; and **F.5** is satisfied because if x is in G we have

$$x(T_aT_b) \underset{(30.2)}{=} (xT_a)T_b \underset{\text{Def.}}{=} (xa)T_b \underset{\text{Def.}}{=} (xa)b \underset{\text{H.4}}{=} x(ab) \underset{\text{Def.}}{=} xT_{ab},$$

so by (30.1) we have $T_aT_b = T_{ab}$, hence

$$(ab)F \underset{\text{Def.}}{=} T_{ab} = T_aT_b \underset{\text{Def.}}{=} (aF)(bF).$$

Because of the isomorphism it follows that the system G' is actually a group [e.g., $T_e = I$ and $T_{a^{-1}} = (T_a)^{-1}$] and the proof is complete.

If the group G is of finite order, it is easy to visualize the transformation T_a in terms of the group table, for the elements x of G occur in the e-column, since $x = xe$, and the images $xT_a = xa$ occur in the a-column. For example, the group of all one-to-one transformations or permutations on three objects, whose table we gave above, can be expressed, according to Cayley's theorem, as a set of six properly chosen one-to-one transformations on six objects, namely, the group elements themselves. Consulting the columns of the group table we have

$$(I, R_1, R_2, V_1, V_2, V_3)T_{R_1} = (R_1, R_2, I, V_3, V_1, V_2),$$
$$(I, R_1, R_2, V_1, V_2, V_3)T_{V_1} = (V_1, V_2, V_3, I, R_1, R_2).$$

By the product rule for transformations

$$(I, R_1, R_2, V_1, V_2, V_3)T_{R_1}T_{V_1} = (R_1, R_2, I, V_3, V_1, V_2)T_{V_1}$$
$$= (V_2, V_3, V_1, R_2, I, R_1).$$

But

$$(I, R_1, R_2, V_1, V_2, V_3)T_{V_2} = (V_2, V_3, V_1, R_2, I, R_1),$$

hence by the equality rule for transformations we have $T_{R_1}T_{V_1} = T_{V_2}$. In the group table we check that $R_1V_1 = V_2$. This agreement is just one instance of the isomorphism demonstrated in the proof of Theorem 5.

From the general viewpoint of trying to obtain the structure theory of a mathematical system, a theorem such as Cayley's can be of considerable advantage. From this point on efforts to obtain the structure theory of groups can be concentrated on transformation groups without unwarranted specialization. The advantage of not having to check the associative property is considerable.

EXERCISES

30.1. Show that the equality defined by *(30.1)* is an equivalence relation. (Hint: Each property of " = " depends on the same property of "E".)

30.2. Show that the product defined by *(30.2)* is well defined; that is, if $T = T_1$ and $U = U_1$, show that $TU = T_1U_1$.

30.3. There are four mappings of a set of two elements into itself; just two of the mappings are one-to-one. Write out the product table for the set of four mappings.

30.4. There are 27 mappings of a set of three elements into itself. Write out the product table for this system arranging the mappings in this order: the six one-to-one mappings; the three three-to-one mappings; the other 18 mappings.

30.5. Show that the group of all one-to-one mappings of a set of n elements onto itself is of order $n!$.

30.6. Show that the (sextic dihedral) group described in Corollary 4.3 for $n = 6$ is isomorphic to the (symmetric) group of all one-to-one mappings of a set of three elements onto itself used to illustrate Corollary 4.2.

30.7. Write out the group table for the (octic) group in Corollary 4.3 when $n = 8$.

30.8. For the set S of all integers x under congruence mod m, consider the set G of all mappings $xT(u, k) \equiv ux + k$ mod m, where u ranges over a reduced residue system mod m and k ranges over a complete residue system mod m. Show that G is a group. Show that G is of order $m\phi(m)$. If $m > 2$, show that G is noncommutative.

30.9. Illustrate Cayley's theorem in detail for each of the two types of groups of order 4 whose tables appear in Chapter 29.

CHAPTER 31

Linear transformations and matrices

31.1. Linear transformations, matrices, and determinants

Consider the set S_2 of all ordered pairs (x, y) of integers x, y, defining
$(x, y) = (u, v)$ if and only if $x = u$ and $y = v$. This set S_2 is called the
set of all lattice points of 2-space.

A transformation T of S_2 defined by

$$(31.1) \qquad (ax + by, cx + dy) = (x, y)T$$

where a, b, c, d are fixed integers, is called a *linear transformation* of S_2.

If we write $(x', y') = (x, y)' = (x, y)T$, then the equations $x' = ax + by$,
$y' = cx + dy$ give another way of describing T. It is evident that T is
completely determined by specifying the values of a, b, c, d and ordering
them correctly, hence a convenient representation for T is to write

$$(31.2) \qquad T = \begin{pmatrix} a & c \\ b & d \end{pmatrix}$$

where the 2-by-2 square array on the right is called a *2-by-2 matrix* and
a, b, c, d are called the *elements* of the matrix. The first column of T

232

determines x' and the second, y'; the first row of T shows the coefficients of x and the second, the coefficients of y.

Let U be a linear transformation of S_2 defined by

$$(x, y)U = (a_1 x + b_1 y, c_1 x + d_1 y)$$

and represented, according to (31.2), by the matrix

$$U = \begin{pmatrix} a_1 & c_1 \\ b_1 & d_1 \end{pmatrix}.$$

M.1: If T and U are linear transformations of S_2, then $T = U$ if and only if $a = a_1$, $b = b_1$, $c = c_1$, $d = d_1$. (In other words, $T = U$ if and only if the matrices representing T and U have their corresponding elements equal.)

Proof: By (30.1), $T = U$ if and only if $(x, y)T = (x, y)U$ for every (x, y) in S_2. In particular we may take $(x, y) = (1, 0)$ to see that

$$(a, c) = (1, 0)T = (1, 0)U = (a_1, c_1)$$

if and only if $a = a_1$, $c = c_1$; and we may take $(x, y) = (0, 1)$ to see that

$$(b, d) = (0, 1)T = (0, 1)U = (b_1, d_1)$$

if and only if $b = b_1$, $d = d_1$.

M.2: If T and U are linear transformations of S_2, then TU is a linear transformation of S_2, and the matrix representing TU is given by

(31.3) $$TU = \begin{pmatrix} aa_1 + cb_1 & ac_1 + cd_1 \\ ba_1 + db_1 & bc_1 + dd_1 \end{pmatrix}$$

Proof: By (30.2) we find

$$\begin{aligned}
(x, y)(TU) &= ((x, y)T)U = (ax + by, cx + dy)U \\
&= ((ax + by)a_1 + (cx + dy)b_1, (ax + by)c_1 + (cx + dy)d_1) \\
&= ((aa_1 + cb_1)x + (ba_1 + db_1)y, (ac_1 + cd_1)x + (bc_1 + dd_1)y).
\end{aligned}$$

Since a, b, c, d, a_1, b_1, c_1, d_1 are integers, so are $aa_1 + cb_1$, $ba_1 + db_1$, $ac_1 + cd_1$, $bc_1 + dd_1$, and TU is seen to have the correct form to be a linear transformation, and by (31.2) the matrix corresponding to TU is precisely that given in (31.3).

At first it would seem difficult to memorize (31.3), but there is an easy device called *matric multiplication* or, *row-by-column multiplication*, which is defined purposely in such a way as to give exactly the result (31.3).

Rule for matric multiplication: To find the element in the ith row and jth column of the matrix TU, find the sum of the products of corresponding elements of the ith row of T and the jth column of U. Thus we find

$$(31.3)' \qquad \begin{pmatrix} a & c \\ b & d \end{pmatrix} \begin{pmatrix} a_1 & c_1 \\ b_1 & d_1 \end{pmatrix} = \begin{pmatrix} aa_1 + cb_1 & ac_1 + cd_1 \\ ba_1 + db_1 & bc_1 + dd_1 \end{pmatrix}.$$

For example, to find the element in the first row and second column of TU, take the first row of T, namely: (a, c) and the second column of U, namely: (c_1, d_1), multiply together their first elements to obtain ac_1 and multiply their second elements to obtain cd_1, and finally take the sum of these products to obtain $ac_1 + cd_1$.

Such a complicated rule for finding the product of two matrices, if presented by itself, might seem highly artificial; but in view of the preceding discussion of products of transformations, applied in particular to products of linear transformations, the rule has quite a satisfactory motivation, resulting in a product-preserving one-to-one correspondence between linear transformations and matrices.

Just as the product of transformations is, in general, not a commutative operation, so the product of matrices might be expected not, in general, to be commutative. To illustrate this remark we compute, by $(31.3)'$, the following products:

$$\begin{pmatrix} 2 & 3 \\ -1 & 0 \end{pmatrix} \begin{pmatrix} 1 & 0 \\ 2 & 1 \end{pmatrix} = \begin{pmatrix} 8 & 3 \\ -1 & 0 \end{pmatrix}, \quad \begin{pmatrix} 1 & 0 \\ 2 & 1 \end{pmatrix} \begin{pmatrix} 2 & 3 \\ -1 & 0 \end{pmatrix} = \begin{pmatrix} 2 & 3 \\ 3 & 6 \end{pmatrix}.$$

By **M.1** we see that these results are not equal.

However, the following result is true, and by our previous work is easily established.

M.3: Multiplication of matrices is an associative operation.

Proof: Each matrix corresponds to a linear transformation and each product of two matrices corresponds to the product of the corresponding linear transformations, as we have previously seen in (31.2), (31.3), $(31.3)'$. However, by **Q.1** in **30.1**, the product of linear transformations is an associative operation; hence the multiplication of matrices is also an associative operation.

Of course, this theorem can also be proved by direct computation from the product rule $(31.3)'$, but the proof here given is much more elegant—particularly if the theory of matrices is extended, as it can be, to other than 2-by-2 matrices.

M.4:   The identity transformation is a linear transformation and the corresponding matrix is given by

$$I = \begin{pmatrix} 1 & 0 \\ 0 & 1 \end{pmatrix}.$$

Proof: By definition $(x, y)I = (x, y)$, hence

$$x' = x = 1 \cdot x + 0 \cdot y, \quad y' = y = 0 \cdot x + 1 \cdot y,$$

so that I is seen to be a linear transformation, and by (31.2) the proper matrix is the one displayed above.

Since the following relation $TI = T = IT$ holds by **Q.2** for all linear transformations, it follows by (31.2), (31.3), $(31.3)'$ that the same relation holds for matrices.

M.5:   A linear transformation T of S_2, represented by the matrix (31.2), has an inverse if and only if $ad - bc$ is a unit, namely $+1$ or -1; and the inverse transformation is a linear transformation.

Proof: Consider the relations $x' = ax + by$, $y' = cx + dy$. By elimination we find

(31.4) $(ad - bc)x = dx' - by'$, $(ad - bc)y = -cx' + ay'$.

Let $t = ad - bc$. By **Q.4** of **30.1**, we know that T has an inverse if and only if T is one-to-one, i.e., if and only if $(x', y') = (x, y)T$ has a unique solution (x, y) for every (x', y') of S_2. Examining (31.4), we see that in order that there be a unique solution, allowing *fractions*, it is necessary and sufficient that $t \neq 0$. But in order for every pair of integers x', y' to determine a *unique* pair of *integers* x, y, we can show that it is necessary and sufficient that $t = +1$ or -1.

If t does not divide a, or if t does not divide b, then if in (31.4) we substitute $x' = 0$, $y' = 1$, we find $tx = -b$, or $ty = a$; hence in the one case, y cannot be an integer, or in the other case, x cannot be an integer. Similarly, if t does not divide c or d, we may substitute $x' = 1$, $y' = 0$ in (31.4) to obtain $tx = d$, $ty = -c$; so that in one case, y cannot be an integer, or in the other case, x cannot be an integer. Thus if T is one-to-one, t must divide a, b, c, d. Hence t^2 must divide $ad - bc = t$, say $t^2 u = t$; then $tu = 1$, so that t must be a unit and either $t = +1$ or $t = -1$.

Conversely, if $t = \pm 1$, then $t^2 = +1$, hence from (31.4) we find

(31.5) $x = tdx' - tby'$, $y = -tcx' + tay'$.

From (31.5) it is clear that every pair of integers x', y' leads to a unique pair of integers x, y; hence T is one-to-one and has an inverse. Moreover, the form of (*31.5*) is such that the inverse of T is seen to be a linear transformation U represented by a matrix

(*31.6*)
$$U = \begin{pmatrix} td & -tc \\ -tb & ta \end{pmatrix}.$$

Definition: If T is the matrix given in (*31.2*), then the function $d(T) = ad - bc$ is called the *determinant* of T.

In terms of this definition, **M.5** may be reworded as follows. A linear transformation T of S_2 has an inverse U if and only if the matrix representing T has a unit determinant $t = d(T) = \pm 1$. Moreover, $d(U) = (td)(ta) - (-tb)(-tc) = t^2(ab - bc) = t = d(T)$.

M.6: The set G of all linear transformations T of S_2, such that $d(T) = \pm 1$, forms a group called the *lattice group*.

Proof: We must show that G has properties **H.1, H.2, H.3. H.1** is satisfied because if T_1 and T_2 are linear transformations of S_2 with $d(T_1) = \pm 1$ and $d(T_2) = \pm 1$, then on the one hand we know by **M.2** that T_1T_2 is a *linear* transformation; and on the other hand we know by **M.5** that T_1 has an inverse U_1 so that $T_1U_1 = U_1T_1 = I$, and that T_2 has an inverse U_2 so that $T_2U_2 = U_2T_2 = I$, whence we can show that U_2U_1 is the inverse of T_1T_2, for using **Q.1** or **M.3**, we have

$$(T_1T_2)(U_2U_1) = T_1(T_2(U_2U_1)) = T_1((T_2U_2)U_1) = T_1(IU_1) = T_1U_1 = I$$

and similarly, $(U_2U_1)(T_1T_2) = I$; but since T_1T_2 *has an inverse*, it follows by **M.5** that $d(T_1T_2) = \pm 1$. Since G includes *all* linear transformations of S_2 of unit determinant, it follows that G satisfies property **H.1**.

H.2 is satisfied because we noted in **M.4** that I is a linear transformation and we note now that $d(I) = 1 \cdot 1 - 0 \cdot 0 = 1$, so that G contains I.

H.3 is satisfied because we noted in **M.5** that the inverse U of a linear transformation T is a linear transformation and we noted in the paragraph preceding **M.6** that $d(U) = d(T)$; since G includes *all* linear transformations of unit determinant, it follows that G includes U. This completes the proof of **M.6**.

M.7: If T and U are linear transformations of S_2, then

$$d(TU) = d(T)d(U).$$

Proof: Using the notation of **M.2**, we find by direct computation, omitting a few terms which cancel, that

$$d(TU) = (aa_1 + cb_1)(bc_1 + dd_1) - (ba_1 + db_1)(ac_1 + cd_1)$$
$$= aa_1dd_1 + cb_1bc_1 - ba_1cd_1 - db_1ac_1$$
$$= (ad - bc)(a_1d_1 - b_1c_1) = d(T)d(U).$$

31.2. Significance of the lattice group for Diophantine problems

We have already indicated in previous chapters that if in a given problem we restrict our attention to those solutions which are integers, then we can agree to describe this restriction by calling our problem a *Diophantine* problem.

If a Diophantine problem involves two variables x and y, then a very powerful simplifying device may often be to replace the two given variables by suitably chosen linear combinations with integer coefficients of two new variables x' and y', so chosen that every pair of integer values of the first two variables will determine a unique pair of integer values for the two new variables, and conversely. In other words we would like to use a *linear transformation* that is *completely reversible in integers*.

But such a transformation is a linear transformation of S_2 and according to **M.5**, it is of necessity one belonging to the lattice group discussed in **M.6**, i.e., a linear transformation of unit determinant and hence possessing an inverse. Moreover from the closure property of the lattice group, the product of any number of these transformations, that is to say the application in convenient sequences of any number of these simplifying transformations, is equal to another of the same kind, that is to say, can be accomplished by a single such transformation.

We observe from Theorem 1 of **6.4** that if we are given a and b, then c and d can be found so that $ad - bc = \pm 1$, if and only if a and b are relatively prime. But this still leaves a good deal of freedom, as we shall show in the next chapter; and from the many corresponding linear transformations that are, as we have shown in **M.5**, *completely reversible in integers*, we can frequently find one or more that will greatly simplify the form of a Diophantine problem, *without losing or gaining* even one extra solution. This technique is well illustrated in the next chapter.

EXERCISES

31.1. Given the matrices

$$T = \begin{pmatrix} 1 & 2 \\ -3 & 2 \end{pmatrix}, \quad U = \begin{pmatrix} 3 & 1 \\ 2 & -5 \end{pmatrix},$$

find TU, UT, $TT = T^2$, and the determinants of the five matrices.

31.2. Prove **M.3** by direct computation.

31.3. Although, in general, $TU \neq UT$ for matrices, show that, always, $d(TU) = d(UT)$ for determinants.

31.4. Using **M.7** give a different proof that the lattice group of **M.6** has closure.

31.5. Show that the lattice group in **M.6** is not commutative.

31.6. Show that the set G of all linear transformations T of S_2 with $d(T) = +1$ is a group, the "direct" lattice group. Decide whether G is commutative.

31.7. Show that the four matrices which follow form a group under matric multiplication:

$$I = \begin{pmatrix} 1 & 0 \\ 0 & 1 \end{pmatrix}, \quad B = \begin{pmatrix} -1 & 0 \\ 0 & 1 \end{pmatrix}, \quad C = \begin{pmatrix} -1 & 0 \\ 0 & -1 \end{pmatrix}, \quad D = \begin{pmatrix} 1 & 0 \\ 0 & -1 \end{pmatrix}.$$

31.8. Show that the four matrices which follow form a group under matric multiplication:

$$I = \begin{pmatrix} 1 & 0 \\ 0 & 1 \end{pmatrix}, \quad A = \begin{pmatrix} 0 & 1 \\ -1 & 0 \end{pmatrix}, \quad A^2 = \begin{pmatrix} -1 & 0 \\ 0 & -1 \end{pmatrix}, \quad A^3 = \begin{pmatrix} 0 & -1 \\ 1 & 0 \end{pmatrix}.$$

31.9. Referring to the previous exercises, define $R = AB$ and $S = BA$ and show that the eight matrices I, A, A^2, A^3, B, D, R, S form a group under matric multiplication isomorphic to the octic group of EX. **30.7.**

31.10. Under matric multiplication the set of all matrices of the form $\begin{pmatrix} 1 & k \\ 0 & 1 \end{pmatrix}$, where k ranges over all integers, forms a group which is isomorphic to the additive group of all integers and to the translation group discussed in **30.2.**

31.11. Consider the mapping $AF = d(A)$ from the system of all linear transformations of S_2 into the system S of all integers. Show that F is an "onto" mapping. Show that F is not one-to-one. Show that F is operation-preserving with respect to the multiplication operations in the two systems.

CHAPTER 32

Introduction to quadratic forms

32.1.   Equivalent functions

It will be evident that this chapter presents generalizations of the material
in Chapter 27 and that it represents an application of the material in the
preceding Chapter 31.

In the present section "function" will be used to mean a polynomial
$f(x, y)$ in two variables with integers as coefficients; in other words, $f(x, y)$
is the sum of a finite number of terms of the type $rx^s y^t$, where r is an integer
and s and t are nonnegative integers.

A function $f(x, y)$ will be said to *represent* an integer n if and only if
there exists a pair of integers x, y (i.e., a lattice point of S_2 as in **31.1**) such
that $f(x, y) = n$. An integer n will be said to be *properly* represented if and
only if there is a representation $f(x, y) = n$ in which x and y are relatively
prime. If a function is such that it represents every integer, the function
will be called *universal*.

A function $F(X, Y)$ will be said to be *equivalent* to a function $f(x, y)$
if and only if there exists a linear transformation T of the lattice group G
of S_2 say,

$$T: \quad x = aX + bY, \quad y = cX + dY, \quad ad - bc = \pm 1,$$

such that $f(x, y) \underset{T}{=} F(X, Y)$.

239

One motivation for this terminology is provided by the following theorem.

F.1:   Equivalent functions represent the same integers.

Proof: We have shown in **M.5** and **M.6** of **31.1**, and in the discussion of **31.4**, how the linear transformations of S_2 which are completely reversible in integers are precisely those of the lattice group of S_2, namely, those of unit determinant. The definition of equivalent functions is phrased to take advantage of this property. For if $f(x, y) \underset{T}{=} F(X, Y)$ and if X, Y are integers such that $F(X, Y) = n$, then the integers x, y defined by $(x, y) = (X, Y)T$ are such that $f(x, y) = n$. Conversely, since T is of unit determinant, there exists an inverse transformation:

$$T^{-1}: \quad X = tdx - tby, \quad Y = -tcx + tay, \quad t = da - cb = \pm 1$$

such that $F(X, Y) \underset{T^{-1}}{=} f(x, y)$. Hence, if x, y are integers such that $f(x, y) = m$, then the integers X, Y defined by $(X, Y) = (x, y)T^{-1}$ are such that $F(X, Y) = m$. Combining these observations, we find that the totalities of integers represented by equivalent functions $f(x, y)$ and $F(X, Y)$ are exactly the same.

For example, if we extend the discussion of **27.3** to all integers x and y, we find that $f(x, y) = x^2 - y^2$ represents all integers n, except those for which $n \equiv 2 \bmod 4$. Using $T: \ x = 2X - 3Y$, $y = X - Y$ which has determinant $+1$, we find

$$f(x, y) \underset{T}{=} (2X - 3Y)^2 - (X - Y)^2 = 3X^2 - 10XY + 8Y^2 = F(X, Y).$$

By **F.1** we can assert that $F(X, Y)$ also represents all integers n, except those for which $n \equiv 2 \bmod 4$. Thus from $f(13, 7) = 120$, we can compute $(13, 7)T^{-1} = (8, 1)$ and assert that $F(8, 1) = 120$.

F.2:   Equivalence of functions is an equivalence relation.

Proof: The proof follows closely the known properties of the lattice group G of S_2 as given in **M.6** of **31.1**. With these group properties proved it is easy to establish that equivalence of functions has the four properties of an equivalence relation.

   (*1*) *Determinative:* given $f(x, y)$ and $F(X, Y)$, either there is or is not a T of G such that $f(x, y) \underset{T}{=} F(X, Y)$.

   (*2*) *Reflexive:* the group G contains I and $f(x, y) \underset{I}{=} f(x, y)$.

(3) *Symmetric:* given that $f(x, y) \underset{T}{=} F(X, Y)$ for a T in G, then there is T^{-1} in G such that $F(X, Y) \underset{T^{-1}}{=} f(x, y)$.

(4) *Transitive:* given that $f(x, y) \underset{T}{=} F(X, Y)$ and $F(X, Y) \underset{U}{=} F_1(X_1, Y_1)$ with T and U in G, then TU is in G and is such that $f(x, y) \underset{TU}{=} F_1(X_1, Y_1)$.

From **F.2** it follows that equivalence of functions divides all functions into mutually exclusive classes of equivalent functions. From **F.1** it follows that all the functions in such an equivalence class represent exactly the same integers. Now to follow out the program outlined in **31.2**, we should seek for each equivalence class some representative, characterized by its simplicity and, if possible, so described that it is canonical, i.e.; so that in an equivalence class there is one and only one function of this description.

In the next section we shall consider certain equivalence classes for which this program can be achieved.

32.2.   Positive definite binary quadratic forms

A *binary quadratic form* is a special function of the type

$$f(x, y) = ax^2 + bxy + cy^2$$

where, of course, a, b, c, are given integers, and since they completely determine the form, the abbreviation $f = [a, b, c]$ is convenient.

F.3:   A function equivalent to a binary quadratic form is a binary quadratic form.

Proof: Let T be a linear transformation of the lattice group G of S_2 defined by

$$T: \quad x = a_1 X + b_1 Y, \quad y = c_1 X + d_1 Y, \quad a_1 d_1 - b_1 c_1 = \pm 1.$$

Then by substitution and expansion we find $[a, b, c] \underset{T}{=} [A, B, C]$,

$$(32.1)\begin{cases} A = aa_1{}^2 + ba_1c_1 + cc_1{}^2 = f(a_1, c_1), \\ B = 2aa_1b_1 + b(a_1d_1 + b_1c_1) + 2cc_1d_1 = f(a_1 + b_1, c_1 + d_1) - A - C, \\ C = ab_1{}^2 + bb_1d_1 + cd_1{}^2 = f(b_1, d_1). \end{cases}$$

Since A, B, C are integers, $[A, B, C]$ is a binary quadratic form.

The *discriminant* of a binary quadratic form a, b, c is defined to be the integer $b^2 - 4ac$.

F.4: Equivalent binary quadratic forms have the same discriminant.

Proof: A straightforward, but tedious simplification, starting from (*32.1*), will show that $B^2 - 4AC = b^2 - 4ac$. However, a simpler proof is obtained by writing (*32.1*) in matric form, as follows:

$$(32.2) \quad \begin{pmatrix} a_1 & c_1 \\ b_1 & d_1 \end{pmatrix} \begin{pmatrix} b & 2a \\ 2c & b \end{pmatrix} \begin{pmatrix} d_1 & c_1 \\ b_1 & a_1 \end{pmatrix} = \begin{pmatrix} B & 2A \\ 2C & B \end{pmatrix}.$$

If to the matric equation (*32.2*) we apply **M.7** and note that even though matric multiplication is not, in general, commutative, the determinants are commutative in their multiplication, then since $(a_1d_1 - b_1c_1)^2 = +1$, we find, rather elegantly, that $b^2 - 4ac = B^2 - 4AC$.

For example, we showed above that $[1, 0, -1]$ and $[3, -10, 8]$ are equivalent. To illustrate **F.4** we can now check that $0^2 - 4((1)-1) = 4 = (-10)^2 - 4(3)(8)$.

Let us describe a form as *positive definite* if it represents, in addition to zero, positive and only positive integers. If there are such forms, then it follows by **F.1** that all forms equivalent to a positive definite form are also positive definite.

F.5: A form $f = [a, b, c]$ is positive definite if and only if

$$a \geqslant 0, \quad c \geqslant 0, \quad a^2 + c^2 > 0, \quad b^2 - 4ac \leqslant 0.$$

Proof: (A) It is clear that a positive definite form must not have $a < 0$, for then $f(1, 0) = a$ would be a negative integer represented by the form; similarly, since $f(0, 1) = c$, it follows that a positive definite form must not have $c < 0$. If $a = b = c = 0$, the form represents only zero and is not positive definite; if $a = c = 0$ and $b \neq 0$, then $f(x, y) = bxy$ so that $f(1, 1) = b$ and $f(1, -1) = -b$, so such a form is not positive definite; therefore a positive definite form must have at least one of a and c positive, i.e., $a^2 + c^2 > 0$. From $f(b, -2a) = -a(b^2 - 4ac)$ it follows that even with $a > 0$, it is necessary to have $b^2 - 4ac \leqslant 0$ to make f positive definite. If $a = 0$, but $c > 0$, then $f(-2c, b) = -cb^2$, hence it is necessary to have $b^2 - 4ac = b^2 = 0$ to make f positive definite. Both of these cases are covered by the requirement $b^2 - 4ac \leqslant 0$.

(B) Conversely, if the conditions mentioned in **F.5** are satisfied, then $f(x, y) = [a, b, c]$, in addition to zero, represents positive and only positive integers. First assume $a > 0$, then $f(1, 0) = a$ shows that f represents at least one positive integer. Secondly, from the following identity:

$$(32.3) \quad 4af(x, y) = 4a(ax^2 + bxy + cy^2) = (2ax + by)^2 - (b^2 - 4ac)y^2,$$

we see, since by hypothesis $b^2 - 4ac \leqslant 0$, that the righthand member of the identity is nonnegative; since $a > 0$, it follows that f is nonnegative.

Finally, if $a = 0$, then $b = 0$ and $c > 0$, so that $f(x, y) = cy^2$ is obviously positive definite.

We shall deal henceforth with positive definite forms, and for each equivalence class of these forms we can establish a canonical form as described in the following two theorems and EX. **32.9**.

F.6:   Any given positive definite form $f = [a, b, c]$ with $b^2 - 4ac < 0$ is equivalent to a form $F = [A, B, C]$ in which

(32.4) $0 \leqslant B \leqslant A$ and $0 < A \leqslant C$.

Proof: By the hypothesis $b^2 - 4ac < 0$ and by **F.5** it follows that both a and c are positive. Both are represented by f. Hence there is a least positive integer A represented by f and an upper limit on its value is already available. By (32.3), or its analogue for $4cf$, the value of A can be found in a finite number of steps. Such an A has a proper representation by f. For if we suppose $f(x_0, y_0) = A$ with $(x_0, y_0) = d$ and $x_0 = X_0 d$, $y_0 = Y_0 d$, then $f(X_0, Y_0) = A/d^2$. Hence if $d > 1$, then A/d^2 would be a positive integer less than A represented by f. Therefore we must have $(x_0, y_0) = 1$. By the Euclid algorithm we know there exist integers r and s so that $r x_0 - s y_0 = 1$. Then $T: \ x = x_0 X + s Y, \ y = y_0 X + r Y$, is a linear transformation belonging to the lattice group G of S_2, for its coefficients are integers and its determinant $+1$. T transforms $[a, b, c]$ into the equivalent form $[A, B', C']$.

The transformation $U_q: \ X = X_1 + q Y_1, \ Y = Y_1$, where q is an integer, is also in the lattice group of S_2, and U_q transforms $[A, B', C']$ into the equivalent form $[A, B^*, C]$ where $B^* = 2qA + B'$. Thus by a suitable choice of q we can make B^* a least absolute value residue of B' mod $2A$; i.e., $-A < B^* \leqslant A$.

If $B^* < 0$, then the transformation $V: \ X_1 = X_2, \ Y_1 = -Y_2$, is in the lattice group of S_2, and V transforms $[A, B^*, C]$ into $[A, B, C]$ where $B = -B^*$. If $B^* \geqslant 0$, we set $B = B^*$. Hence in both cases we have $0 \leqslant B \leqslant A$.

By the transitive property in **F.2** it follows that $[a, b, c]$ is equivalent to $[A, B, C]$. By **F.4** it follows that these forms have the same discriminant. By the hypothesis $B^2 - 4AC = b^2 - 4ac < 0$. Then since $A > 0$, it follows that $C > 0$. Furthermore by **F.1**, A is the least positive integer represented by $[a, b, c]$ and by $[A, B, C]$; hence $A \leqslant C$.

This completes the proof of the theorem. A form with the properties (32.4) will be called a *reduced* form.

For example, if given $f = [4, -27, 48]$, we check that $b^2 - 4ac = -39$, so the form is positive definite and of negative discrimant. It is clear that $A \leqslant 4$. From (32.3) we write

$$16A = (8x - 27y)^2 + 39y^2 \leqslant 64$$

which requires $y = 0$ or $y = 1$. The first case requires $x = 0$ and $A = 0$; or $x = 1$ and $A = 4$. The second case requires both $(8x - 27)^2 \leqslant 25$ and $(8x - 27)^2 \equiv 9 \bmod 16$ so that only two solutions are found: either $x = 3$ and $A = 3$; or $x = 4$ and $A = 4$. Thus the correct value of A is 3 with the proper representation $f(3, 1) = 3$. The transformation $T: x = 3X + 2Y$, $y = X + Y$, takes $[4, -27, 48]$ into $[3, -9, 10]$. Since $-9 = 6(-2) + 3$, we may use $U_2: X = X_1 + 2Y_1$, $Y = Y_1$, to transform $[3, -9, 10]$ into $[3, 3, 4]$ which is a reduced form. The next theorem guarantees that we cannot, by some other sequence of transformations, arrive at any other reduced form.

F.7: In each class of equivalent positive definite forms of negative discriminant there is one and only one reduced form.

Proof: By **F.6** there is at least one reduced form in every class of equivalent positive definite forms of negative discriminant. Let us suppose that $[a, b, c]$ and $[A, B, C]$ are two equivalent reduced forms, each satisfying the conditions (32.4) so $0 \leqslant b \leqslant a$, $0 < a \leqslant c$; $0 \leqslant B \leqslant A$, $0 < A \leqslant C$. Let us suppose that these forms are equivalent under a transformation T such that the relations (32.1) hold.

It is no restriction to assume $a \geqslant A$. From $(a_1 \pm c_1)^2 \geqslant 0$ it follows that $a_1{}^2 + c_1{}^2 \geqslant 2|a_1c_1|$. From $0 \leqslant b \leqslant a$, whether $a_1c_1 \geqslant 0$ or $a_1c_1 < 0$, we have $ba_1c_1 \geqslant -a|a_1c_1|$. Then since $c \geqslant a$, we may use (32.1) to see that

$$A = aa_1{}^2 + ba_1c_1 + cc_1{}^2 \geqslant 2a|a_1c_1| - a|a_1c_1| = a|a_1c_1|.$$

Hence $a \geqslant A \geqslant a|a_1c_1|$, so $1 \geqslant |a_1c_1|$.

If $|a_1c_1| = 0$, and $a_1 = 0$, then $c_1 \neq 0$, for $a_1d_1 - b_1c_1 = \pm 1$; then $a \geqslant A = cc_1{}^2 \geqslant c \geqslant a$ shows $A = a$. A similar argument holds when $|a_1c_1| = 0$ and $c_1 = 0$. If $|a_1c_1| = 1$, the concluding line of the last paragraph shows $a \geqslant A \geqslant a$, so that $A = a$. Thus in every case we have $A = a$.

If $c = a = A = C$, we may use **F.4** and $b^2 - 4ac = B^2 - 4AC$ to conclude that $b^2 = B^2$. Since b and B are nonnegative, it follows that $b = B$, hence in this case the reduced forms are identical.

In the remaining case it is no restriction to consider $c > a$, rather than $C > A$, inasmuch as we have already shown $a = A$. Then the inequality established above is more restrictive and instead of $A \geqslant a|a_1c_1|$, we may say $A > a|a_1c_1| = A|a_1c_1|$, so $|a_1c_1| = 0$.

If $a_1 = 0$, then $c_1 \neq 0$, for $a_1d_1 - b_1c_1 = \pm 1$; furthermore, $|b_1c_1| = 1$, so $c_1{}^2 = 1$. Then $a = A = cc_1{}^2 = c$, a contradiction of the assumption $c > a$, so this case cannot arise.

If $a_1 \neq 0$, then $c_1 = 0$, and as above $a_1d_1 = +1$ or $a_1d_1 = -1$. From (32.1) we may write

$$B = 2aa_1b_1 + b(a_1d_1 + b_1c_1) + 2cc_1d_1 = 2aa_1b_1 + ba_1d_1.$$

If $a_1 d_1 = 1$, then $B - b = 2aa_1b_1$ is a multiple of $2a$; but with $0 \leqslant b \leqslant a$, $0 \leqslant B \leqslant A = a$, we have $-a \leqslant B - b \leqslant a$. Hence it follows that $a_1 b_1 = 0$; since $a_1 \neq 0$, we have $b_1 = 0$. Either $a_1 = 1$, $d_1 = 1$; or $a_1 = -1$, $d_1 = -1$. In these cases the corresponding transformations $T = I$ or $T = -I$ are such that $B = b$ and $C = c$.

If $a_1 d_1 = -1$, then $B + b = 2aa_1b_1$. Since $0 \leqslant B + b \leqslant 2a$, we have two cases to consider. If $B + b = 0$, then $B = b = 0$, and also $a_1 b_1 = 0$ so that $b_1 = 0$; then either $a_1 = 1$, $d_1 = -1$; or $a_1 = -1$, $d_1 = 1$; in either case the transformation T thus determined is such that $C = c$. If $B + b = 2a$, then $B = b = a$, and $a_1 b_1 = 1$; then either $a_1 = 1$, $b_1 = 1$, $d_1 = -1$; or $a_1 = -1$, $b_1 = -1$, $d_1 = 1$; in either case the transformation T thus determined is such that $C = ab_1^2 + bb_1 d_1 + cd_1^2 = a - b + c = c$.

Thus in every case reduced and equivalent forms have been shown to be identical, which completes the proof of **F.7**.

The final note of clarification is contained in the following theorem, which carries the warning that there may be more than one reduced form of a given discriminant but tempers the warning with words of finiteness.

F.8: There are only a finite number of reduced forms with the same discriminant.

Proof: From the condition (*32.4*) we have $B^2 \leqslant A^2 \leqslant AC < 4AC$ or $B^2 - 4AC < 0$, so a reduced form is automatically positive definite. Let us set $K = 4AC - B^2 > 0$. Then $4A^2 \leqslant 4AC = B^2 - (B^2 - 4AC) \leqslant A^2 + K$, so that $3A^2 \leqslant K$. Hence if K is fixed, there are only a finite number of choices of A. The conditions $0 \leqslant B \leqslant A$ and $B^2 \equiv -K \bmod 4A$ show that there are only a finite number of B's to go with a choice of A. As soon as A and B are selected, C is already fixed by $4AC = B^2 + K$. In short, there are only a finite number of reduced forms of a given discriminant, $-K$.

An immediate corollary, of course, is that there are only a finite number of equivalence classes of positive definite forms of a given negative discriminant. For by **F.7** each such class contains one and just one reduced form. Since by **F.8** there are only a finite number of these reduced forms, there are just the same number of classes.

For example, if $K = 6$, then $3A^2 \leqslant 6$, shows $A = 1$; but since neither $B = 0$ nor $B = 1$ solves $B^2 \equiv -6 \bmod 4$, there are *no* reduced forms, and *no* positive definite forms, of discriminant -6. But if $K = 7$, then $3A^2 \leqslant 7$, shows $A = 1$, and $B = 1$ (but not $B = 0$) solves $B^2 \equiv -7 \bmod 4$; hence there is one, and just one, class of positive definite forms of discriminant -7, and this class is represented by its only reduced form $[1, 1, 2]$.

With these ideas as background Hermite gave a simple proof of the theorem of **27.1**, which we restate as follows:

F.9: Every prime of the form $4k + 1$ can be represented as the sum of two squares.

Proof: Since -1 is a quadratic residue of the prime $p = 4k + 1$, there are integers s and t such that $s^2 + 1 = tp$. Hence the form $[t, 2s, p]$ with $p > 0$, $t > 0$, and discriminant $(2s)^2 - 4tp = -4$ is positive definite. When $K = 4$, we have $3A^2 \leqslant 4$, so $A = 1$; then from $B^2 \equiv -4 \bmod 4$, only the solution $B = 0$ satisfies $0 \leqslant B \leqslant A$; and for this solution $C = 1$. Thus there is one and only one reduced form of discriminant -4 and it is $[1, 0, 1]$. By **F.7** it follows that $[t, 2s, p]$ and $[1, 0, 1]$ are equivalent, for they have the same discriminant and there is only the one reduced form with this discriminant. By **F.1** these equivalent forms represent the same integers. But it is clear that $F(X, Y) = [t, 2s, p]$ represents p, inasmuch as $F(0, 1) = p$. Hence it follows that $[1, 0, 1]$ represents p. However, $f(x, y) = [1, 0, 1] = x^2 + y^2$ is the familiar sum of two squares, now written as a binary quadratic form. Hence p may be written as the sum of two squares.

The literature about quadratic forms and universal functions is extensive. But among modern writers, few, except Dickson, include the topic because Dickson and his students have written so extensively on the subject; so it is to this author's books we refer the student who may wish to pursue the subject in greater detail.

EXERCISES

32.1. Prove that $f(x, y) = x^3 + y^3$ is equivalent to
$$F(X, Y) = 37X^3 - 90X^2Y + 72XY^2 - 19Y^3.$$

32.2. (a) Using $T: x = 5X + 2Y$, $y = 7X + 3Y$, find the form which is T-equivalent to $f(x, y) = [3, 5, 1]$.

(b) Check that the equivalent forms of part (a) do have the same discriminant.

32.3. Decide which of the following forms are positive definite: (a) $4xy$; (b) $x^2 + 3xy + 2y^2$; (c) $-x^2 + 3xy - 12y^2$; (d) $x^2 + 3xy + 3y^2$.

32.4. Find all the reduced forms of discriminant -104.

32.5. Find the reduced form equivalent to
$$37x^2 - 194xy + 255y^2.$$

32.6. Define $f(x, y)$ to be *strictly* equivalent to $F(X, Y)$ if and only if $f(x, y) = \underset{T}{=} F(X, Y)$ where $T: x = aX + bY$, $y = cX + dY$ has $ad - bc = +1$. Show that strict equivalence of functions is an equivalence relation.

32.7. Show that any given positive definite binary quadratic form $[a, b, c]$ of negative discriminant is strictly equivalent to a reduced form A, B, C where either (1) $0 < A < C$, $-A < B \leqslant A$; or (2) $0 < A = C$, $0 \leqslant B \leqslant A$.

32.8. Show that two reduced forms of the type described in EX. **32.7** which are strictly equivalent are identical.

32.9. Show that in each class of equivalent positive definite forms of zero discriminant there is one and only one form $[A, 0, 0]$ with $0 < A$.

We do not find career men
among those who make a career of
just getting by.—F. R. KAPPEL

CHAPTER 33

Congruence modulo a subgroup

33.1. Subgroups

A typical maneuver in studying a mathematical system is to determine all subsystems of the system, for these often serve to characterize the parent system and to suggest ways in which larger systems can be constructed from smaller, thus helping to reach the major goal of structure theory. We can illustrate the procedure by studying the notion of a subgroup.

Definition: A set H of elements belonging to a group G is said to form a subgroup of G if and only if H itself is a group, using the same equivalence relation and the same group operation which hold in G.

It is clear that H must satisfy postulates **H.1**, **H.2**, **H.3**, **H.4**, but because **H.4** holds for the group operation in G, and the same operation is to be used for H, this particular postulate will not need to be checked. Of course by Theorem 2 the identity of H will have to be the same as for G; and the inverse elements remain the same.

For example, from Theorem 5 in Chapter 30 it follows that the group of all one-to-one transformations of m objects contains as a subgroup, in the sense of isomorphism, each and every group of order m. At first this idea astounds us with its universality. Apparently to find all groups of order m, all we need do is construct this parent group and find all its

248

subgroups of order m. But practically, the idea is fruitless, for the simple reason that the parent group has order $m!$ which makes such an investigation tedious.

A proper subgroup of G is a group different from G and e, which are subgroups of G, but which are considered as trivial examples.

We present two theorems that offer both practical and theoretical tests for deciding whether a subset H of G is a subgroup of G.

Theorem 6: A subset H of a group G is a subgroup of G if and only if h_1 and h_2 in H implies that $h_1{}^{-1}h_2$ is in H.

Proof: (A) Suppose the condition $h_1{}^{-1}h_2$ in H is satisfied for all h_1 and h_2 in H. In particular, take $h_2 = h_1$; then H contains $h_1{}^{-1}h_1 = e$, so **H.2** is satisfied. Then take $h_2 = e$ to see that for every h_1 in H, $h_1{}^{-1}e = h_1{}^{-1}$ is in H; so **H.3** is satisfied. Finally, from the previous step and Corollary 2.2 in Chapter 29 we find that $h_1 h_2 = (h_1{}^{-1})^{-1}h_2$ is in H for every h_1 and h_2 in H; so **H.1** is satisfied. Therefore H is a subgroup of G.

(B) If H is a subgroup of G so that H satisfies **H.1**, **H.2**, **H.3**, it is clear that if h_1 and h_2 are in H, then $h_1{}^{-1}h_2$ must be in H.

For example, if G is the group of all integers under ordinary equality and the operation of addition, then a subgroup H is formed by all multiples of a fixed integer m. For if $h_1 = sm$ and $h_2 = tm$ are taken as typical members of H, we can see that the $h_1{}^{-1}h_2$ of Theorem 6 is $-(sm) + tm = (-s + t)m$, which is a multiple of m and hence in H. Note that with one exception such a subgroup is of infinite order. If we recall **L.3** in Chapter 2 it is easy to show that these are the only subgroups of G.

33.2.   Left-congruence

The following definition should seem familiar to a student of number theory already acquainted with the congruence idea. However, in the work which follows, the general group G is not commutative, so the convention of multiplication on the left must be consistently used. (We could agree to work on the right equally well.)

Definition: If H if a subset of G and if g_1 and g_2 are in G, write $g_1 \equiv g_2 \bmod H$ and say that "g_1 is left-congruent to g_2 modulo H" if and only if there exists an element h in H such that $g_1 = hg_2$.

Theorem 7: Left-congruence modulo H is an equivalence relation for the group G if and only if H is a subgroup of G.

Proof: (*1*) Left-congruence mod H is determinative by definition, for (Theorem 2) $h = g_1 g_2^{-1}$ either is or is not in H.

(*2*) Left-congruence mod H is reflexive if and only if $g \equiv g \bmod H$ for every g in G; but this requires $g = hg$ with h in H, and by Corollary 2.1 this condition is satisfied if and only if H contains e, i.e., if and only if H satisfies **H.2**.

(*3*) Left-congruence mod H is symmetric if and only if $g_1 \equiv g_2 \bmod H$ implies $g_2 \equiv g_1 \bmod H$. By definition the first condition means $g_1 = hg_2$ with h in H; hence $g_2 = h^{-1}g_1$. But by Theorem 2 there is a unique solution x in G to the equation $g_2 = xg_1$. Thus the second condition $g_2 \equiv g_1 \bmod H$ holds if and only if H contains $x = h^{-1}$. Now for every h in H there is at least one pair of elements in G—namely, g_2 and $g_1 = hg_2$ for which $g_1 \equiv g_2 \bmod H$. Hence left-congruence mod H is symmetric if and only if H satisfies **H.3**.

(*4*) Left-congruence mod H is transitive if and only if $g_1 \equiv g_2 \bmod H$ and $g_2 \equiv g_3 \bmod H$ imply $g_1 \equiv g_3 \bmod H$. The assumed conditions mean $g_1 = h_1 g_2$ and $g_2 = h_2 g_3$ with h_1 and h_2 in H, so that $g_1 = h_1(h_2 g_3) = (h_1 h_2)g_3$ using properties **H.1** and **H.4** of G. But by Theorem 2 there is a unique solution x in G to the equation $g_1 = xg_3$. Thus the third condition $g_1 \equiv g_3 \bmod H$ holds if and only if H contains $h_1 h_2$. Now for every h_1 and h_2 in H, there is at least one set of three elements in G—namely, g_3, $g_2 = h_2 g_3$, and $g_1 = h_1 g_2$ for which $g_1 \equiv g_2 \bmod H$ and $g_2 \equiv g_3 \bmod H$. Hence left-congruence mod H is transitive if and only if H satisfies **H.1**.

Since (*2*), (*3*), (*4*) show that **E.2**, **E.3**, **E.4** for left-congruence mod H are equivalent, respectively, to **H.2**, **H.3**, **H.1** for H, we have proved Theorem 7.

Suppose H is a subgroup of G, then left-congruence mod H is an equivalence relation dividing the elements of G exhaustively into mutually exclusive classes of left-congruent elements. These classes may be called *left-cosets* of G modulo H.

Corollary 7.1: The left-cosets of G modulo H all have the cardinality of H.

Proof: We recall the definition of cardinal number and see that we must establish a one-to-one mapping between each left-coset of G mod H and H itself. Let g be any element of G and let the left-coset containing g be indicated as the g-coset. We claim that the correspondence defined by $hF = hg$ is a one-to-one mapping between H and the left g-coset of G mod H.

F.1: If h is in H, then $hF = hg$ is in the g-coset for $hg \equiv g \bmod H$.

F.2: If $h_1 = h_2$, then $h_1 F = h_1 g = h_2 g = h_2 F$ by property **H.1** of G.

F.3: If g' is in the g-coset mod H, so that $g' \equiv g$ mod H, then $g' = hg$ where h is in H, hence $g' = hF$.

F4: If $h_1 F = h_2 F$, then $h_1 g = h_2 g$, and by Theorem 2 we have $h_1 = h_2$.

Corollary 7.2: If G is a group of finite order m and H is a subgroup of G of order k, then k must divide m.

Proof: By the preceding corollary the left-cosets of G mod H are each of order k. Since left-congruence is an equivalence relation, the left-cosets include all of G without overlapping. Since G is of finite order, there are only a finite number c of left-cosets, and $m = ck$.

The cardinal number of the left-cosets of a subgroup H of a group G is called the *index* of H in G.

Referring to the example of the preceding section where G consists of all integers under ordinary equality and the operation of addition, let H be the subgroup of G consisting of all multiples of m. We find that $a \equiv b$ mod H if and only if $a = sm + b$, but this is precisely the condition for $a \equiv b$ mod m, the congruence mod m which we studied so intensively in earlier chapters. The left-cosets mod H are nothing more in this case than the residue classes modulo m. Although both G and H are infinite (when $m \neq 0$) the index of H in G is finite, and we are familiar from **G.1** in Chapter 13 with the fact that index $H = m$.

Let us examine the noncommutative group of order 6 given in Chapter 30 for its subgroups and corresponding left-cosets. Let us use the notation $H = (h_1 = e, h_2, \ldots)$ for a subgroup H; and for the left a-coset of G mod H let us write $Ha = (h_1 a = a, h_2 a, \ldots)$. For the fact that G can be divided exhaustively into nonoverlapping cosets let us write $G = H \oplus Ha \oplus \ldots$, where we have recognized that $H = He$ is itself a left-coset and we assume that a is not in H. If more than two cosets are involved the $\oplus$ is meant to imply, without further explicit description, that the cosets are nonoverlapping. For the group in question the only possible subgroups must be of orders 1, 2, 3, or 6, and the complete breakdown is given as follows:

$$
\begin{aligned}
G &= (I) \oplus (R_1) \oplus (R_2) \oplus (V_1) \oplus (V_2) \oplus (V_3) \\
&= (I, V_1) \oplus (R_1, V_3) \oplus (R_2, V_2) \\
&= (I, V_2) \oplus (R_1, V_1) \oplus (R_2, V_3) \\
&= (I, V_3) \oplus (R_1, V_2) \oplus (R_2, V_1) \\
&= (I, R_1, R_2) \oplus (V_1, V_2, V_3) \\
&= (I, R_1, R_2, V_1, V_2, V_3).
\end{aligned}
$$

The index of the subgroup (I) is 6; the index for each of the subgroups (I, V_1) and (I, V_2) and (I, V_3) is 3; the index for the subgroup (I, R_1, R_2) is 2; and the index of the subgroup G is 1.

33.3. Cyclic subgroups

It is customary in group theory to use exponents in the same fashion as in ordinary multiplication. If a is in G, we define (I) $a^1 = a$, and (II) $a^{k+1} = a^k a$, where the product intended in (II) is the group product of G and k is any positive integer. The motivation for (I) and (II), of course, is the possibility of using mathematical induction to establish the exponent rules: $a^r a^k = a^{r+k}$ and $(a^r)^k = a^{rk}$. We must caution at once that one rule used in ordinary multiplication is true, in general, only for commutative groups—namely, $(ab)^k = a^k b^k$.

The rules of exponents are extended to apply to a^k where k is any integer by defining $a^0 = e$ and $a^{-1} = $ inverse of a. Neither of these definitions should come as any surprise.

Theorem 8: If a is a fixed element of G, the set H of all elements of G of the form a^k, where k is an integer, form a commutative subgroup of G, called the *cyclic* subgroup generated by a.

Proof: If H contains a^r and a^k, then $a^r a^k = a^{r+k}$ is contained in H, so H has property **H.1**. By definition H contains $a^0 = e$, so H has property **H.2**. By definition H contains a^{-1}, so H has property **H.3**.

Corollary 8.1: If G is of finite order and a is any element of G, there exists a positive integer r such that $a^r = e$.

Proof: Suppose G is of order m; then in the set of $m + 1$ elements $e, a, a^2, \ldots, a^m$ some two must be equal, say $a^s = a^t$, where $t = r + s$ with $r > 0$. Then $ea^s = a^s = a^t = a^{r+s} = a^r a^s$, so by Theorem 2 we have $a^r = e$.

Since $a^r = e$ implies that $a^{-1} = a^{r-1}$, it follows that in dealing with finite groups it is not necessary to use negative exponents.

If there exists a positive integer r such that $a^r = e$, then the least positive integer r such that $a^r = e$ is called the *period* of a.

Corollary 8.2: If G is of order m and a is of period r, then r must be a divisor of m.

Proof: If a is of period r then exactly as in **G.15.2** of Chapter 19 we can show that $a^x = a^y$ if and only if $x \equiv y \bmod r$. Hence the subgroup H generated by a has exactly r distinct elements. By Corollary 7.2 it follows that r must divide m.

Of course G itself may be generated by some element a, and in such a case G is called a *cyclic group*. For example, the set G of all integers under ordinary equality and the operation of addition is an infinite cyclic group generated by the integer $a = 1$. Note that in this case a does not have a period, so to obtain the whole group it is necessary to use zero and negative exponents—or rather, since the group operation is addition, we must use zero and negative multiples of a.

The group $G(m)$ of integers under congruence mod m and addition of residue classes forms a finite cyclic group of order m generated by the 1-class.

In the sense of isomorphism the examples just given represent every possible cyclic group.

Corollary 8.3:   If p is a prime, then in the sense of isomorphism there is just one group G of order p.

Proof: (A) We know there is at least one group of order p, namely, $G(p)$, the residue classes of integers mod p under addition.

(B) Let G' be any group of order p, a prime. Since $p \geqslant 2$, G' contains at least one element a such that $a \neq e$. By the Corollaries 8.1 and 8.2 we know that a is of period r where r divides p. But $r \neq 1$ because $a^1 = a \neq e$, so it follows since p is a prime that $r = p$. Thus the subgroup of G' generated by a is G' itself. Hence the elements of G' may be represented as $u^0 = e, a^1 = a, a^2, \ldots, a^{p-1}$.

(C) It is easy to show $G(p)$ isomorphic to G' by use of the mapping $(i\text{-class})F = a^i$. This mapping F is one-to-one since the equivalence relation for both groups is determined in the same way: $a^i = a^j$ in G' if and only if $i \equiv j \bmod p$, which is exactly the equivalence relation in $G(p)$. For essentially the same reason F is operation-preserving:

$$((i\text{-class}) + (j\text{-class}))F = ((i + j)\text{-class})F = a^{i+j}$$
$$= a^i a^j = (i\text{-class})F(j\text{-class})F.$$

It is clear that there is only one type of group of order 1 consisting of the identity element e and the simple product rule $ee = e$; in the sense of isomorphism we know from Corollaries 8.3 and 3.1 all groups of orders 2, 3, 4, and 5. Since these are all commutative groups, we have shown that the noncommutative group of lowest order is of order 6.

33.4.   Invariant subgroups and quotient groups

It is clear that a definition "a is right-congruent to b mod H if and only if there exists an element h in H such that $a = bh$" will lead to results exactly parallel to Theorem 7 and Corollary 7.1, with classes of right-congruent elements defined as right-cosets, and with $G = H \oplus aH \oplus \cdots$ as a subdivision of G into exhaustive, nonoverlapping right-cosets.

For the example used previously

$$G = (I, V_1) \oplus (R_1, V_3) \oplus (R_2, V_2)$$

using left-cosets, but

$$G = (I, V_1) \oplus (R_1, V_2) \oplus (R_2, V_3)$$

using right-cosets; so we see that left- and right-cosets do not always contain the same elements.

On the other hand,

$$G = (I, R_1, R_2) \oplus (V_1, V_2, V_3)$$

using left-cosets, and

$$G = (I, R_1, R_2) \oplus (V_1, V_3, V_2)$$

using right-cosets; so in this instance, although the elements occur in a different order, it is correct to say that the left- and right-cosets, as sets, do contain exactly the same elements.

To distinguish these possibilities let us proceed as follows:

Definition: A subgroup H of a group G is said to be an *invariant* subgroup of G if and only if for every element a in G the left a-coset and the right a-coset of G modulo H contain exactly the same elements.

Reviewing the definitions of cosets we see that an invariant subgroup H must have the property that for every a in G and every h in H there must exist an h' in H such that $ha = ah'$. It is then obvious that every subgroup of a commutative group is invariant (using $h' = h$), but the example used above shows that there can be invariant, as well as non-invariant, subgroups of noncommutative groups.

Consider left-cosets modulo a subgroup H of a group G and make the following definition of the *product* of two left-cosets:

(33.1) $(a\text{-coset})(b\text{-coset}) = (ab\text{-coset})$.

Theorem 9: The product defined by *(33.1)* of left-cosets modulo a subgroup H of a group G is well defined if and only if H is an invariant subgroup of G.

Proof: If a and b are in G, if a_1 is left-congruent to a modulo H and if b_1 is left-congruent to b modulo H, to tell whether *(33.1)* is well defined we must investigate conditions under which $a_1 b_1$ is left-congruent to ab modulo H. In other words, we are given h_1 and h_2 in H such that $a_1 = h_1 a$

and $b_1 = h_2b$, and we question whether the x of G which by Theorem 2 solves $a_1b_1 = xab$ is in H. Substitution shows $h_1ah_2b = xab$ so that $ah_2 = h_1^{-1}xa$. This condition is satisfied by an x in H if and only if there is an element $h_3 = h_1^{-1}x$ in H such that $ah_2 = h_3a$. Since a is any element in G and h_2 is any element in H, the requirement that h_3 exist in H is satisfied if and only if H is an invariant subgroup of G.

Theorem 10:   If H is an invariant subgroup of G, then the cosets of G modulo H under the equivalence relation of congruence modulo H and under the operation *(33.1)* of coset-multiplication form a group called the *quotient group* of G mod H and designated G/H.

Proof: Since the covering hypothesis is that H is an invariant subgroup of G it is not necessary to speak of left- or right-cosets, or to distinguish left- and right-congruence mod H.

From *(33.1)* and Theorem 9 we know that coset-multiplication is closed and well-defined; so G/H has property **H.1.** The (e-coset) $= H$ serves as the identity for *(33.1)*; so G/H has property **H.2.** The (a^{-1}-coset) serves as the inverse of the (a-coset) for *(33.1)*; so G/H has property **H.3.** Since multiplication in G is associative, it follows that coset-multiplication defined by *(33.1)* is associative; so G/H has property **H.4.** This completes the proof of Theorem 10.

One example of Theorem 10 is already well known to us, for the group $G(m)$ in Example 2 of Chapter 29 is the quotient group of G, the set of all integers under ordinary equality and addition, modulo the subgroup H consisting of all multiples of m. H is invariant because G is commutative, the cosets of G modulo H are residue classes, and the coset-multiplication in *(33.1)* is the operation of addition of residue classes studied in **G.3** of Chapter 13.

But in Theorem 10 we have a significant generalization of our previous work, and in succeeding chapters we can exploit this theorem in several ways.

The example above illustrates one general fact worth elaboration. The quotient group G/H obtained from Theorem 10 is a new system, not to be imagined as a subgroup of G—and in general G/H is not even isomorphic to a subgroup of G. Witness the above example where $G(m) = G/H$ is finite, but except for the trivial case of the subgroup consisting of the identity 0, all other subgroups of G are infinite.

Perhaps another example will help illustrate this point and also help us visualize Theorems 9 and 10 as splitting up G into cosets which multiply in orderly fashion. For if we see the group table of G arranged in proper coset "blocks," we can read off the table for G/H and have a better appreciation of that word "quotient."

We start with the quaternion group which is a noncommutative group of order 8 with the following table:

I	A	B	C	D	E	F	U
A	U	C	E	I	F	B	D
B	F	U	A	C	I	D	E
C	B	D	U	E	A	I	F
D	I	F	B	U	C	E	A
E	C	I	D	F	U	A	B
F	E	A	I	B	D	U	C
U	D	E	F	A	B	C	$I.$

We may show that $H = (I, U)$ is an invariant subgroup of G directly by noting the same breakdown of G into left- and right-cosets mod H, namely, $G = (I, U) \oplus (A, D) \oplus (B, E) \oplus (C, F)$; or we may proceed indirectly to rearrange the group table and then appeal to Theorem 9:

I	U	A	D	B	E	C	F
U	I	D	A	E	B	F	C
A	D	U	I	C	F	E	B
D	A	I	U	F	C	B	E
B	E	F	C	U	I	A	D
E	B	C	F	I	U	D	A
C	F	B	E	D	A	U	I
F	C	E	B	A	D	I	$U.$

The extra lines help us see how the coset-multiplication is well defined: for example, whether we pick A or D from the coset (A, D) and multiply by B or E from the coset (B, E), we get either C or F which are in the coset (C, F). The extra lines help us see G/H as that particular kind of a group of order 4 in which every element (now, of course, the "elements" are cosets) is self-inverse. But in the quaternion group G only two elements are self-inverse. So it is impossible to find a subgroup of G which is isomorphic to G/H.

EXERCISES

33.1. For the octic group (EXS. **30.7** and **31.9**) determine all subgroups and all invariant subgroups. In particular, show that the subgroup made up of I and B is not invariant.

33.2. By considering determinants show that the direct lattice group (EX. **31.6**) is an invariant subgroup of the complete lattice group on S_2.

33.3. For any group (finite or infinite) show that a subgroup of index 2 is always invariant. Give a new proof of EX. **33.2.**

33.4. Show that the set H of all matrices of the form $\begin{pmatrix} u & x \\ 0 & v \end{pmatrix}$, where u, v, x are integers and $uv = \pm 1$, is a subgroup of the lattice group G on S_2, but is not an invariant subgroup.

33.5. Show that the translation group H_1 (EX. **31.10**) is an invariant subgroup of H (EX. **33.4**). Show that H_1 is not an invariant subgroup of the lattice group G on S_2.

33.6. Referring to EX. **33.5**, show that the quotient group H/H_1 is isomorphic to the noncyclic group of order 4 (EX. **31.7**).

33.7. Referring to EX. **33.4**, show that the set of all matrices in H having $v = 1$ is an invariant subgroup H_2 of H. (Note that H_2 is the group of all reflections and translations of S.)

33.8. Consider the set C of all elements c of a group G such that $cx = xc$ for every x in G. Show that C is an invariant subgroup of G. C is called the *center* of G.

33.9. Referring to EX. **33.8** and **33.4**, show that the center of H is of order 2.

33.10. Show that the dihedral group H of order $2m$, $m > 2$, described in Corollary 4.3 of **30.2**, may be represented by all matrices of the form $\begin{pmatrix} u & k \\ 0 & 1 \end{pmatrix}$ whose elements are residue classes of integers mod m with $u \equiv \pm 1 \bmod m$. Show that the center of H is of order 1 or 2, depending upon whether m is odd or even.

33.11. The group G of order $m\phi(m)$ in EX. **30.8** may be represented by all matrices, mod m, of the form $\begin{pmatrix} u & k \\ 0 & 1 \end{pmatrix}$ where $(u, m) = 1$. Show that H (EX. **33.10**) is an invariant subgroup of G.

33.12. Show that a cyclic group of order n contains a subgroup of order d for every divisor d of n. (See G.15.3 in **19.1**.)

33.13. Recall EX. **29.8**. Use Corollary 8.2 and obtain a new proof of Euler's theorem (**G.10** in **18.4**).

CHAPTER 34

Direct products

34.1.   Direct products

Let us illustrate a way in which larger mathematical systems can be constructed from known constituents. Suppose we are given a system S_1 with elements $a_1, b_1, \ldots$, an equivalence relation $a_1 \, \mathbf{E}_1 \, b_1$ or $a_1 \, \mathbf{E}_1 \, b_1$, and an ordered binary operation $a_1 b_1$; and a system S_2 with elements $a_2, b_2, \ldots$, an equivalence relation $a_2 \, \mathbf{E}_2 \, b_2$ or $a_2 \, \mathbf{E}_2 \, b_2$, and an ordered binary operation $a_2 b_2$.

Consider a new system S, called the *direct product* of S_1 and S_2, indicated by $S = S_1 \otimes S_2$, defined in the following way: as the elements of S use all ordered pairs (a_1, a_2) in which a_1 belongs to S_1 and a_2 belongs to S_2; as an equivalence relation for S use $(a_1, a_2) \, \mathbf{E} \, (b_1, b_2)$ if and only if $a_1 \, \mathbf{E}_1 \, b_1$ and $a_2 \, \mathbf{E}_2 \, b_2$; as an ordered binary operation for S use

$$(34.1) \qquad\qquad (a_1, a_2)(b_1, b_2) \, \mathbf{E} \, (a_1 b_1, a_2 b_2)$$

where the first component of the new product operation is determined by the known operation $a_1 b_1$ in S_1, and the second component is determined by the known operation $a_2 b_2$ in S_2.

258

We leave as easy exercises the proofs that E is indeed an equivalence relation for S; if S_1 and S_2 are of orders m_1 and m_2, respectively, then S is of order $m = m_1 m_2$; and if the operations in S_1 and S_2 are closed and well defined, then the operation (34.1) in S is closed and well defined.

34.2. Direct product of groups

Let us apply the general discussion in the preceding section to the special case of groups.

Theorem 11:   The direct product $G = G_1 \otimes G_2$ of two given groups G_1 and G_2 is a group. G is commutative if and only if both G_1 and G_2 are commutative.

Proof: The remarks in **34.1** indicate that (34.1) is a closed and well-defined operation because the group operations in G_1 and G_2 have these properties; so G has property **H.1**. If e_1 and e_2 are the identities of G_1 and G_2, respectively, then (e_1, e_2) is the identity for the operation (34.1); so G has property **H.2**. It is easy to see that $(a_1, a_2)^{-1} \, E \, (a_1^{-1}, a_2^{-1})$; so G has property **H.3**. The componentwise multiplication in (34.1) shows that G must have the associative property **H.4** because each of G_1 and G_2 has this property. This completes the proof that G is a group. The final remark about G being commutative or noncommutative follows, just like all the other properties, from the componentwise nature of the product (34.1).

A host of groups conceptually new to us are at once available as we form the direct product of two (or, by iteration, of any finite number of) groups previously studied. Of course, some of these groups may be isomorphic to groups previously described; for example, $G(2) \otimes G(2)$; the so-called "four-group," is isomorphic to the group G_2 in Corollary 3.1; and $G(2) \otimes G(3)$ is isomorphic to $G(6)$. Some of the direct product groups may be isomorphic to others: for example, $G_1 \otimes G_2$ is always isomorphic to $G_2 \otimes G_1$; and we write $G_1 \otimes G_2 \otimes G_3$, rather than $G_1 \otimes (G_2 \otimes G_3)$, because the latter group is isomorphic to $(G_1 \otimes G_2) \otimes G_3$.

A way in which the direct product idea is a partial counterpart of the quotient group idea is revealed in the following corollary.

Corollary 11.1:   In the direct product group $G = G_1 \otimes G_2$, the set H_1 of all elements of the form (a_1, e_2) is an invariant subgroup of G; H_1 is isomorphic to G_1; and the quotient group G/H_1 is isomorphic to G_2.

Proof: We leave as an exercise the proof that the correspondence $(a_1, e_2)F_1 = a_1$ is an isomorphism between H_1 and G_1, so that H_1 is a subgroup of G. To show that H_1 is an invariant subgroup of G we must show that the solution (x, y) of $(b_1, b_2)(a_1, e_2) = (x, y)(b_1, b_2)$ is in H_1. But from (34.1) this solution, which is unique by Theorem 2, is easily seen to be $(x, y) = (b_1 a_1 b_1^{-1}, e_2)$ which *is* in H_1. Finally, the correspondence $(H_1(b_1, b_2))F_2 = b_2$ is readily shown to be an isomorphism mapping the cosets $H_1(b_1, b_2)$ of G/H_1 onto the elements b_2 of G_2.

However, it is not true that one can obtain all groups of a given order as the direct product of groups of lower order. For example, we have already observed that groups of orders 2, 3, and 4 are commutative, so if we use them to form direct product groups of orders 6 or 8, we shall obtain commutative groups. But we have already produced some noncommutative groups of these orders.

Corollary 11.2: If $a = (a_1, a_2, \ldots, a_t)$ is an element of $G = G_1 \otimes G_2 \otimes \cdots \otimes G_t$ and if a_i has the period r_i in G_i, then a has the period r where r is the least common multiple of the r_i.

Proof: When the product rule (34.1) is extended to t components we find $a^r = e$ in G if and only if $a_i^r = e_i$ in G_i for $i = 1, 2, \ldots, t$. But this holds if and only if $r \equiv 0 \bmod r_i$ for $i = 1, 2, \ldots, t$. This system of congruence conditions can be satisfied and the minimum positive value for r is the least common multiple of the r_i.

With the aid of Corollary 11.2 and EX. **29.11** which states that under isomorphism an element must map into an element of the same period, we can readily show that some groups are nonisomorphic. Thus if p is a prime there are at least two nonisomorphic commutative groups of order p^2—namely, $G(p^2)$ and $G(p) \otimes G(p)$, for the first has a generator of period p^2, but the second has no elements of period p^2. (As a matter of fact, it is possible to show that in the sense of isomorphism there are no other groups of order p^2, commutative or noncommutative!) Similarly, there are at least three nonisomorphic commutative groups of order p^3—namely, $G(p^3)$, $G(p) \otimes G(p^2)$, and $G(p) \otimes G(p) \otimes G(p)$, distinguished from one another by elements of maximum periods p^3, p^2, and p, respectively. The same argument will distinguish many groups, although it may be necessary to examine elements other than those of maximum period. Thus $G(4) \otimes G(8)$ and $G(2) \otimes G(2) \otimes G(8)$ both have 16 elements of the maximum period 8, but they are not isomorphic, for the first group has 12 elements of period 4 whereas the second has only eight such elements.

34.3.   Commutative groups of order p^k

The remarks closing the last section are special cases of the following theorem which seems worth developing since it uses many concepts from our previous study of number theory and gives us some insight into structure theory.

Theorem 12: If p is a prime and if $G = G(p^{k_1}) \otimes G(p^{k_2}) \otimes \cdots \otimes G(p^{k_t})$, where $1 \leqslant k_1 \leqslant k_2 \leqslant \cdots \leqslant k_t$, let $Q(j)$ be the number of k_x satisfying $k_x \geqslant j$; let $R(0) = 0$, and if $1 \leqslant i \leqslant k_t$, let $R(i) = \sum Q(j)$ summed over $j = 1, 2, \ldots, i$; then the number $N(i)$ of elements of G of period p^i is given by $N(0) = 1$ and by

$$N(i) = p^{R(i)} - p^{R(i-1)}, \qquad 1 \leqslant i \leqslant k_t.$$

Proof: (A) For a cyclic group $G(p^k)$ the method of proof in **G.15.3** of **19.1** applies directly (replacing e by p^k and E by p^i) to show that the number of elements of period p^i when $0 \leqslant i \leqslant k$ is given by $\phi(p^i)$. Then the first theorem in **11.4** shows that the number of elements of periods p^s where $p^s \leqslant p^i$ is given by p^i.

(B) From Corollary 11.2 we see that an element a of G is of period p^i if and only if p^i is the least common multiple of the periods p^{s_x} of a_x in $G(p^{k_x})$ for $x = 1, 2, \ldots, t$. Using the maximum exponent idea in **8.4** we find requirements are that

(1) $i \geqslant s_x$,   for $x = 1, 2, \ldots, t$; and
(2) $i = s_x$,   for at least one value of x.

To help us count the number of ways that $a = (a_1, \ldots, a_m, a_{m+1}, \ldots, a_t)$ can be chosen consistent with (1) and (2) let us set $m = t - Q(i)$.

Since $s_x \leqslant k_x$, it is impossible to satisfy (2) except in the $Q(i)$ cases where $k_x \geqslant i$. So for the cases where $x \leqslant m$, we consider only the condition (1) and see that a_x can be chosen in p^{k_x} ways.

For the $Q(i)$ cases where $m + 1 \leqslant x \leqslant t$ we must select the a_x in such a way that both (1) and (2) are satisfied. From (A) we know that (1) can be satisfied in p^i ways and (2) in $\phi(p^i)$ ways. However, to count the a's without repetition, we shall fix x and suppose that $s_y \leqslant i - 1$ when $m + 1 \leqslant y < x$, $s_x = i$, $s_y \leqslant i$ when $x < y \leqslant t$.

With this notation established the number of a's of period p^i is given by extending the following sum over $x = m + 1, m + 2, \ldots, t$:

$$N(i) = \sum p^{k_1} \cdots p^{k_m} (p^i - 1)^{x - (m+1)} \phi(p^i)(p^i)^{t-x}.$$

By setting $S = it - (i - 1)(m + 1)$ we may rewrite $N(i)$ in the form

$$N(i) = p^{k_1} \cdots p^{k_m} \phi(p^i) \sum p^{S-x}.$$

Since we may write

$$\phi(p^i) = p^{i-1}(p - 1), \qquad \sum p^{S-x} = p^{S-t} \sum p^{t-x} = p^{S-t}(p^{Q(i)} - 1)/(p - 1)$$

we can set $T = k_1 + \cdots + k_m + S - t + i - 1$ and obtain

$$N(i) = p^T(p^{Q(i)} - 1).$$

From the definitions of m and S we find that

$$T = k_1 + \cdots + k_m + (i - 1)Q(i).$$

(C) To complete the proof we need to show that $T = R(i - 1)$, which is equivalent to showing $T + Q(i) = R(i)$. A geometric description of this identity makes it easy to see. Let the $k_1, k_2, \ldots, k_t$ be represented in a tableau of t rows and k_t columns in which the first k_i positions of the ith row are filled with 1's and the remaining positions with 0's. Then $Q(j)$ is the sum of the elements of the jth column; and $R(i)$ is the cumulative sum of the elements in the first i columns. When this latter sum is formulated in terms of rows, the rows are abbreviated to a length i; when $x \leqslant m$, so that $k_x < i$, the contribution to the sum is k_x; but when $m + 1 \leqslant x$ so that $k_x \geqslant i$, the contribution to the sum is i, and there are $Q(i)$ such rows. Thus $R(i) = k_1 + \cdots + k_m + iQ(i) = T + Q(i)$.

For example, consider the group $G = G(p^2) \otimes G(p^4) \otimes G(p^4) \otimes G(p^5)$ which is of order p^{15}, but can have elements only of periods $1, p, p^2, p^3, p^4, p^5$. From the tableau we readily compute $Q(i)$ and $R(i)$.

k_1	1	1	0	0	0
k_2	1	1	1	1	0
k_3	1	1	1	1	0
k_4	1	1	1	1	1
$Q(i)$	4	4	3	3	1
$R(i)$	4	8	11	14	15

Then

$$N(5) = p^{15} - p^{14}, \qquad N(4) = p^{14} - p^{11}, \qquad N(3) = p^{11} - p^8,$$
$$N(2) = p^8 - p^4, \qquad N(1) = p^4 - 1, \qquad N(0) = 1.$$

Corollary 12.1: If p is a prime and k a positive integer, there are at least as many nonisomorphic commutative groups of order p^k as there are ways of partitioning k in the form

$$k = k_1 + k_2 + \cdots + k_t, \qquad 1 \leqslant k_1 \leqslant k_2 \leqslant \cdots \leqslant k_t, \qquad 1 \leqslant t.$$

Proof: (A) For each partitioning there is a corresponding direct product group $G = G(p^{k_1}) \otimes G(p^{k_2}) \otimes \ldots \otimes G(p^{k_i})$ which is of order p^k and which is commutative.

(B) By Theorem 12 any two of these groups, say G and G', corresponding to different partitions are nonisomorphic, because for at least two values of i they differ in the number $N(i)$ of elements of period p^i. We leave the details as EX. **34.6**.

It would take us too far afield to prove, what is the fact, that in the sense of isomorphism there are no commutative groups of order p^k, other than those given in Corollary 12.1.

At this point we shall conclude our study of group theory *per se* and pass on to the study of other mathematical systems. Since these systems are based upon the concept of a group, what we have learned will be continuously in use.

A course devoted to the study of groups would pursue at greater length each of the ideas we have introduced—using transformation groups, invariant subgroups, cyclic groups, quotient groups, direct product groups, many-to-one operation preserving mappings called *homomorphisms*, etc., etc., to attack the problem of structure. The problem is not solved for all groups, but for some important classes of groups the structure theory is completely known: for example, the structure of all finite, commutative groups is known. We hope our readers are challenged by these introductory chapters to make their way to the frontiers of knowledge.

EXERCISES

34.1. Verify the remarks in the last paragraph of **34.1**.

34.2. Write out the group table for the direct product G of the cyclic group of order 2 and the dihedral group of order 6, arranged in a way to show that G is isomorphic to the dihedral group of order 12.

34.3. In the proof of Corollary 11.1 verify that the mappings F_1 and F_2 are isomorphisms.

34.4. As in the example following Theorem 12, find the number of elements of various periods for the group

$$G = G(p) \otimes G(p^4) \otimes G(p^5) \otimes G(p^5).$$

34.5. Repeat the previous exercise for the group

$$G = G(p) \otimes G(p^2) \otimes G(p^3) \otimes G(p^4) \otimes G(p^5).$$

34.6. Complete the proof of (B) in Corollary 12.1.

34.7. Apply Corollary 12.1 with $p_1 = 2$ and $p_2 = 3$ and then use the direct product concept to show there are at least six nonisomorphic commutative groups of order 72.

CHAPTER 35

Rings, domains, and fields

35.1.   Introduction to rings

Next we shall consider a *ring*, which is more complicated than a group, because it has two operations, but is rather obviously algebraic in nature, since these operations are called *addition* and *multiplication* and have at least some of the familiar properties associated with these names.

Definition: A ring is a mathematical system R with at least two elements $a, b, \ldots$; an equivalence relation, usually written $a = b$ or $a \neq b$; and two ordered binary operations: one called *addition* with a "sum" indicated by $a + b$; and the other called *multiplication* with a "product" indicated by ab. A ring is subject to the following postulates:

R.1: R is a commutative group under addition;

R.2:   Multiplication in R is closed, well defined, and associative;

R.3:   Multiplication is left- and right-distributive over addition: viz., if a, b, c are in R, then $a(b + c) = ab + ac$ and $(b + c)a = ba + ca$.

Usually the identity of addition is called the *zero* of the ring and is designated by z or 0. Similarly, we use a familiar name for the inverse of an element a under addition and call it the *negative* of a, designated by $-a$.

264

To show that this set of postulates is consistent we note that the set J of all integers is a ring under ordinary equality, addition, and multiplication. Or to put the matter a different way, we have been assuming since Chapter 1 that J has all the properties required of a ring. If the logic of *assuming* that J is a ring is bothersome, the reader is asked to wait until Chapters 43 and 44 where this matter is approached in another way. Meanwhile with J as a fundamental example of a ring we can proceed to construct many other rings.

To compare the rings R and R' we need to extend the notion of isomorphism to cover preservation of two operations. A correspondence $aF = a'$ between the ring R and the ring R' is said to be an isomorphism if and only if

(*1*) F is a one-to-one mapping between R and R';

(*2*) F is operation-preserving with respect to the operations of addition in the two systems: if a and b are in R, then $(a + b)F = aF + bF$, where the first $a + b$ is the sum in R, and the second $aF + bF$ is the sum in R';

(*3*) F is operation-preserving with respect to the operations of multiplication in the two systems: if a and b are in R, then $(ab)F = (aF)(bF)$, where the first ab is the product in R, and the second $(aF)(bF)$ is the product in R'.

Since we have agreed to use the name "zero" for the identity of addition in a ring, there will be no confusion if we henceforth use the word "identity" only in reference to the multiplication of the ring.

We note that postulate **R.2** does not require that a ring possess a left-, or right-, or two-sided identity. Later we shall show an example in which a ring has a left-identity but not a right-identity. For the moment we are content with two simple observations.

First, if R has a two-sided identity e, so that a in R implies $ea = a = ae$, then e is unique; for if f is also a two-sided identity of R, then $f = ef = e$.

Second, if R has any type of identity and R is isomorphic to R', then R' must possess an identity of the same type; for this is an easy consequence of properties (*1*) and (*3*) of the isomorphism.

As an example of a ring without an identity consider, within the ring J, the subsystem J_m consisting of all integers which are multiples of a fixed integer $m > 1$. In the study of groups we noted that J_m is a subgroup of J under addition. Since it is intended that the product rule in J_m be the same as in J, the only detail to be checked to make sure that J_m is a ring is the closure property in **R.2**. But closure is assured, since $(sm)(tm) = (smt)m$ is in J_m. We know that J has a two-sided identity, the integer 1, which by the first observation above is unique. Since J_m has the same product rule as J, but does not contain 1, it follows that J_m does not have a two-sided identity. Of course J_m does not have a one-sided identity either, because J_m, like J, has commutative multiplication.

It is now easy to see that the postulates for a ring are not categorical. For we noted above that an isomorphism must map an identity element into an identity element; so the ring J is not isomorphic to the ring J_m when $m > 1$, since the first ring has an identity, but the second has none.

Even when R has an identity, we note that **R.2** does not require that R shall have left-, or right-, or two-sided inverses. One reason for this situation is related to the following theorem.

Theorem 1: In a ring R the zero z has the property that if a is in R, then $az = z = za$.

Proof: Using the convention of writing justifications under the equivalence signs, we have

$$z + az \underset{\textbf{R.2,R.1}}{=} az \underset{\textbf{R.1,R.2}}{=} a(z + z) \underset{\textbf{R.3}}{=} az + az,$$

where in the first use of **R.2** we need closure, and in the second, the well-defined property. Since R is a group under addition, Theorem 2 of **29.3** applies, and we conclude that $z = az$, since there must be a unique solution to the equation $x + az = az$. Similarly, we may use the second part of **R.3** to show that $za = z$.

Theorem 1 is sometimes phrased as follows: "In a ring the zero is an annihilator for multiplication."

An immediate consequence of Theorem 1 is that in a ring it is impossible for the zero to have an inverse. For Theorem 1 indicates that z can have an inverse only if z is an identity of the ring. But Theorem 1 also shows that z cannot be an identity of the ring, since the ring is assumed to have at least two elements.

A less obvious consequence is the familiar "rules of signs" for multiplication.

Corollary 1.1: If a and b are in a ring R, then $-(ab) = a(-b)$.

Proof: Using appropriate postulates and Theorem 1, indicated as **T.1**, we have

$$-(ab) + ab \underset{\textbf{R.1}}{=} z \underset{\textbf{T.1}}{=} az \underset{\textbf{R.1,R.2}}{=} a((-b) + b) \underset{\textbf{R.3}}{=} a(-b) + ab.$$

But in the additive group of R there is a unique solution to the equation $x + ab = z$; hence $-(ab) = a(-b)$.

We leave as exercises the proofs that $-(ab) = (-a)b$ and that $(-a)(-b) = ab$.

By Theorem 1 we see that in a ring R the equation $zx = z$ is solved by $x = b$ for every b in R; and if $a \neq z$, the equation $ax = z$ has at least one solution $x = z$. With this situation as motivation, we make the following definition:

Definition: An element a of R is a proper left-divisor of zero if and only if $a \neq z$ and there exists an element b in R with $b \neq z$ such that $ab = z$.

Similar definitions may be made for proper right- and proper two-sided divisors of zero.

Theorem 2: If R is a ring with a left-identity in which every $a \neq z$ has a left-inverse, then R has no proper left-divisor of zero.

Proof: Suppose that x solves $ax = z$ with $a \neq z$. If R is a ring with a left-identity e and a has a left-inverse a^{-1}, then from Theorem 1 and the associative property in **R.2** we find

$$x = ex = (a^{-1}a)x = a^{-1}(ax) = a^{-1}z = z.$$

But if x must be z, then a is not a proper left-divisor of zero.

The cardinal number of the set of all elements in R is called the *order* of R.

Theorem 3: For every integer $m > 1$ there exists at least one ring of order m.

Proof: Consider the set $J(m)$ of all residue classes of integers modulo the fixed integer $m > 1$. In our study of congruence mod m in Chapter 14 we have already shown all the necessary properties of the equivalence relation and of the addition and multiplication of residue classes to show that $J(m)$ is a ring of order m.

Corollary 3.1: The ring $J(m)$ has an identity and exactly $\phi(m)$ elements have inverses. If m is composite, $J(m)$ has proper divisors of zero. If p is prime, $J(p)$ has no proper divisors of zero.

Proof: These results are just restatements of propositions in Chapter 14 such as **G.7.2**.

A ring is called *commutative* if and only if a and b in R implies $ab = ba$. Thus far all the examples we have produced have been commutative rings. In the next section we shall discover a number of noncommutative rings.

35.2. Matric rings

Following the plan in Chapter 31 we may introduce the idea of a mathematical system $M(R)$ whose elements are all the 2-by-2 matrices:

$$A = \begin{pmatrix} a_{11} & a_{12} \\ a_{21} & a_{22} \end{pmatrix}, \qquad B = \begin{pmatrix} b_{11} & b_{12} \\ b_{21} & b_{22} \end{pmatrix},$$

whose entries $a_{11}, a_{12}, a_{21}, a_{22}$ are elements of a given ring R, with the double subscript notation a_{ij} to indicate the element in the ith row and jth column of the matrix A. We know from Chapter 34 how to motivate the following componentwise definitions:

(35.1) $A = B$ if and only if $a_{11} = b_{11}, a_{12} = b_{12}, a_{21} = b_{21}, a_{22} = b_{22}$;

(35.2)
$$A + B = \begin{pmatrix} a_{11} + b_{11} & a_{12} + b_{12} \\ a_{21} + b_{21} & a_{22} + b_{22} \end{pmatrix};$$

and we know from Chapter 31 how to motivate the following row-by-column definition of a matric product:

(35.3)
$$AB = \begin{pmatrix} a_{11}b_{11} + a_{12}b_{21} & a_{11}b_{12} + a_{12}b_{22} \\ a_{21}b_{11} + a_{22}b_{21} & a_{21}b_{12} + a_{22}b_{22} \end{pmatrix}.$$

Theorem 4: The system $M(R)$ of all 2-by-2 matrices, with entries from a ring R, is itself a ring under matric equality *(35.1)*, the matric sum *(35.2)*, and the matric product *(35.3)*.

Proof: It is easy to check directly that the new equality $A = B$ defined in *(35.1)* is an equivalence relation, because of its componentwise nature and the fact that the relation $a_{ij} = b_{ij}$ in R is known to be an equivalence relation. Likewise, it is easy to check that $M(R)$ is a commutative group under the matric sum *(35.2)*, because R is known to form a commutative group under the addition $a + b$ and *(35.2)* simply extends this property component by component. In particular, we discover that the zero and negative for $M(R)$ are given by

$$Z = \begin{pmatrix} z & z \\ z & z \end{pmatrix}, \qquad -A = \begin{pmatrix} -a_{11} & -a_{12} \\ -a_{21} & -a_{22} \end{pmatrix}.$$

But a more sophisticated way for us to reach these same conclusions is to note that $M(R)$ is isomorphic to the direct product $M' = R \otimes R \otimes R \otimes R$ of four copies of R, as far as the operations of addition are concerned. Although an element A of $M(R)$ is arranged as a 2-by-2 array (to facilitate the definition of AB), whereas a corresponding element A' of M' is arranged as a 1-by-4 array, say $(a_{11}, a_{12}, a_{21}, a_{22})$, there is no other difference in the componentwise nature of the definitions of equality and group operations. Then we can appeal to Theorem 11 of Chapter 34 to claim that M' and $M(R)$ have property **R.1**.

It is obvious that the matric product (*35.3*) is closed and well defined because the two operations in R which are used are both known to have these properties. It is a little more difficult to check the associative law directly, but if we set $S = A(BC)$ and $T = (AB)C$ we find

$$s_{ij} = a_{i1}(b_{11}c_{1j} + b_{12}c_{2j}) + a_{i2}(b_{21}c_{1j} + b_{22}c_{2j}),$$
$$t_{ij} = (a_{i1}b_{11} + a_{i2}b_{21})c_{1j} + (a_{i1}b_{12} + a_{i2}b_{22})c_{2j}.$$

In showing $s_{ij} = t_{ij}$ we must remember that the multiplication in R is not assumed to be commutative. However, by using the two distributive laws, the associative multiplication, and the associative and commutative addition, we see that $s_{ij} = t_{ij}$. Hence by (*35.1*) we have $S = T$. Again a more sophisticated proof is available. We can study the linear transformations of the lattice space $S_2(R)$ of all ordered pairs (a, b), where a and b are in R, and establish the analog of **M.2** in **31.1**. Then the associative property for the matric product (*35.3*) will follow from the associative law for the product of transformations.

We check directly that $M(R)$ satisfies **R.3**. For if we set $S = A(B + C)$ and $T = AB + AC$ we find from (*35.2*) and (*35.3*) that

$$s_{ij} = a_{i1}(b_{1j} + c_{1j}) + a_{i2}(b_{2j} + c_{2j}),$$
$$t_{ij} = (a_{i1}b_{1j} + a_{i2}b_{2j}) + (a_{i1}c_{1j} + a_{i2}c_{2j}).$$

The known properties of R, particularly the left-distributive law, show that $s_{ij} = t_{ij}$. Then from (*35.1*) it follows that $S = T$. In a similar way, but using the right-distributive property in R, we can show the right-distributive property for $M(R)$.

Corollary 4.1: If R has a left-identity e, then $M(R)$ has a left-identity

$$I = \begin{pmatrix} e & z \\ z & e \end{pmatrix}.$$

Proof: From (*35.2*) and Theorem 1 we have

$$\begin{pmatrix} e & z \\ z & e \end{pmatrix}\begin{pmatrix} a & c \\ b & d \end{pmatrix} = \begin{pmatrix} ea + zb & ec + zd \\ za + eb & zc + ed \end{pmatrix} = \begin{pmatrix} a & c \\ b & d \end{pmatrix}.$$

Corollary 4.2: The ring $M(R)$ has a proper left-divisor of zero.

Proof: Since R has at least two elements, R must contain at least one element $a \neq z$. Then the matrices

$$A = \begin{pmatrix} z & z \\ a & z \end{pmatrix}, \qquad B = \begin{pmatrix} z & z \\ z & a \end{pmatrix},$$

have the properties: $A \neq Z$, $B \neq Z$, $AB = Z$.

Corollary 4.3: The property that R is commutative is inherited by $M(R)$ if and only if R has the property that if a and b are in R, then $ab = z$.

Proof: If there are elements a and b in R such that $ab \neq z$, then if

$$A = \begin{pmatrix} z & z \\ z & a \end{pmatrix} \text{ and } B = \begin{pmatrix} z & z \\ b & z \end{pmatrix}, \text{ we have } AB = \begin{pmatrix} z & z \\ ab & z \end{pmatrix}. \text{ Since } AB \neq Z,$$

but $BA = Z$, we know that $M(R)$ is not commutative.

But if $ab = z$ for every a and b in R, then by (35.3) $AB = Z = BA$ for every A and B in $M(R)$, so $M(R)$ is commutative, albeit in a very special way.

The Corollary 4.3 reminds us to mention that any commutative group G which contains at least two elements can be used to generate a ring R. Take the elements and equivalence relation of G as the elements and equivalence relation of R, let the group operation of G be considered the addition of R, and simply define every product in R to be z (the identity of G). Postulates **R.2** and **R.3** are then satisfied in a trivial way. Such a ring R may be called a *nil-ring* of level 2, since the product of any two elements is zero.

An example of a noncommutative ring of finite order with a two-sided identity is provided by $M(J(m))$ when $m > 1$, for $J(m)$ has the 1-class as its identity; so Corollary 4.1 shows that $M(J(m))$ has a left-identity, and it is easy to check that this is also a right-identity. Since $J(m)$ contains an element e for which $ee \neq z$, we can apply Corollary 4.3 to see that $M(J(m))$ is noncommutative. Finally, since $J(m)$ is of order m, we see that $M(J(m))$ is of order m^4.

For an example of a ring with a left-identity, but no right-identity, consider the subsystem M' of $M(J)$ containing all matrices which have identical rows:

$$A = \begin{pmatrix} a_1 & a_2 \\ a_1 & a_2 \end{pmatrix}, \quad B = \begin{pmatrix} b_1 & b_2 \\ b_1 & b_2 \end{pmatrix}, \dots.$$

It is not hard to check that M' forms a commutative group under matric addition; in fact M' is isomorphic to $J \otimes J$. Matric multiplication is well defined, associative, and left- and right-distributive over addition, so all that remains to show M' is a ring is to check the closure property. But closure is assured for by (35.3) we have

$$AB = \begin{pmatrix} (a_1 + a_2)b_1 & (a_1 + a_2)b_2 \\ (a_1 + a_2)b_1 & (a_1 + a_2)b_2 \end{pmatrix},$$

and we see that AB is in M' since the two rows are identical. We also see that $AB = B$ can be satisfied for every B in M' if and only if $a_1 + a_2 = 1$. Thus M' has a plentiful supply of left-identities.

On the other hand, if we try to satisfy $AB = A$ for every A in M', we are unsuccessful, for the requirements $(a_1 + a_2)b_1 = a_1$, $(a_1 + a_2)b_2 = a_2$, which are imposed by (35.1) can be met when $a_1 = 1$, $a_2 = 0$ only by $b_1 = 1$, $b_2 = 0$; but this pair of values of b_1 and b_2 will not work when $a_1 = 0$, $a_2 = 1$. This shows that M' has no right-identity.

35.3.   Domains and fields

The particular kinds of rings we study next stand in close relation to the theory of numbers.

Definition: A domain D is a commutative ring which has an identity and which has no proper divisors of zero.

Definition: A field F is a commutative ring which has an identity and in which every nonzero element has an inverse.

We appeal to Theorem 2 for an immediate proof that every field is a domain.

We use the example of the ring of integers to prove that not every domain is a field. For although J is commutative and has an identity and has no proper divisors of zero, we also know that the only elements of J which have inverses are the units $+1$ and -1.

Indeed, we think of J as the prototype of all domains; but our motive in studying the abstract domain remains the same as in the study of any mathematical system—we hope the abstract study will throw new light on the concrete example from which we begin. For example, it may reveal that some results, which we might be inclined to take for granted in J, actually require proof, because they are not true in all domains. Such, for example, is the idea of unique factorization.

Before we present other examples of domains and fields, let us note two simple theorems.

Theorem 5:   In a domain D the cancellation law of multiplication is valid: If a, b, c are in D and $a \neq z$, then $ab = ac$ implies $b = c$.

Proof: We use Corollary 1.1, denoted by **C.1.1**, to help justify

$$\underset{\text{R.3}}{a(-c + b)} = \underset{\text{C.1.1}}{a(-c) + ab} = \underset{\text{H,R.1}}{-ac + ab} = \underset{\text{R.1}}{-ac + ac} = z.$$

But $a \neq z$ and D is a domain with no proper divisors of zero, hence $-c + b = z$. But $-c + c = z$ and D is a group under addition, so that the equation $-c + x = z$ has a unique solution; hence $b = c$.

Theorem 6: In a field F if $a \neq z$, the equation $ax = b$ has a unique solution—namely, $x = a^{-1}b$.

Proof: If we review the additional postulates which convert a ring into a field from the standpoint of group theory, we find that the nonzero elements of a field must form a commutative group. For **R.2** already shows that the product has properties **H.1** and **H.4**; and when we postulate the commutative property and the existence of the identity and inverses, we have added properties **H.5**, **H.2**, and **H.3**. Then the conclusion in Theorem 6 is just a restatement of Theorem 2 of **29.3**, applied to the multiplicative group of nonzero elements of F.

We have not yet mentioned examples to show that the postulates for a field are consistent and not-categorical.

Theorem 7: If p is a prime, the ring $J(p)$ of residue classes of integers mod p is a field of order p. The nonzero classes of $J(p)$ form a cyclic group of order $p - 1$.

Proof: Let us recall Theorem 3 and Corollary 3.1 which show that $J(p)$ is a commutative ring of order p with an identity element and with $\phi(p) = p - 1$ classes which have inverses. But there are only $p - 1$ nonzero classes, so $J(p)$ is a field.

When we demonstrated in **G.17.1** of Chapter 19 the existence of a primitive root mod p, we showed the existence of a generator for all the nonzero classes, so these form a cyclic group of order $p - 1$.

If we return to the discussion following **G.3** in **13.3** we can see the addition and multiplication tables for $J(5)$ written out in detail. In the product table we see confirmation of zero's role as an annihilator; and we see that the nonzero elements form a cyclic group of order 4.

At a later stage of development of the theory it is possible to show that in the sense of isomorphism there is no other field of order p, so we may begin speaking of $J(p)$, in honor of its discoverer, as "*the* Galois field of order p."

35.4. Matric domains and fields

If R is a *commutative* ring and if

$$T = \begin{pmatrix} a & c \\ b & d \end{pmatrix}$$

is a matrix in $M(R)$, there is no difficulty in defining $d(T) = ad - bc$ to be the determinant of T and in showing that the analog of **M.7** in **31.1** is valid, so that for matrices T and U in $M(R)$ we have $d(TU) = d(T)d(U)$. Then the analog of **M.5** is as follows:

Theorem 8: If R is a commutative ring with an identity, the necessary and sufficient condition that a matrix T in $M(R)$ has an inverse in $M(R)$ is that $d(T)$ has an inverse in R.

Proof: On the one hand, if we suppose that U exists so that $TU = I$, we have $e = d(I) = d(TU) = d(T)d(U)$, so that $d(U)$ is the inverse of $d(T)$ in R.

Conversely, if $d(T) = t$ has an inverse u in R, so that $tu = e$, then

$$U = \begin{pmatrix} ud & -uc \\ -ub & ua \end{pmatrix}$$

is readily checked by *(35.3)* to be the inverse of T in $M(R)$.

It will make an interesting application of some of our earlier number theory to prove the following theorem.

Theorem 9: If p is an odd prime, if q is not a quadratic residue mod p, and if M' is the set of all matrices of $M(J(p))$ of the form

$$A = \begin{pmatrix} a_1 & a_2 \\ qa_2 & a_1 \end{pmatrix}, \qquad B = \begin{pmatrix} b_1 & b_2 \\ qb_2 & b_1 \end{pmatrix}, \ldots,$$

then M' is a field of order p^2 under matric equality, addition and multiplication.

Proof: Since M' is a subset of $M(J(p))$, matric equality is an equivalence relation for M'; and since A is uniquely determined by choosing a_1 and a_2, it follows that M' is of order p^2. We check directly that

$$A + B = \begin{pmatrix} a_1 + b_1 & a_2 + b_2 \\ q(a_2 + b_2) & a_1 + b_1 \end{pmatrix}, \quad Z = \begin{pmatrix} 0 & 0 \\ q0 & 0 \end{pmatrix}, \quad -A = \begin{pmatrix} -a_1 & -a_2 \\ q(-a_2) & -a_1 \end{pmatrix}$$

are all in M'; we know that matric addition is associative and commutative; so we conclude that M' has property **R.1**. We check that

$$AB = \begin{pmatrix} a_1b_1 + qa_2b_2 & a_1b_2 + a_2b_1 \\ q(a_2b_1 + a_1b_2) & qa_2b_2 + a_1b_1 \end{pmatrix} = BA, \quad I = \begin{pmatrix} 1 & 0 \\ q0 & 1 \end{pmatrix}$$

are all in M'; we know that matric multiplication is associative and distributive over addition; so we conclude not only that M' has properties **R.2** and **R.3**, but also that M' is a commutative ring with an identity.

It remains to show that if A is in M' and if $A \neq Z$, then A^{-1} exists and is in M'. From Theorem 8 the test for the existence of A^{-1} in $M(J(p))$ is that $d(A)$ have an inverse in $J(p)$. Since $J(p)$ is a field, this is equivalent to showing $d(A) \not\equiv 0 \bmod p$.

Consider the possibility $d(A) = a_1{}^2 - qa_2{}^2 \equiv 0 \bmod p$. If $a_2 \not\equiv 0$, we find $q \equiv (a_2{}^{-1}a_1)^2 \bmod p$, contradicting the assumption that q is not a quadratic residue mod p. If $a_2 \equiv 0$, we find $a_1 \equiv 0 \bmod p$, contradicting the assumption that $A \neq Z$. Hence A^{-1} exists in $M(J(p))$; and according to the last part of Theorem 8, if u is the inverse of $d(A)$ in $J(p)$, then

$$A^{-1} = \begin{pmatrix} ua_1 & -ua_2 \\ q(-ua_2) & ua_1 \end{pmatrix};$$

but this is of the correct form to be in M'. This completes the proof of Theorem 9.

It is interesting to investigate the situation comparable to that in Theorem 9 when we replace the field $J(p)$ by the domain J. The result (see **Q.1** of **36.1**) is that we obtain domains, but not fields. The arithmetic of such domains provides some instructive comparisons with the familiar arithmetic in J. To these topics we devote the next chapter.

EXERCISES

35.1. Modify the proof of Corollary 1.1 and show that $-(ab) = (-a)b$ and that $(-a)(-b) = ab$.

35.2. Take R to be the ring $J(2)$ of residue classes of J mod 2. Verify that $M(J(2))$ is a ring of $n = 16$ matrices whose additive group is isomorphic to $G(2) \otimes G(2) \otimes G(2) \otimes G(2)$. Verify that the corresponding ring M' whose matrices have identical rows (analogous to that described in **35.2**) contains just $n' = 4$ matrices, $s' = 2$ of which are left-identities, and $t' = 2$ of which are left-annihilators.

35.3. Repeat EX. **35.2** with m, instead of $m = 2$, obtaining $n = m^4$, $n' = m^2$, $s' = m$, and $t' = m$.

35.4. If $R = J(10)$ apply Theorem 8 to the system $M(J(10))$. Find the inverse of the matrix A and show that B does not have an inverse:

$$A = \begin{pmatrix} 3 & 2 \\ 4 & 5 \end{pmatrix}, \quad B = \begin{pmatrix} 2 & 1 \\ 3 & 4 \end{pmatrix}.$$

35.5. As a corollary to Theorem 8 show that the set of all matrices T in $M(R)$ for which $d(T)$ is a unit of R [that is, $d(T)$ has an inverse in R] forms a group G under matric multiplication.

35.6. If $R = J(2)$, show that the group G in EX. **35.5** is a noncommutative group of order 6.

35.7. Write out the addition and multiplication table for the field of nine matrices, obtained from Theorem 9 when $p = 3$ and $q = 2$.

35.8. Write out the addition and multiplication tables and show that the following matrices from $M(J(2))$ form a field of order 4:

$$Z = \begin{pmatrix} 0 & 0 \\ 0 & 0 \end{pmatrix}, \quad I = \begin{pmatrix} 1 & 0 \\ 0 & 1 \end{pmatrix}, \quad A = \begin{pmatrix} 0 & 1 \\ 1 & 1 \end{pmatrix}, \quad A^2 = \begin{pmatrix} 1 & 1 \\ 1 & 0 \end{pmatrix}.$$

35.9. For a ring R with identity e define a new operation, called *padding*, by $a \oplus b = a + b + e$. Retaining the same equality that holds in R, show that R is a commutative group under the operation of padding. In particular, find the "zero" of padding.

35.10. Continue EX. **35.9.** Define a new operation, called *addiplication*, by $a \odot b = ab + a + b$. Show that addiplication is associative and has an identity e'.

35.11. Continue EXS. **35.9** and **35.10.** Show that addiplication is left- and right-distributive over padding.

35.12. Combine the previous three exercises to show that R is a ring R' under the operations of padding and addiplication. Prove that R is isomorphic to R'. (Hint: An isomorphism must map zero into "zero" and identity into "identity.")

35.13. If $R = J(m)$ show that the group G of unit matrices of $M(J(m))$, obtained in EX. **35.5**, is of order $n = m\phi(m)S(m)$, where $S(m)$ is the multiplicative function defined by $m^2 = \Sigma\, S(d)$, summed over all positive divisors of m. If $m = \Pi\, p_i{}^{a_i}$, then $S(m) = m^2\, \Pi\, (p_i{}^2 - 1)/p_i{}^2$.

When I use a word, it means just
what I choose it to mean—neither more,
nor less.

—H. DUMPTY; L. CARROLL; C. DODGSON

CHAPTER 36

The fundamental theorem reconsidered

36.1. The domain $J\sqrt{q}$

The following theorem is the analog of Theorem 9 when we replace the field $J(p)$ by the domain J.

Q.1: If q is not a perfect square of J and if $J\sqrt{q}$ is the set of all matrices of $M(J)$ of the form

$$A = \begin{pmatrix} a_1 & a_2 \\ qa_2 & a_1 \end{pmatrix}, \qquad B = \begin{pmatrix} b_1 & b_2 \\ qb_2 & b_1 \end{pmatrix}, \ldots,$$

then $J\sqrt{q}$ is a domain, but not a field, under matric equality, addition, and multiplication.

Proof: The proof that $J\sqrt{q}$ is a commutative ring with an identity is word for word like that in Theorem 9 of **35.4**.

We digress for a moment to show that if B is in $J\sqrt{q}$, then $d(B) = 0$ if and only if $B = Z$. For $d(B) = b_1{}^2 - qb_2{}^2 = 0$ requires both $b_1 = 0$ and $b_2 = 0$, because by hypothesis q is not a perfect square of J.

Suppose A and X are in $J\sqrt{q}$ and that $AX = Z$. Then $0 = d(Z) = d(AX) = d(A)d(X)$. If $A \neq Z$, then $d(A) \neq 0$; but J is a domain, so this

276

forces $d(X) = 0$, which implies $X = Z$. Thus A is not a proper divisor of zero; hence $J\sqrt{\bar{q}}$ is a domain.

Furthermore, $J\sqrt{\bar{q}}$ is not a field, for from Theorem 8 we know A has an inverse in $M(J)$ if and only if $d(A)$ is a unit of J. But $d(A) = a_1{}^2 - qa_2{}^2$; so if, say, $a_1 = 0$, $a_2 = 2$, then $d(A) = -4q \neq \pm 1$, so that A does not have an inverse in $M(J)$, certainly not in $J\sqrt{\bar{q}}$.

Q.2: In the domain $J\sqrt{\bar{q}}$ the subsystem K of all matrices of the form $\begin{pmatrix} a & 0 \\ 0 & a \end{pmatrix}$ forms a domain isomorphic to J.

Proof: It is easy to see that the correspondence $\begin{pmatrix} a & 0 \\ 0 & a \end{pmatrix} = aF$ is a one-to-one correspondence between J and K and that it preserves both the operations of addition and multiplication in the respective systems, for

$$(a + b)F = \begin{pmatrix} a + b & 0 \\ 0 & a + b \end{pmatrix} = \begin{pmatrix} a & 0 \\ 0 & a \end{pmatrix} + \begin{pmatrix} b & 0 \\ 0 & b \end{pmatrix} = aF + bF,$$

$$(ab)F = \begin{pmatrix} ab & 0 \\ 0 & ab \end{pmatrix} = \begin{pmatrix} a & 0 \\ 0 & a \end{pmatrix}\begin{pmatrix} b & 0 \\ 0 & b \end{pmatrix} = (aF)(bF).$$

Henceforth, with **Q.2** in mind, we agree to write aI for $\begin{pmatrix} a & 0 \\ 0 & a \end{pmatrix}$, whenever convenient.

Q.3: The domain $J\sqrt{\bar{q}}$ contains a solution of the equation $X^2 = qI$.

Proof: According to the convention introduced above, the equation under consideration and a solution appear as follows:

$$\begin{pmatrix} x_1 & x_2 \\ qx_2 & x_1 \end{pmatrix}^2 = \begin{pmatrix} q & 0 \\ 0 & q \end{pmatrix}, \qquad X = \begin{pmatrix} 0 & 1 \\ q & 0 \end{pmatrix}.$$

The theorems **Q.1**, **Q.2**, and **Q.3** show us that $J\sqrt{\bar{q}}$ is a domain which may be thought of as an *extension* of the domain J; for not only does $J\sqrt{\bar{q}}$ contain a *subsystem* K behaving just *like* J, but also $J\sqrt{\bar{q}}$ contains *other elements* of a different character, for in the domain J the equation $x^2 = q$, corresponding to $X^2 = qI$, has no solution. Now we can see a motive for naming the matrix

$$\begin{pmatrix} 0 & 1 \\ q & 0 \end{pmatrix} = \sqrt{\bar{q}}$$

and using the symbol $J\sqrt{\bar{q}}$ to describe the domain.

The above discussion is not quite complete, for we need to show that if there were an isomorphism F between $J\sqrt{q}$ and J, the equation $X^2 = qI$ *must* correspond to the equation $x^2 = q$. But we know the identities of multiplication must correspond, so $IF = 1$; an isomorphism must preserve addition, hence $(kI)F = k$ for every $k > 0$ in J; and an isomorphism must preserve negatives, hence $(-kI)F = -k$. Thus whether q is positive or negative, we must have $(qI)F = q$. So if there is an isomorphism F, a solution X of $X^2 = qI$ implies $x^2 = (XF)^2 = X^2F = (qI)F = q$. This validates the conclusion that $J\sqrt{q}$ is not isomorphic to J.

If we note that

$$\begin{pmatrix} a_1 & a_2 \\ qa_2 & a_1 \end{pmatrix} = \begin{pmatrix} a_1 & 0 \\ 0 & a_1 \end{pmatrix} + \begin{pmatrix} 0 & a_2 \\ qa_2 & 0 \end{pmatrix} = \begin{pmatrix} a_1 & 0 \\ 0 & a_1 \end{pmatrix} + \begin{pmatrix} a_2 & 0 \\ 0 & a_2 \end{pmatrix}\begin{pmatrix} 0 & 1 \\ q & 0 \end{pmatrix}$$

and abbreviate $(a_2I)\sqrt{q}$ to just $a_2\sqrt{q}$, we see that a suitable notation for an element A of $J\sqrt{q}$ is provided by $A = a_1I + a_2\sqrt{q}$.

If one has already established the properties of the real and complex number systems, so that a number $\sqrt{q}$ is available, this suggests a new way of defining a domain isomorphic to $J\sqrt{q}$. However, as we shall see, the construction of the real and complex number systems involves a rather nonarithmetical study of infinite sets; so there is considerable logical merit in this approach where $\sqrt{q}$ turns out to be a certain matrix whose elements are ordinary integers.

Certainly the notation $A = a_1I + a_2\sqrt{q}$ has considerable mnemonic value, for with its aid the rules for equality, addition, and multiplication within $J\sqrt{q}$ may be abbreviated and readily reconstructed.

Thus if the elements of $J\sqrt{q}$ are written as $A = a_1I + a_2\sqrt{q}$, $B = b_1I + b_2\sqrt{q}, \ldots$, then

(1) $A = B$ if and only if $a_1 = b_1$, $a_2 = b_2$;

(2) $A + B = (a_1 + b_1)I + (a_2 + b_2)\sqrt{q}$;

(3) $AB = (a_1b_1 + a_2b_2q)I + (a_1b_2 + a_2b_1)\sqrt{q}$.

In particular, what was previously found as a matric product may now be found, if so desired, by manipulating these particular matrices in the same fashion as quadratic surds in algebra.

Our discussion above showed that $J\sqrt{q}$ is not isomorphic to J. The following corollary extends this observation.

Q.3.1: If q_1 and q_2 are not squares in J and if q_1 and q_2 are distinct, then $J\sqrt{q_1}$ and $J\sqrt{q_2}$ are not isomorphic.

Proof: The same argument used in comparing $J\sqrt{q}$ and J shows that an isomorphism F between $J\sqrt{q_1}$ and $J\sqrt{q_2}$ must have the property

$(kI)F = kI$ for every k in J. Then since **Q.3** shows that $X^2 = q_1 I$ has a solution in $J\sqrt{q_1}$, it follows, under the isomorphism, that $(XF)^2 = X^2 F = (q_1 I)F = q_1 I$ must have a solution in $J\sqrt{q_2}$.

However, $(x_1 I + x_2\sqrt{q_2})^2 = q_1 I$ requires $x_1^2 + x_2^2 q_2 = q_1$ and $2x_1 x_2 = 0$. These conditions demand $x_2 = 0$ or $x_1 = 0$, but not both.

If $x_2 = 0$, then $q_1 = x_1^2$, a contradiction, since q_1 is not a square.

If $x_1 = 0$, then $q_1 = x_2^2 q_2$. This implies q_1 and q_2 must be of the same sign. Since $q_1 \neq q_2$, we may assume $|q_2| > |q_1|$; so that no suitable integer x_2 can be found.

36.2. Divisibility properties in a domain

With **Q.1** in mind to show that $J\sqrt{q}$ is as much deserving the title domain as is J, we attempt a division of the elements of any domain into classes according to divisibility properties, just as was done for the domain J in **6.1**.

If a, b, c are in a domain and $c = ab$, we call c a *multiple* of b; and b, a *divisor* or *factor* of c. The zero z is exceptional from this point of view, being a multiple of every element, so we put zero in a class by itself.

If there are elements a and b in a domain such that $ab = e$, then a and b will be called *units*. Every domain has at least two units e and $-e$. In **Q.5** we show that some of the domains $J\sqrt{q}$ have infinitely many units.

If an element p in a domain is not a unit and is such that $p = ab$ implies that either a or b must be a unit, then p is called a *prime*. Note that if a domain is a field, there can be no primes, for every nonzero element in a field is a unit. There exists a domain which is not a field in which there are no primes; but in each of the domains $J\sqrt{q}$ we can exhibit some primes.

Any element of a domain that is not zero, not a unit, and not a prime is called *composite*.

Thus on the basis of rather simple divisibility properties the elements of a domain will fall, in general, into four distinct categories.

In discussing the questions of divisibility for the domain $J\sqrt{q}$ we find that the determinant $d(A) = d(a_1 I + a_2\sqrt{q}) = a_1^2 - a_2^2 q$ plays an important role. If we define $\overline{A} = a_1 I - a_2\sqrt{q}$ as the *conjugate* of A, then an alternate definition for $d(A)$ is the following: $A\overline{A} = d(A)I$. From either point of view we see that $d(A)$ is an ordinary integer. Furthermore, the following theorem shows that every factorization of elements in $J\sqrt{q}$ is accompanied by a factorization of ordinary integers in J.

Q.4: If A and B are in $J\sqrt{q}$, then $d(AB) = d(A)d(B)$.

Proof: This is merely a special case of **M.7** which we have used several times previously. An alternate proof for this particular case is provided by observing that

$$\overline{AB} = (a_1b_1 + a_2b_2q)I - (a_1b_2 + a_2b_1)\sqrt{q}$$
$$= (a_1I - a_2\sqrt{q})(b_1I - b_2\sqrt{q}) = \overline{A}\,\overline{B}.$$

Then since multiplication in $J\sqrt{q}$ is associative and commutative we have

$$d(AB)I = AB\overline{AB} = AB\overline{A}\overline{B} = A\overline{A}B\overline{B} = d(A)Id(B)I = d(A)d(B)I;$$

so by *(35.1)* it follows that $d(AB) = d(A)d(B)$.

Q.5:   An element U of $J\sqrt{q}$ is a unit, if and only if $d(U) = \pm 1$.

Proof: This is a special case of Theorem 8: An element A of $M(J)$ has an inverse in $M(J)$ if and only if $d(A)$ has an inverse in J. However, the only units of J are ± 1. So a necessary condition for U of $J\sqrt{q}$ to be a unit is that $d(U) = t = \pm 1$. Conversely, if this condition is satisfied, we can proceed as suggested in Theorem 9 to show that $U^{-1} = t\overline{U}$ is in $J\sqrt{q}$.

Q.5.1:   If $q < -1$, then $J\sqrt{q}$ has two units: $\pm I$. If $q = -1$, then $J\sqrt{q}$ has four units: $\pm I$, $\pm \sqrt{q}$. If $q > 0$, then $J\sqrt{q}$ has infinitely many units.

Proof: If $q < -1$, the only solution of $a_1{}^2 - a_2{}^2 q = \pm 1$ in integers of J is obtained when $a_2 = 0$ and $a_1 = \pm 1$. If $q = -1$, the only solutions of $a_1{}^2 + a_2{}^2 = \pm 1$ are $a_2 = 0$, $a_1 = \pm 1$; and $a_1 = 0$, $a_2 = \pm 1$.

If $q > 0$ and there can be found a unit $U_1 = u_1I + u_2\sqrt{q}$ with $u_1 > 1$, then $u_1{}^2 - u_2{}^2 q = \pm 1$ shows $u_2 \neq 0$. But $\overline{U}_1$ is also a unit, and whichever of U_1 or $\overline{U}_1$ has $u_2 > 0$ will be called U. Then U^k is also a unit, because $d(U^k) = (d(U))^k = (\pm 1)^k = \pm 1$; and U^t is distinct from U^k when $t > k$, because the components of U, $U^2, \ldots, U^k, U^{k+1}, \ldots$ are increasing sequences. This follows by induction if we set $U^k = x_1I + x_2\sqrt{q}$ and $U^{k+1} = y_1I + y_2\sqrt{q}$, so that $y_1I + y_2\sqrt{q} = (x_1I + x_2\sqrt{q})(u_1I + u_2\sqrt{q})$. When $k = 1$, we have $u_1 > 1$ and $u_2 \geqslant 1$. We assume $x_1 > 1$ and $x_2 \geqslant 1$. Then

$$y_1 = x_1u_1 + x_2u_2q > x_1, \quad y_2 = x_1u_2 + x_2u_1 > x_2.$$

So from one unit U of this kind, we find infinitely many.

However, it is not so easy to guarantee the existence of a unit U with $u_1 > 1$. If q is small, we can produce U by trial: for example, if $q = 3$, use $u_1 = 2$, $u_2 = 1$; if $q = 5$, use $u_1 = 2$, $u_2 = 1$; if $q = 7$, use $u_1 = 8$, $u_2 = 3$; if $q = 10$, use $u_1 = 3$, $u_2 = 1$. In general, it is possible to find U with $u_1 > 1$ by using the method of continued fractions to be explained in a subsequent chapter.

Q.5.2:   The domain $J\sqrt{\bar{q}}$ contains primes.

Proof: For a given prime p of J either there does or does not exist an element A in $J\sqrt{\bar{q}}$ such that $d(A) = \pm p$.

Case 1:   If there is no A in $J\sqrt{\bar{q}}$ such that $d(A) = \pm p$, then pI is a prime of $J\sqrt{\bar{q}}$. For $pI = AB$ implies $p^2 = d(A)d(B)$. Then the unique factorization in J implies, since $d(A) \neq \pm p$, $d(B) \neq \pm p$, that one of A or B has determinant ± 1. By **Q.5** it follows that A or B is a unit; hence pI is a prime.

Case 2:   If there exists an A in $J\sqrt{\bar{q}}$ such that $d(A) = \pm p$, then A is a prime of $J\sqrt{\bar{q}}$. For $A = RS$ implies $d(A) = d(R)d(S) = \pm p$. Hence one of R or S has determinant ± 1. By **Q.5** it follows that R or S is a unit of $J\sqrt{\bar{q}}$. Hence A is a prime.

For the elements of a domain let us define a to be an *associate* of b if and only if there exists a unit u such that $a = ub$.

Q.6:   Being an associate is an equivalence relation for a domain.

Proof: By definition the concept of being an associate is determinative. Since e is a unit, $a = ea$ shows that a is an associate of itself, so the concept is reflexive. If u is a unit, there is a companion unit v so that $vu = e$; hence if $a = ub$, then $va = v(ub) = (vu)b = eb = b$; so the concept is symmetric. If u and u_1 are units, so is uu_1, since $(uu_1)^{-1} = u_1^{-1}u^{-1}$; since $a = ub$, $b = u_1c$ imply $a = ub = u(u_1c) = (uu_1)c$, the concept is transitive. This establishes **Q.6**.

From **Q.6** it follows that the elements of a domain are divided exhaustively into mutually exclusive classes of associated elements. Moreover, the division preserves the concepts of the zero, units, primes, and composite elements. The zero is in a class by itself; and all the units fall into one class. If one member of a class is a prime, so are all the others. If one member of a class is composite, so are all of its associates.

These last remarks follow since if c and c' are associates we have $c = uc'$, $c' = vc$ with $vu = e$. Then if $c = ab$, we can derive $c' = a'b'$ where $a' = va$, $b' = b$; or conversely, with $a = ua'$, $b = b'$. Hence if one of a or b must be a unit, so must one of a' or b'; and conversely. Or if neither a nor b is a unit; then neither a' nor b' is a unit.

If we suppose $c = ab$, it is simple to take any unit u and its companion unit v such that $vu = e$, and to write $c = avub = a_1b_1$ where $a_1 = av$ and $b_1 = ub$. We shall not consider two such factorizations, which differ only because factors have been replaced by their associates, as being distinct.

In our first discussion of the fundamental theorem of arithmetic for integers of J, we limited the argument to positive integers. Had we considered all ordinary integers, we would have had to state the theorem in such a way as to allow for the replacement of pairs of primes by their associates, pq by $(-p)(-q)$, or the replacement of p by $(-1)(-p)$. With this in mind, we could restate the fundamental theorem for J as follows: Every integer of J, not zero or a unit, can be factored into a product of primes and a unit, and this factorization is unique except for the order of the prime factors and the replacement of a prime factor by an associate, accompanied by an appropriate change in the unit factor.

We must make these same considerations when we discuss factorization in an arbitrary domain, and in some of the cases where the domain has a great multiplicity of units, and hence of associates, the situation is even more critical. When we compare the primes of one factorization with those of another factorization which is claimed to be distinct, it will be necessary to guarantee that the primes used in one factorization are not associates of the primes used in the other factorization.

With these preliminary remarks in mind the following sections gain in interest.

36.3.   The domain $J\sqrt{3}$ does have unique factorization

The main step in establishing the result used as the title of this section will be to show that $J\sqrt{3}$ has a division algorithm. Every other detail of the proof will follow the pattern in **6.3**, **8.1**, and **8.2** with minor changes to accommodate the fact that $J\sqrt{3}$ has infinitely many units.

Q.7:   If A and B are in $J\sqrt{3}$ and $B \neq Z$, there exist Q and R in $J\sqrt{3}$, such that $A = QB + R$ and $0 \leqslant |d(R)| < |d(B)|$.

Proof: Compute $d(B) = t$ noting that $t \neq 0$ since $B \neq Z$. Consider $\bar{B}A = s_1 I + s_2 \sqrt{3}$, and from the least absolute value division algorithm in J determine q_1, v_1 and q_2, v_2 such that

$$s_1 = q_1 t + v_1, \quad 0 \leqslant 2|v_1| \leqslant |t|; \quad s_2 = q_2 t + v_2, \quad 0 \leqslant 2|v_2| \leqslant |t|.$$

Define $Q = q_1 I + q_2 \sqrt{3}$, $V = v_1 I + v_2 \sqrt{3}$, and $R = A - QB$. From $\bar{B}A = Qt + V$ we find $V = A\bar{B} - Q(tI) = (A - QB)\bar{B} = R\bar{B}$. Then $d(V) = v_1{}^2 - 3v_2{}^2 = d(R)d(B) = d(R)t$, so that

$$4|d(R)|\,|t| = 4|v_1{}^2 - 3v_2{}^2| \leqslant 3|t|^2 < 4|t|^2,$$

which implies $|d(R)| < |t| = |d(B)|$ and completes the proof.

With **Q.7** supplying a division algorithm, it is easy to develop all the details of an Euclidean algorithm and to prove the existence of a greatest common divisor, exactly as in the theorem of **6.3**, although the part about uniqueness has a new twist since $J\sqrt{3}$ has infinitely many units. Next we can prove the analog of the fundamental lemma in **6.1**, exactly as before, except in speaking of the divisors of a prime p we now have an infinite list—namely, all units u and all associates pu.

Q.8:   If N is any element of the domain $J\sqrt{3}$ which is not zero and not a unit, then N can be written

$$N = UP_1{}^{a_1}P_2{}^{a_2} \cdots P_k{}^{a_k},$$

where U is a unit, where k is a positive integer, where each a_i is a positive integer, where each P_i is a prime of $J\sqrt{3}$, where the $P_1, P_2, \ldots, P_k$ have the property that no two are associated, and the representation is unique except for the order in which the primes are given and for the replacement of a prime by any one of its associates and an accompanying replacement of U.

Proof: The proof is similar in spirit to that given in **6.2**.

(A) We show the existence of at least one representation of this form by an induction argument on $|d(N)|$. Since N is not zero or a unit, the argument begins with $|d(N)| = 2$. There are such elements (for example, $I + \sqrt{3}$) and by **Q.5.3** we know they are primes, so that a representation of the desired form is at once available. If we assume that a representation of this form have been found for all elements A for which $2 \leqslant |d(A)| \leqslant n$, we can proceed to the case $|d(N)| = n + 1$. If there is no such N or if N is prime, there is no more to prove. But if such an N is composite, so that $N = AB$ where neither A nor B is a unit, then $d(N) = d(A)d(B)$ where $d(A) \neq \pm 1$ and $d(B) \neq \pm 1$. Hence $2 \leqslant |d(A)| \leqslant n$ and $2 \leqslant |d(B)| \leqslant n$. So by the induction hypothesis, representations for A and B are available. Combining these, by the associative and commutative properties, we obtain a representation of the desired form for $N = AB$.

(B) We assume two representations for the same element, say,

$$UP_1{}^{a_1}P_2{}^{a_2} \cdots P_k{}^{a_k} = VQ_1{}^{b_1}Q_2{}^{b_2} \cdots Q_m{}^{b_m}.$$

By the fundamental lemma which is valid for this domain as has been explained above, the prime P_1 must divide some one of the primes Q in the second factorization, and these can be reordered so that P_1 divides Q_1. But because both are primes, P_1 must be an associate of Q_1, say $U_1P_1 = Q_1$. Assume, say, $a_1 \leqslant b_1$. Then by the cancellation law in the domain (Theorem 5 of **35.3**) we find

$$UU_1{}^{a_1}P_2{}^{a_2} \cdots P_k{}^{a_k} = VQ_1{}^{b_1 - a_1}Q_2{}^{b_2} \cdots Q_m{}^{b_m}.$$

Unless $b_1 = a_1$ we reach a contradiction; for if $b_1 > a_1$, then Q_1 must divide some one of the primes P_j on the left. But none of these primes are associated with P_1 and hence cannot be associated with Q_1. Repeating this argument and supposing, say, $m > k$, we arrive at

$$UU_1{}^{a_1}U_2{}^{a_2} \cdots U_k{}^{a_k} = VQ_{k+1}{}^{a_{k+1}} \cdots Q_m{}^{a_m}.$$

But this is a contradiction since a prime cannot be a divisor of a unit. Hence $m = k$ and $V = UU_1{}^{a_1}U_2{}^{a_2} \cdots U_k{}^{a_k}$. Thus the proof of the uniqueness of the representation—except for order, and associates, and modifying the unit factor—is complete.

36.4.   Some domains which do not have unique factorization

We show two examples of domains which do not have a fundamental theorem for their arithmetic. Superficially, the examples seem alike, but actually they differ considerably in the ways in which they can be modified to restore some semblance of unique factorization.

Q.9:   The domain $J\sqrt{5}$ does not have unique factorization.

Proof: All that is necessary is to produce one counterexample. Consider $4I = (2I)(2I) = (I + \sqrt{5})(-I + \sqrt{5})$. We can show that each of $2I$, $I + \sqrt{5}$, $-I + \sqrt{5}$ is a prime of $J\sqrt{5}$ and that $2I$ is not an associate of $I + \sqrt{5}$ or $-I + \sqrt{5}$. By the standards proposed as a test, this implies that we do not have unique factorization.

Let C be any one of $2I$, $I + \sqrt{5}$, $-I + \sqrt{5}$. If $C = AB$, then $4 = d(C) = d(A)d(B)$. We can show that $d(A) \neq \pm 2$, hence the only possibility of factorization is for $d(A)$ or $d(B)$ to have the value ± 1, hence A or B is a unit, and C is a prime. The missing detail is easy since $d(a_1 I + a_2 \sqrt{5}) = a_1{}^2 - 5a_2{}^2 \equiv a_1{}^2 \not\equiv \pm 2 \bmod 5$, because ± 2 are not quadratic residues mod 5.

Moreover, if $2I = (xI + y\sqrt{5})(\pm I + \sqrt{5})$, then $2 = \pm x + 5y$, $0 = x \pm y$ which requires $2 = 4y$. But this is impossible for an integer y of J. Hence $2I$ is not an associate of either $I + \sqrt{5}$ or $-I + \sqrt{5}$.

Q.10:   The domain $J\sqrt{10}$ does not have unique factorization.

Proof: As a counterexample we use

$$6I = (2I)(3I) = (2I + \sqrt{10})(-2I + \sqrt{10}).$$

As in **Q.9** we note that $d(a_1 I + a_2 \sqrt{10}) = a_1{}^2 - 10a_2{}^2 \equiv a_1{}^2 \bmod 5$; hence $d(A) \ne \pm 2, \pm 3$. Then if C stands for any one of $2I$, $3I$, $2I + \sqrt{10}$, $-2I + \sqrt{10}$, we note that $d(C) = 4, 9, -6, -6$, respectively. In every case, since $d(A) \ne \pm 2, \pm 3$, we find that $C = AB$ and the accompanying $d(C) = d(A)d(B)$ requires that one of A or B is a unit; hence C is a prime. Moreover, no prime of the first factorization is an associate of a prime in the second factorization, inasmuch as associated primes must have determinants with the same absolute value.

Before discussing further the anomalies presented by **Q.9** and **Q.10** it is desirable to discuss some domains other than $J\sqrt{q}$ which are subsystems of $M(J)$.

36.5.   Domains in $M(J)$

For the discussion to follow we will need a lemma which is a special case of the Hamilton-Cayley theorem in the theory of matrices.

Lemma: If A belongs to $M(J)$ and $t(A) = a_{11} + a_{22}$, then

$$A(t(A)I - A) = d(A)I.$$

Proof: The proof is by direct check:

$$\begin{pmatrix} a_{11} & a_{12} \\ a_{21} & a_{22} \end{pmatrix} \begin{pmatrix} a_{22} & -a_{12} \\ -a_{21} & a_{11} \end{pmatrix} = \begin{pmatrix} d(A) & 0 \\ 0 & d(A) \end{pmatrix}.$$

We call $t(A)$ the *trace* of A.

Let us consider the problem of finding every possible domain D, in the sense of isomorphism, which is a subsystem of the ring of matrices $M(J)$.

First, let us suppose that every element A in D has $d(A) = 0$. If there is such a domain, its identity E cannot be the familiar I. The conditions $EE = E$ and $d(E) = 0$ may be combined with the lemma to show $(t(E) - 1)E = Z$. We cannot have $E = Z$, for the domain D must contain at least one nonzero element; hence we must have $t(E) = 1$. Then since D is an additive group, we see that D must contain kE for every k in J. On the other hand, suppose A is in D. Then the conditions $EA = A = AE$, combined with $d(E) = 0$, require $A = kE$ (see EX. **36.7**). Consequently, D must be exactly the set of all matrices of the form kE. It is easy to check that this set is a domain isomorphic to J.

Second, let us suppose that D contains some matrix A with $d(A) \ne 0$. Then the identity E of D must satisfy $EA = A$, so $d(E)d(A) = d(A)$; but

$d(A) \neq 0$ implies $d(E) = 1$. Comparing the domain requirement $EE = E$ and $d(E) = 1$ with the lemma, we find $I = E(t(E) - 1)$. Using determinants we find $1 = (t(E) - 1)^2$ so $t(E) = 0$ or $t(E) = 2$. In the first case we would have $E = -I$, but this will not satisfy $EE = E$. In the second case we find $E = I$, as probably anticipated.

Thus we assume D contains I; and as a consequence of being an additive group, D must contain kI for every k in J. The simplest possibility is that D contains only the matrices kI and so is isomorphic, once more, to J.

Next suppose D contains some matrices not of the form kI, say, P. Then D must contain $Q = P - p_{11}I$. Suppose, tentatively, that $p_{12} = 0$. Then

$$Q = \begin{pmatrix} 0 & 0 \\ p_{21} & p_{22} - p_{11} \end{pmatrix}$$

and the lemma shows $Q(t(Q)I - Q) = Z$. Certainly, $Q \neq Z$, for if $Q = Z$, then $P = p_{11}I$, a contradiction. Also $t(Q)I - Q$ is in D and $t(Q)I - Q \neq Z$, for if $t(Q)I - Q = Z$, then $P = p_{22}I$, a contradiction. But these results show that Q is a proper divisor of zero, but this is not permissible in a domain. Therefore, we must have $p_{12} \neq 0$.

Of all the elements P, and $-P$, which are in D and not of the form kI, all having $p_{12} \neq 0$, or $-p_{12} \neq 0$, there must be at least one, say, B, with a least positive value for b_{12}. (This is an application of **L.3** in **2.4**.)

Suppose $p_{12} = qb_{12} + r_{12}$, $0 \leqslant r_{12} < b_{12}$, then $R = P - qB$ is in D. If $r_{12} \neq 0$, then R is in D, but not of the form kI, which contradicts the choice of B, since $r_{12} < b_{12}$. Therefore, $r_{12} = 0$, and R, being in D, must have the form kI. Hence P has the form $P = kI + qB$, $q \neq 0$.

In other words, any domain D which is a subsystem of $M(J)$ and not made up exclusively of matrices of the form kI is a collection of all matrices of the form $kI + qB$ where B is a fixed matrix with $b_{12} \neq 0$. However, not every B of this type leads to a domain D.

From the lemma we have $B^2 - t(B)B + d(B)I = Z$ and hence

(36.1) $\qquad (2B - t(B)I)^2 = (t^2(B) - 4d(B))I = \Delta(B)I,$

where for brevity we have introduced $\Delta(B) = t^2(B) - 4d(B)$. We call $\Delta(B)$ the *discriminant* of B. If $\Delta(B) = m^2$ in J, then since D is a domain, we would have $2B - t(B)I = \pm mI$. But B has $b_{12} \neq 0$ and cannot satisfy this equation. Hence if D is to be a domain, we must add the condition that $\Delta(B)$ is not a perfect square in J.

Conversely, if $\Delta(B)$ is not a perfect square in J and $b_{12} \neq 0$, then the set $J(B)$ of all matrices of $M(J)$ of the form $A = a_1I + a_2B$ is a domain. The proof is as follows:

Since $b_{12} \neq 0$, it is easy to check that $J(B)$ forms a commutative group under addition isomorphic to $J \otimes J$. From the lemma we have $B^2 = t(B)B - d(B)I$, so $J(B)$ has the product rule:

$$(a_1 I + a_2 B)(b_1 I + b_2 B)$$
$$= (a_1 b_1 - a_2 b_2 d(B))I + (a_1 b_2 + a_2 b_1 + a_2 b_2 t(B))B.$$

Thus multiplication in $J(B)$ is closed, well defined, associative, and commutative and has the identity I. All that remains is to show that $J(B)$ has no proper divisors of zero.

Assume $A = a_1 I + a_2 B$ has $d(A) = 0$. Then we find

$$(a_1 + a_2 b_{11})(a_1 + a_2 b_{22}) - (a_2 b_{21})(a_2 b_{12}) = a_1{}^2 + t(B)a_1 a_2 + d(B)a_2{}^2 = 0;$$

but this implies

$$(2a_1 + t(B)a_2)^2 = a_2{}^2 \, \Delta(B).$$

Unless $a_1 = 0$ and $a_2 = 0$, this contradicts the hypothesis that $\Delta(B)$ is not a perfect square in J. Hence if A is in $J(B)$, then $d(A) = 0$ if and only if $A = Z$. Consequently if A and X are in $J(B)$ and $AX = Z$, then $d(A)d(X) = 0$; so if $A \neq Z$, then $d(A) \neq 0$; which forces $d(X) = 0$ which implies $X = Z$. Therefore, $J(B)$ has no proper divisors of zero.

Finally, we want to determine just how the particular domains $J\sqrt{q}$ fit into this description of all possible domains $J(B)$.

Recall that $\Delta(B) = t^2(B) - 4d(B)$ is not a square in J.

Case 1: Suppose $t(B) = 2s$; then $\Delta(B) = 4q$ where q is not a square in J. From (36.1) we have

$$(2B - 2sI)^2 = 4qI = (2\sqrt{q})^2$$

where $\sqrt{q}$ is the matrix used in defining $J\sqrt{q}$. If we assume $b_{12} > 0$, then we have $B = sI + \sqrt{q}$, and a simple mapping F is available to show that $J(B)$ is isomorphic to $J\sqrt{q}$—namely,

$$(a_1 I + a_2 B)F = (a_1 + sa_2)I + a_2\sqrt{q}.$$

Case 2: Suppose $t(B) = 2s + 1$, then $\Delta(B) = 4u + 1 = q$ is not a square in J. We note that this case arises only when $q \equiv 1 \bmod 4$. From (36.1) we have

$$(2B - (2s + 1)I)^2 = (4u + 1)I = \begin{pmatrix} -1 & 2u \\ 2u & 1 \end{pmatrix}^2 ;$$

then $B = sI + H$ where $H = \begin{pmatrix} 0 & u \\ u & 1 \end{pmatrix}$, and it is a simplifying gesture to notice that $J(B)$ is isomorphic to $J(H)$.

We can see that $(2H - I)^2 = qI$ so that this domain $J(H)$ contains a proper subdomain $J(2H)$ which is isomorphic to $J\sqrt{q}$ under the mapping

$$(a_1I + a_22H)F = (a_1 + a_2)I + a_2\sqrt{q}.$$

That $J(2H)$ is contained properly in $J(H)$ is shown by the fact that $2X = I + \sqrt{q}$ is not solvable in $J\sqrt{q}$, but the equation in $J(H)$ which would correspond to this under an isomorphism is solved by H.

Hence when $q \not\equiv 1 \bmod 4$, $J\sqrt{q}$ is a maximal domain, but when $q \equiv 1 \bmod 4$, $J\sqrt{q}$ can be imbedded in a larger domain $J(H)$.

We summarize the work of this section as follows:

Q.11: In the sense of isomorphism, the domains J, $J\sqrt{q}$, and $J(H)$ constitute all the possible domains which are subsystems of the ring $M(J)$.

36.6. Methods of restoring unique factorization

If we examine $J\sqrt{5}$ in the light of **36.5** we find $5 \equiv 1 \bmod 4$, so we may imbed $J\sqrt{5}$ in the domain $J(H)$ where $H = \begin{pmatrix} 0 & 1 \\ 1 & 1 \end{pmatrix}$. Then it is not too hard to prove the analog of **Q.7** and go on to prove that $J(H)$ has unique factorization. The negative example in **Q.9** is no longer valid, for $2I$ and $I + \sqrt{5}$, which were not associates in $J\sqrt{5}$, have images in $J(H)$ which are associates. The presence of more units in the latter case turns the trick; in fact H itself is a unit, since $d(H) = -1$. Then $(I + \sqrt{5})F^{-1} = 2H = (2I)H$ is an associate of $(2I)F^{-1} = 2I$.

The classical study of algebraic integers limits itself in the quadratic case to a study of $J\sqrt{q}$ when $q \not\equiv 1 \bmod 4$; and the study of $J(H)$ when $q \equiv 1 \bmod 4$. We shall explain one reason for this limitation: the domains $J\sqrt{q}$ when $q \equiv 1 \bmod 4$ provide perfectly good examples of nonunique factorization; but the remedy, called the *theory of ideals*, which is known to be effective in all the classical domains, is simply not effective here. Despite the beauty of the theory of ideals one gains a false impression of its power if one considers only domains where it is effective.

When we consider the result in **Q.10** for $J\sqrt{10}$ where $q \not\equiv 1 \bmod 4$, we are faced with one of the classical cases of nonunique factorization. In such a domain the ordinary definition of greatest common divisor in **6.2** is simply nonsense. Thus the only common divisors of $A = 6I$ and $B = 4I + 2\sqrt{10}$ are $2I$, $2I + \sqrt{10}$, and I, and all their multitudinous associates; but no one of these is divisible by all the others!

However, remember that in **7.4** the notion of greatest common divisor (a, b) was approached in a different way by considering the *set* of all integers of the form $xa + yb$ where x and y run over J. Perhaps it will not be too surprising to learn that in classical domains, where unique factorization of elements may be lacking, a substitute definition of greatest common divisor is simply to consider certain *sets*, called *ideals*. Thus (a) means the set $\{xa\}$ and (a, b) means the set $\{xa + yb\}$ where x and y run over the whole domain; there are similar definitions for (a, b, c) and (a, b, c, d). Ideal equality is defined as *set identity*; and ideal multiplication is defined by $(a, b)(c, d) = (ac, ad, bc, bd)$. By this rather remarkable scheme unique factorization is restored.

Thus for the example used in **Q.10** it turns out in terms of ideals that

$$(6I) = (2I, \sqrt{10})(2I, \sqrt{10})(3I, I + \sqrt{10})(3I, 2I + \sqrt{10}).$$

One method of associating these ideal factors yields

$$(2I) = (2I, \sqrt{10})(2I, \sqrt{10}), \quad (3I) = (3I, I + \sqrt{10})(3I, 2I + \sqrt{10});$$

but another way of associating them yields

$$(2I + \sqrt{10}) = (2I, \sqrt{10})(3I, 2I + \sqrt{10}),$$
$$(-2I + \sqrt{10}) = (2I, \sqrt{10})(3I, I + \sqrt{10}).$$

This application of the theory of ideals is classical but too long for inclusion here. The interested student should pursue the matter under the topical heading "algebraic integers."

EXERCISES

36.1. As in the discussion of **Q.5.1**, by trial produce units $u_1 I + u_2\sqrt{q}$ with $u_1 > 1$ for the domains determined by $q = 2, 6, 8, 11$.

36.2. Illustrate **Q.5.2** when $q = 7$ by showing that pI is a prime when $p = 5$, 11, 13, 17 (Hint: EX. **22.7**): and that pI is not a prime when $p = 2, 3$, 7, 19.

36.3. Establish the analogue of **Q.7** for $q = 2, q = -1, q = -2$.

36.4. Modify the proof of **Q.7** and establish the analogue of **Q.7** for $q = 7$. (Hint: If $x = v_1/t$, $y = v_2/t$, consider $-1 < x^2 - 7y^2 < 1$ as in analytic geometry; for $|x| \leqslant 1/2$, $|y| \leqslant 1/2$ if $-1 < x^2 - 7y^2$, make no change in the proof; but if $x^2 - 7y^2 \leqslant -1$, replace x by $x \pm 1$ as $x \gtrless 0$ and replace q_1 by $q_1 \mp 1$.)

36.5. Try the hint given in EX. **36.4** for the case $q = 5$, and note that the only failure is for $x = 1/2$, $y = 1/2$.

36.6. Show that $2I$, $3I$, and $I + \sqrt{-5}$ are primes in $J\sqrt{-5}$, and not associates. Show that $J\sqrt{-5}$ does not have unique factorization.

36.7. For matrices in $M(J)$ show that the conditions $t(E) = 1$, $d(E) = 0$, $AE = A = EA$ imply $A = kE$. In fact, $k = t(A)$.

36.8. Show that the system H of all integers $x \equiv 1 \mod 3$ is a group under multiplication. Show that H does not have unique factorization into "primes" by considering $1870 = 10 \cdot 187 = 22 \cdot 85 = 34 \cdot 55$. Show how to construct other counterexamples.

36.9. The reduced residue classes mod m form a group G under multiplication. Let H be a *proper* subgroup of G. Show that H determines a subsystem of J which does not have unique factorization into "primes." [Hint: Let u_1 and u_2 be distinct elements in the u-coset of G/H where u is not in H; let v_1 and v_2 be distinct elements in the v-coset, where $uv \equiv 1 \mod m$; consider $(u_1 v_1)(u_2 v_2) = (u_1 v_2)(u_2 v_1)$.]

36.10. If R is a ring, define a new operation $a \circ b$, called "doubling," by $a \circ b = ab + ab$. (a) Show that doubling is associative and distributive over addition, so that the system U consisting of the elements of R under the equality and addition of R, and the operation of doubling, is a ring. (b) If R has an identity e, show that U has an identity if and only if $2e$ is a unit of R. (c) Show that U is isomorphic to the ring of matrices of $M(R)$ of the form $\begin{pmatrix} a & a \\ a & a \end{pmatrix}$. (B. Jacobson.)

36.11. If a ring does not have an identity, define an element p to be a prime if and only if p cannot be written in the form $p = ab$. Referring to EX. **36.10**, take $R = J$ so that U does not have an identity. (a) Prove that a is prime in U if and only if a is odd. (b) Prove that U does not have unique factorization into primes. (Consider $18 = 1 \circ 9 = 3 \circ 3$.)

CHAPTER 37

Quotient fields

37.1. The quotient field of a domain

In Chapter 35 the fields exhibited in Theorems 7 and 9 are all of finite
order. The present discussion will produce some fields of infinite order.

We start from a given domain D and construct a new system $Q(D)$,
defining each new symbol, relation, and operation in terms of previously
known symbols, relations, and operations. We shall use the term
"quotient" or "quotient number" for our new elements, instead of the
overworked word "fraction," but as a symbol we shall use the familiar a/b.

Definitions: A "quotient" of $Q(D)$, indicated a/b, is an ordered pair
of elements a and b of the domain D, with $b \neq z$; the first element a is
called the *numerator*; the second element b, the *denominator*.

Equality in $Q(D)$ is defined by

(37.1) $\qquad\qquad a/b = c/d$ if and only if $ad = bc$ in D.

Addition in $Q(D)$ is defined by

(37.2) $\qquad\qquad a/b + c/d = (ad + bc)/bd.$

Multiplication in $Q(D)$ is defined by

(37.3) $\qquad\qquad\qquad (a/b)(c/d) = ac/bd.$

291

Note again how each definition uses only concepts and operations available in D. This is brought out frequently in the proofs which follow.

U.1: If D is a domain the system $Q(D)$ of all quotient numbers a/b with $b \neq z$, under the equality (37.1), addition (37.2), and multiplication (37.3), is a field, called the *quotient field* of D.

Proof: (A) The equality (37.1) is an equivalence relation for $Q(D)$.

Since the components of the quotients are elements of D for which the rules of multiplication and equality are known, the relation defined by (37.1) is determinative. The relation (37.1) is reflexive, for from the commutative property in D we have $ab = ba$, which by (37.1) implies $a/b = a/b$. The relation (37.1) is symmetric, for $a/b = c/d$ implies $ad = bc$; but because of the commutative multiplication in D and the symmetric property of the equality in D this implies $cb = da$; hence by (37.1) we have $c/d = a/b$. The relation (37.1) is transitive, for if $a/b = c/d$ and $c/d = g/f$, then by (37.1) we have $ad = bc$ and $cd = dg$; employing the well-defined and associative multiplication in D, we have $(ad)f = (bc)f = b(cf) = b(dg)$. By definition the quotient c/d has $d \neq z$; hence we may use the commutative and cancellation properties of D to conclude that $af = bg$; but by (37.1) this implies $a/b = g/f$.

(B) Under the addition (37.2) the system $Q(D)$ is a commutative group.

Since D is closed under both addition and multiplication, the combinations $ad + bc$ and bd are in D; since D has no proper divisors of zero, if $b \neq z$ and $d \neq z$, then $bd \neq z$; hence the operation defined in (37.2) is closed.

If $a/b = a'/b'$ and $c/d = c'/d'$, we have $ab' = ba'$ and $cd' = dc'$ in D. Then operating in D we have

$$(ad + bc)b'd' = (ab')dd' + bb'(cd') = (ba')dd' + bb'(dc')$$
$$= bd(a'd' + b'c').$$

By (37.1) this implies $(ad + bc)/bd = (a'd' + b'c')/b'd'$. Then by (37.2) and the transitive property of the equality (37.1) we find $a/b + c/d = a'/b' + c'/d'$ which shows that (37.2) is a well-defined operation.

If z and e are the zero and identity of D, we find that the quotient z/e is a suitable zero for the operation (37.2), since using well-known properties of z and e in D we have

$$z/e + a/b = (zb + ea)/eb = (z + a)/b = a/b.$$

As a negative for a/b we may use $(-a)/b$, for

$$(-a)/b + a/b = ((-a)b + ba)/bb = (-(ab) + ab)/bb = z/bb = z/e,$$

where the last step is justified by using (37.1).

To show that (37.2) is associative, we note that in D

$$\{(ad + bc)f + (bd)g\}b(df) = (bd)f\{a(df) + b(cf + dg)\}.$$

Using (37.1) and (37.2) we conclude first that

$$(ad + bc)/bd + g/f = a/b + (cf + dg)/df;$$

then having already proved that (37.2) is well defined, we use (37.2) again to see that $(a/b + c/d) + g/f = a/b + (c/d + g/f)$.

Finally, we check that the addition (37.2) is commutative; for from properties of D we have $(ad + bc)db = bd(cb + da)$, hence by (37.1) we have $(ad + bc)/bd = (cb + da)/db$, which by (37.2) implies

$$a/b + c/d = c/d + a/b.$$

(C) The operation (37.3) is closed, well defined, associative, commutative, and has an identity in $Q(D)$.

Since D is closed under multiplication, both ac and bd are in D; since D has no proper divisors of zero, $b \neq z$ and $d \neq z$ imply $bd \neq z$; hence the operation (37.3) is closed. If $a/b = a'/b'$ and $c/d = c'/d'$, so that $ab' = ba'$ and $cd' = dc'$, then in D we have

$$(ac)(b'd') = (ab')(cd') = (ba')(dc') = (bd)(a'c').$$

By (37.1) this implies $ac/bd = a'c'/b'd'$; then by (37.3) and the transitive property of (37.1) we have $(a/b)(c/d) = (a'/b')(c'/d')$, so the operation (37.3) is well defined.

To show that (37.3) is associative we note that in D $\{(ac)g\}\{b(df)\} = \{(bd)f\}\{a(cg)\}$. Using (37.1) and (37.3) we conclude first that $(ac/bd)(g/f) = (a/b)(cg/df)$; then having already proved that (37.3) is well defined, we apply (37.3) again to see that $\{(a/b)(c/d)\}(g/f) = (a/b)\{(c/d)(g/f)\}$.

We check that (37.3) is commutative; for from properties of D we know $(ac)(db) = (bd)(ca)$; hence by (37.1) we have $ac/bd = ca/db$, which by (37.3) implies $(a/b)(c/d) = (c/d)(a/b)$.

The quotient e/e makes a suitable identity for $Q(D)$ since

$$(e/e)(a/b) = ea/eb = a/b.$$

(D) The product (37.3) is distributive with respect to the addition (37.2). For in terms of elements of D we have

$$(ad + bc)g(bf)(df) = (bd)f\{ag(df) + (bf)cg\}.$$

Then using (37.1) we have $(ad + bc)g/(bd)f = \{ag(df) + (bf)cg\}/(bf)(df)$. Using (37.2) and (37.3) we find first that

$$\{(ad + bc)/bd\}(g/f) = (ag/bf) + (cg/df);$$

then using the well-defined properties of (37.2) and (37.3), we see that

$$(a/b + c/d)(g/f) = (a/b)(g/f) + (c/d)(g/f)$$

which is the required distributive property.

(E) The nonzero elements of $Q(D)$ form a commutative group under the operation (37.3).

Before discussing this result we must check that $x/y = z/e$ according to (37.1) if and only if $xe = yz$, hence if and only if $x = z$. Thus a quotient a/b of $Q(D)$ is a nonzero quotient if and only if $a \neq z$.

To prove (E) we note first that the nonzero quotients of $Q(D)$ are closed under (37.3) since $a \neq z$ and $c \neq z$ imply $ac \neq z$. We check that the identity e/e is nonzero. We find that each nonzero quotient a/b has a companion quotient b/a which exists in $Q(D)$ because $a \neq z$ and which is nonzero because $b \neq z$; and this companion is an inverse for a/b since by (37.3) and (37.1) we have $(a/b)(b/a) = ab/ba = e/e$. That the product (37.3) is associative and commutative for the nonzero elements of $Q(D)$ follows from the work in (C).

This completes the proof of **U.1.**

U.1.1: The quotient field $Q(D)$ contains a subsystem K, made up of all quotients of the form k/e, which is isomorphic to D.

Proof: The correspondence $(k/e)T = k$, which is clearly onto D, is an isomorphism between K and D. Certainly T is one-to-one since $k/e = m/e$ if and only if $k = ke = em = m$; and T is operation-preserving for

$$(k/e + m/e)T = ((ke + em)/ee)T = ((k + m)/e)T$$
$$= k + m = (k/e)T + (m/e)T$$

and

$$((k/e)(m/e))T = (km/ee)T = (km/e)T = km = (k/e)T(m/e)T.$$

U.1.2: For a field F, the quotient field $Q(F)$ is isomorphic to F.

Proof: If $b \neq z$, then b^{-1} exists in F. The correspondence T defined by $(a/b)T = ab^{-1}$ is an isomorphism between $Q(F)$ and F. The mapping T is onto F, since $(c/e)T = ce^{-1} = c$ for every c in F; T is one-to-one because in $Q(F)$ we have $a/b = c/d$ if and only if $ad = bc$ in F, which is equivalent to $ab^{-1} = cd^{-1}$; and T is operation-preserving because $(bd)^{-1} = b^{-1}d^{-1}$ so that

$$(a/b + c/d)T = ((ad + bc)/bd)T$$
$$= (ad + bc)b^{-1}d^{-1} = ab^{-1} + cd^{-1} = (a/b)T + (c/d)T,$$

$$((a/b)(c/d))T = (ac/bd)T = acb^{-1}d^{-1} = ab^{-1}cd^{-1} = (a/b)T(c/d)T.$$

With **U.1** and **U.1.1** in mind we have a motive for calling the quotient field $Q(D)$ an extension of D; but we realize from **U.1.2** that $Q(D)$ is a proper extension of D, i.e., $Q(D)$ is not isomorphic to D only when the domain D is not a field.

37.2.   The rational field

The particular quotient field $Q(J)$ is called the *rational field*. We shall use for it the special notation Ra, and we shall call its elements *rational numbers* or *ordinary fractions*. The use of the adjective "rational" is based on the meaning "quotient" or "ratio" and has no intentional relation to the meaning "sensible."

From **U.1.1** we know that the rational field Ra contains a subset K, made up of all rational numbers of the form $a/1$, which is isomorphic to the domain J of all integers. It is natural to combine terminologies and henceforth to think of each integer a interchangeably with its isomorphic image $a/1$ as a *rational integer* and to describe the entire collection J or K as the *rational domain*. Sometimes we will use for J or K the notation $[Ra]$.

It is worth reconsidering the equivalence relation (37.1) for the particular case of Ra, since the investigation of the equivalence classes involves a small piece of number theory. Since the rational number a/b has $b \neq 0$, we note that $d = (a, b)$ is defined and that $a = Ad, b = Bd$ with $(A, B) = 1$ and $B \neq 0$. We may even agree to choose d to agree in sign with b and have $B > 0$.

By (37.1) it follows that $a/b = Ad/Bd = A/B$ since $(Ad)B = (Bd)A$. Thus any given rational number is equal to one with a positive denominator in which numerator and denominator are relatively prime. On the other hand if $x/y = A/B$ where $(A, B) = 1$, then by (37.1) we have $xB = yA$. But by Theorem 2 of **6.4** this implies $x = kA, y = kB$ where k is an integer. Conversely, for any integer $k \neq 0$, we find kA/kB is defined and $kA/kB = A/B$.

In summary, all rational numbers are divided by (37.1) into classes of equal numbers, such that in each class there is one and only one rational number A/B with $(A, B) = 1$ and $B > 0$; all numbers of the form kA/kB with $k \neq 0$ belong to the class, and every number in the class is of this form. We say that A/B with $(A, B) = 1$ and $B > 0$ is a *canonical*, or *reduced*, rational number; or that such a rational number is in *lowest terms*.

For example, $-30/12$, $15/-6$, $-10/4$ are all in the same class whose canonical representative is $-5/2$; and every number in this class is represented by $-5k/2k$ with k an integer and $k \neq 0$.

37.3.   The matric ring $M(Ra)$

If the integer q is not a perfect square in the domain J, then the corresponding rational integer $q/1$ is not a perfect square in the field Ra. For by (37.1) the equation $(x/y)^2 = q/1$ in Ra requires $x^2 = qy^2$ in J. Since $y \neq 0$ we require $x \neq 0$. If q is negative, there is obviously no solution. If q is positive, we may consider the standard form of each side of the equation. On the left every exponent is even; on the right, since q is not a perfect square, $q > 1$, so that at least one exponent is odd; this contradiction shows that no solution can be found.

Suppose that $q/1$ is not a perfect square in Ra. Within the matric ring $M(Ra)$ consider the subsystem $Ra\sqrt{q}$ made up of all matrices of the form

$$\begin{pmatrix} x_1/y_1 & x_2/y_2 \\ x_2q/y_2 & x_1/y_1 \end{pmatrix}.$$

Exactly as in **Q.1** of **36.1** we can show that $Ra\sqrt{q}$ is a domain, containing a solution $\begin{pmatrix} 0 & 1 \\ q & 0 \end{pmatrix}$ of the matric equation $X^2 = qI$, and, as before, we designate this matrix as $\sqrt{q}$. Then the matrices in $Ra\sqrt{q}$ may be written $A = (x_1/y_1)I + (x_2/y_2)\sqrt{q}$ and we may proceed to show that $Ra\sqrt{q}$ is a field. For if $A \neq Z$, not both x_1 and x_2 are zero; hence $d(A) = (x_1^2y_2^2 - x_2^2y_1^2q)/y_1^2y_2^2 \neq 0$; so the matrix $(x_1/y_1d(A))I - (x_2/y_2d(A))\sqrt{q}$ is in $Ra\sqrt{q}$ and serves as A^{-1}.

An alternate way of realizing the structure of $Ra\sqrt{q}$ is provided by the following theorem.

U.2: If q is not a square in J, then the quotient field $Q(J\sqrt{q})$ is isomorphic to $Ra\sqrt{q}$.

Proof: The elements of $Q(J\sqrt{q})$ are of the form A/B where $A = a_1I + a_2\sqrt{q}$, $B = b_1I + b_2\sqrt{q} \neq Z$. Using $\bar{B} = b_1I - b_2\sqrt{q} \neq Z$, we find from (37.1) that $A/B = A\bar{B}/B\bar{B} = A\bar{B}/d(B)I$. This suggests that the correspondence

$$(A/B)T = A\bar{B}/d(B) = \left(\frac{a_1b_1 - a_2b_2q}{d(B)}\right)I + \left(\frac{a_2b_1 - a_1b_2}{d(B)}\right)\sqrt{q}$$

may be an isomorphism between $Q(J\sqrt{q})$ and $Ra\sqrt{q}$.

The mapping T is onto $Ra\sqrt{q}$ since

$$\{(x_1y_2I + x_2y_1\sqrt{q})/y_1y_2I\}T = (x_1/y_1)I + (x_2/y_2)\sqrt{q}.$$

The mapping T is one-to-one since $A/B = C/D$ in $Q(J\sqrt{q})$ if and only if $AD = BC$ in $J\sqrt{q}$, which implies $A\bar{B}D\bar{D} = B\bar{B}C\bar{D}$ or $A\bar{B}d(D) = C\bar{D}d(B)$ which holds if and only if $A\bar{B}/d(B) = C\bar{D}/d(D)$ in $Ra\sqrt{q}$.

The mapping T preserves sums since

$$(A/B + C/D)T = ((AD + BC)/BD)T = (AD + BC)\overline{BD}/d(BD)$$
$$= (AD + BC)\bar{B}\bar{D}/d(B)d(D)$$
$$= (A\bar{B}d(D) + C\bar{D}d(B))/d(B)d(D)$$
$$= (A\bar{B}/d(B)) + (C\bar{D}/d(D)) = (A/B)T + (C/D)T;$$

and T preserves products since

$$((A/B)(C/D))T = (AC/BD)T = AC\overline{BD}/d(BD) = AC\bar{B}\bar{D}/d(B)d(D)$$
$$= (A\bar{B}/d(B))(C\bar{D}/d(D)) = (A/B)T(C/D)T.$$

It may be helpful to diagram the alternate constructions of these isomorphic fields.

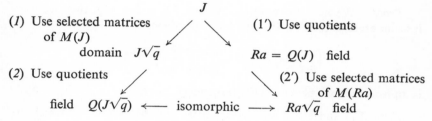

(1) Use selected matrices
   of $M(J)$
      domain $J\sqrt{q}$

(1') Use quotients

$Ra = Q(J)$ field

(2) Use quotients

(2') Use selected matrices
   of $M(Ra)$

field $Q(J\sqrt{q})$ $\longleftarrow$ isomorphic $\longrightarrow$ $Ra\sqrt{q}$ field

U.2.1:   The field $Ra\sqrt{q}$ contains a domain isomorphic to $J\sqrt{q}$.

Proof: This is a corollary of **U.2** and **U.1.1**. The precise form of the mapping is given by $(a_1I + a_2\sqrt{q})T = (a_1/1)I + (a_2/1)\sqrt{q}$ which is an isomorphism between $J\sqrt{q}$ and a subsystem of $Ra\sqrt{q}$, made up of all matrices $x_1I + x_2\sqrt{q}$ where x_1 and x_2 are rational integers.

U.2.2:   If $q \equiv 1 \bmod 4$, then $Ra\sqrt{q}$ contains a domain isomorphic to $J(H)$.

Proof: The correspondence $(a_1I + a_2H)T = ((2a_1 + a_2)/2)I + (a_2/2)\sqrt{q}$ maps $J(H)$ isomorphically onto a subsystem K of $Ra\sqrt{q}$ made up of all matrices $x_1I + x_2\sqrt{q}$ where either x_1 and x_2 are both rational integers, or both are halves of odd rational integers. We leave the details as an exercise.

We showed that $J\sqrt{q_1}$ and $J\sqrt{q_2}$ are not isomorphic when $q_1 \neq q_2$; when $q \equiv 1 \bmod 4$, the domain $J(H)$ is not isomorphic to $J\sqrt{q}$; and the various $J(H)$ are not isomorphic to each other when $q_1 \neq q_2$. But this situation is not preserved when we consider the corresponding quotient fields.

U.3: If $q_2 = m^2 q_1$, where q_1 is not a square in J and $m \neq 0$, then $Q(J\sqrt{q_2})$ is isomorphic to $Q(J\sqrt{q_1})$.

Proof: Because of **U.2** it will suffice to compare $Ra\sqrt{q_2}$ and $Ra\sqrt{q_1}$. We leave it as an exercise to show that the correspondence

$$((x_1/y_1)I + (x_2/y_2)\sqrt{q_2})T = (x_1/y_1)I + (mx_2/y_2)\sqrt{q_1}$$

is an isomorphism between $Ra\sqrt{q_2}$ and $Ra\sqrt{q_1}$.

U.3.1: If q is not a square in J and $q \equiv 1 \bmod 4$, then $Q(J(H))$ is isomorphic to $Q(J\sqrt{q})$.

Proof: We need to recall the relation $2H = I + \sqrt{q}$; then we leave it as an exercise to show that the correspondence

$$\left(\frac{a_1 I + a_2 H}{b_1 I + b_2 H}\right) T = \frac{(2a_1 + a_2)I + a_2\sqrt{q}}{(2b_1 + b_2)I + b_2\sqrt{q}}$$

is an isomorphism between $Q(J(H))$ and $Q(J\sqrt{q})$.

From **U.3** and **U.3.1** we see that if we seek fields $Q(J\sqrt{q})$ which are distinct in the sense of isomorphism, it will suffice to deal with the case $q = -1$ (the so-called Gaussian field) and the cases where $q = \pm p_1 p_2 \cdots p_k$ in which no prime p_i is repeated. Such numbers are called *square-free*. Moreover, from **U.1.1** and the line of reasoning in **Q.3.1** it follows that distinct square-free rational integers q_1 and q_2 will lead to nonisomorphic fields $Q(J\sqrt{q_1})$ and $Q(J\sqrt{q_2})$.

EXERCISES

37.1. Complete the proof of **U.2.2**.

37.2. Complete the proof of **U.3**.

37.3. Complete the proof of **U.3.1**.

37.4. Show that the Gaussian field $Ra\sqrt{-1}$ does not contain any element $X = (x_1/y_1)I + (x_2/y_2)\sqrt{-1}$, solving $X^2 = 2I$.

37.5. Return to EXS. **25.1**, **25.2**, and **25.3** and interpret these results in terms of rational numbers.

37.6. Apply EX. **25.2** to show there is no rational number x/y such that

$$\frac{3}{2}\left(\frac{x}{y}\right)^3 + \frac{1}{4}\left(\frac{x}{y}\right) = \frac{1}{2}.$$

37.7. Define a point (x, y) of a rectangular coordinate system to be a "rational point" if and only if *both* x and y are rational numbers.

(a) Describe accurately all the *infinitely many rational points* on the locus of $x^2 + y^2 = 1$.

(b) Prove that there are *only four rational points* on the locus of $x^4 + y^4 = 1$.

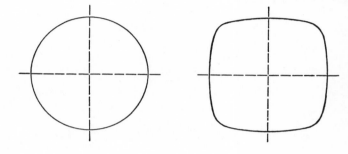

When you come to a hard or dreary
passage, pass it over; and then come back
to it after you have seen its importance
or found the need for it later on.

—G. CHRYSTAL

CHAPTER 38

Ordered rings

38.1. Ordered rings

A quick review of **1.3** will help the reader see that the following definition extends to more general systems some ideas originally applied to the familiar domain of integers.

Definition: A ring R is said to be *ordered* if and only if there is a set P of nonzero elements of R, called the *positive* elements of R, such that:

V.1: If a is in P and $A = a$, then A is in P;

V.2: If a is in R and $a \neq z$, then exactly one of a or $-a$ is in P;

V.3: If a and b are in P, then $a + b$ is in P;

V.4: If a and b are in P, then ab is in P.

We assume that J is an ordered domain, and then we consider some other rings to see if they are ordered. The requirements are so severe that many rings are not ordered rings. We make several preliminary observations.

(*1*) If a is in P and if, as usual, we define $1a = a$, and $(k + 1)a = ka + a$, then we can use **V.3** and mathematical induction to assert that ka is in P for every positive integer k in J. If these positive elements are not
300

all distinct, then there exists a positive integer $m > 1$ such that $ma = z$. But then a and $(m - 1)a$ are both in P, but their sum is not in P, contradicting **V.3**. In other words, if R contains a nonzero element whose additive period is finite, then R is not an ordered ring. As a corollary we see that if a ring R is of finite order, then R is not an ordered ring. For example, the Galois field $J(p)$ in **35.3** is not an ordered field.

(2) If a ring R has proper divisors of zero, then R is not an ordered ring. For $ab = z$ with $a \neq z$ and $b \neq z$ implies $(-a)b = z$, $a(-b) = z$, $(-a)(-b) = z$. According to **V.2** exactly one of a or $-a$ and exactly one of b or $-b$ is in P; thus one of the four listed products violates **V.4**. For example, the matric ring $M(J)$ is not an ordered ring, since $M(J)$ does have proper divisors of zero.

(3) If R is an ordered ring, then every nonzero element of R which can be written as the square of a number in R must be in P. For if $a = x^2$, by the rules of sign in R we must also have $a = (-x)^2$. If $a \neq z$, then $x \neq z$, hence by **V.2** one of x or $-x$ is in P, and by **V.4** it follows that a is in P.

If q is not a square in J and if q is not a positive integer of J, we can show that $J\sqrt{q}$ as in **36.1** is not an ordered domain. For $I^2 = I$ shows by (3) that I must be in P. Then by (1) we know $(-q)I$ must be in P. But $\sqrt{q}\sqrt{q} = qI$ must be in P by (3). To have both qI and $(-q)I = -(qI)$ in P contradicts **V.2**.

After these negative experiences, let us show that there exist ordered rings other than J. A trivial example is provided by the subring J_m of J made up of all multiples of a fixed integer $m > 1$; for a suitable set of positive elements of J_m is given by those elements of J_m which are positive integers of J. The following example is more important.

Theorem: The rational field Ra is an ordered field.

Proof: Let a/b be a nonzero element of Ra, so that both a and b are nonzero integers of J, where we assume that J is known to be an ordered domain. Define a/b to be a positive fraction if and only if ab is a positive integer.

(*V.1*) To show that being positive is well defined, we first note that $a/b = A/B$ implies $aB = bA$, so $a \neq 0$, $B \neq 0$ imply $A \neq 0$. Then $abAB = (bA)^2$ is a positive integer of J; hence AB is positive if and only if ab is positive. Thus A/B is a positive fraction if and only if a/b is a positive fraction.

(*V.2*) Since exactly one of $(-a)b = -(ab)$ and ab is a positive integer of J, it follows that exactly one of $-(a/b) = (-a)/b$ and a/b is a positive fraction.

(*V.3*) If a/b and c/d are positive fractions so that ab and cd are positive integers, then $(ad + bc)bd = abd^2 + cdb^2$ is a positive integer which shows that $(ad + bc)/bd = a/b + c/d$ is a positive fraction.

($V.4$) Similarly, $acbd = (ab)(cd)$ is a positive integer which shows that $ac/bd = (a/b)(c/d)$ is a positive fraction.

38.2. An order relation for an ordered ring

The motivation for the use of the adjective "ordered" is revealed in what follows. If R is an ordered ring we may define an order relation in R, written $a < b$ and read "a is less than b" or written $b > a$ and read "b is greater than a," as follows:

(38.1) $a < b$ if and only if $b - a$ is a positive element of R.

We establish a number of properties of the relation (38.1).

W.1: The order relation (38.1) is well defined.

Proof: If $b = B$ and $a = A$ and $a < b$ we must show $A < B$. Since addition is well defined in R we have $b - a = B - A$ so the desired result follows from (38.1) and **V.1**.

W.2: The order relation (38.1) is trichotomous.

Proof: If a and b are in R, we must show that one and only one of the three cases $a < b$, $a = b$, $a > b$ must hold. From **V.2** we know that $b - a$ must satisfy exactly one of the conditions of being a positive element of R, of being zero, or of having $-x = a - b$ be a positive element of R. The trichotomy then follows from (38.1) and the uniqueness of negatives in R.

As a corollary of **W.2** we know that exactly one of the cases $z < b$, $z = b$, $z > b$ must hold. But this has a special interpretation since $z < b$ implies $b - z = b$ must be a positive element of R; and $z > b$ implies $z - b = -b$ must be a positive element of R.

In other words, from this point on, we may characterize

the positive elements b of R by $z < b$;
the zero element of R by $b = z$;
the nonzero elements of R
   such that $-b$ is positive   by $b < z$.

W.3: The order relation (38.1) is transitive.

Proof: We must show if $a < b$ and $b < c$, then $a < c$. By hypothesis and (38.1) $b - a = x_1$ and $c - b = x_2$ are positive elements of R; then by V.3 we know $x_1 + x_2 = b - a + c - b = c - a$ is a positive element of R; hence by (38.1) we have $a < c$.

W.4:   The order relation (38.1) is preserved under the addition of any element of R to both sides of the relation.

Proof: If $a < b$ and x is in R, we must show $a + x < b + x$. Since $(b + x) - (a + x) = b - a$, the desired result follows from (38.1) and **V.1**.

W.5:   If $a < b$, then $ax < bx$, $ax = bx$, $ax > bx$ as $z < x$, $x = z$, $x < z$, respectively.

Proof: In the discussion following **W.2** we noted that $z < x$ implies that x is positive; the hypothesis $a < b$ implies from (38.1) that $b - a$ is positive; property **V.4** implies that $(b - a)x = bx - ax$ is positive; hence by (38.1) we have $ax < bx$.

If $x = z$, then $bx = bz = z = az = ax$.

If $x < z$, then $-x$ is positive; hence by **V.4** we have $ax - bx = (-x)(b - a)$ is positive, so $ax > bx$.

Let us examine the order relation (38.1) for the ordered field Ra. We have $c/d < a/b$ if and only if $a/b - c/d = (ad - bc)/bd$ is a positive fraction; hence if and only if $(ad - bc)bd$ is a positive integer.

If we standardize the fractions to a form where all denominators are of the same sign, then $bd > 0$, so the test $a/b > c/d$ can be reduced to checking $ad > bc$. But unless we observe the standardization this check is not well defined. Thus $2/3 > 4/15$ because $30 > 12$; however, if we innocently replace $2/3$ by $-2/-3$ and try the same test, we are led falsely to think $-2/-3 < 4/15$ because $-30 < -12$. The test that is always valid is the one in the preceding paragraph which shows $-2/-3 > 4/15$ because $(ad - bc)bd = (-30 - (-12))(-45) > 0$.

38.3. Absolute value in an ordered ring

In the discussion to follow we shall adopt the usual notation $a \leqslant b$ to mean either $a < b$ or $a = b$.

In an ordered ring R we may define an absolute value $|a|$ as follows:

(38.2)
$$\begin{cases} \text{if } z \leqslant a, \text{ then } |a| = a; \\ \text{if } a \leqslant z, \text{ then } |a| = -a. \end{cases}$$

The following results are easily established by examining separately a small number of cases.

A.1: $|a| \geqslant z$.

A.2: $|a| = z$ if and only if $a = z$.

A.3: $|ab| = |a|\,|b|$.

A.4: $|a + b| \leqslant |a| + |b|$.

We give just one sample proof—a special case of **A.4**.

Suppose $a < z < b$ and that $|a| \geqslant |b|$. These hypotheses and (38.2) imply $-a \geqslant b$. Hence **W.4** implies $a + b \leqslant z$; therefore (38.2) shows $|a + b| = -(a + b) = -a - b$. On the other hand, the hypotheses and (38.2) imply $|a| + |b| = -a + b$. So to establish **A.4** for this particular case we need to show $-a - b \leqslant -a + b$. By **W.4** this is equivalent to showing $z \leqslant b + b$. But we are given $z < b$, so we may apply **W.4** to conclude $z < b = b + z < b + b$; then from **W.3** we have $z < b + b$, which is enough to complete the proof.

There is a temptation here to apply **W.5** and argue from $z < 2e$ and $z < b$ that $z < 2b$; but there is no reason, in general, that an ordered ring R need contain an identity e. Witness the example J_m when $m > 1$.

In particular, since Ra is an ordered field, we may define an absolute value $|a/b|$ which will have properties **A.1**, **A.2**, **A.3**, **A.4** and be of considerable use in later chapters.

38.4. Well-ordered rings

Given a set S of elements in an ordered ring R, if there exists an element x in the set S such that $x \leqslant y$ for every y of the set S, then x is called a *least element* of the set S.

An ordered ring R is said to be *well-ordered* if and only if every non-empty set S, finite or infinite, of positive elements of R has a least element.

In our earlier chapter on mathematical induction one of the alternate forms of mathematical induction, designated as **L.3**, shows that the domain J of integers is assumed to be a well-ordered domain.

Let us show that not every ordered ring is well-ordered. For a counter-example we may use the rational field Ra, which we showed to be an ordered field in **38.1**. Let A/B be a fixed positive fraction. Consider the set S of all positive fractions x/y such that $x/y > A/B$. The set S is non-empty for $2A/B > A/B$. But S has no least element, for if we suppose a/b is least such that $a/b > A/B$, then $x/y = (a/b + A/B)(1/2)$ provides a contradiction, for we can show $a/b > x/y = a/2b + A/2B > A/B$. From **W.4** each of these inequalities will hold if we can show $a/2b > A/2B$; but this follows readily by applying **W.5** to $a/b > A/B$ with $0 < 1/2$. Thus Ra is not well-ordered.

On the other hand, J is not the only well-ordered ring, for the ring J_m of all multiples of a fixed integer m is well-ordered under the same ordering that obtains in J. However, when $m > 1$, J_m is not a domain because of one deficiency—the lack of an identity. There is considerable logical importance attached to the following theorem, so we dignify it with a separate section.

38.5.   Categorical characterization of the rational domain J

Theorem: In the sense of isomorphism there is only one well-ordered domain.

Proof: Let D be a well-ordered domain. A domain possesses an identity e. In an ordered domain every square is a positive element; hence $e = ee$ is a positive element. By **V.3** the positive elements are closed under addition; hence if we define (I) $1e = e$ and (II) $(k + 1)e = ke + e$, then we see by mathematical induction that ke is a positive element of D for every *positive* integer k in J. If we define $0e = z$ and $(-k)e = -(ke)$ and use the additive properties of D, we find that D must contain ke for *every* integer k in J. Furthermore, using the ordering in D we find if r and s are in J, then $re < se$ in D if and only if $r < s$ in J.

We want to show that if D is a well-ordered domain and y is in D, then y must be of the form ke with k in J. Suppose y is not of the form ke; then $y \neq z$ for $z = 0e$, and hence by **V.2** exactly one of y or $-y$ is a positive element of D. Then the set S of positive elements of D which are not of the form ke with k in J is nonempty. Since D is assumed to be well-ordered it follows that S must contain a least element x.

We show first that we cannot have $z < x < e$, for then by **W.5** we have $z = zx < xx < ex = x < e$ where xx is a positive element of D. If $xx = ke$ for some k in J, then we have $0e < ke < 1e$ in D, which implies $0 < k < 1$ in J, a contradiction. (For in J the assumption of mathematical induction in the form **L.3** implies that if there is any positive integer k with the property $0 < k < 1$, then there is a least such integer, say m. But $0 < m < 1$ implies $0 < mm < m < 1$, and the existence of mm contradicts the minimal property of m.) Hence xx is a positive element of D not of the form ke with k in J. But $xx < x$ contradicts the minimal property of x, so this case $z < x < e$ cannot occur.

We cannot have $x = e = 1e$, so we use **W.2** to see we must have $z < e < x$. By **W.5** this is equivalent to $-x < -e < z$. By **W.4** this implies $z = x - x < x - e < x + z = x$. Hence $x - e$ is a positive element of D less than x. By the minimal property of x it follows that $x - e$ is of the form ke with k in J. But then $x = ke + e = (k + 1)e$ is of forbidden form.

These contradictions show that every element of the well-ordered domain D must be of the form ke with k in J. The natural correspondence $(ke)T = k$ is an isomorphism between D and J, which completes the proof of the theorem.

At the risk of being repetitious let us outline our logical position. We assume there exists a well-ordered domain J; then the theorem assures us that in the sense of isomorphism there is no other well-ordered domain. At first the assumption may overwhelm us, but then we realize that in developing mathematical systems we must have some initial systems; and the theorem restores our confidence, for it shows that the combined hypotheses of being a domain and being well-ordered are a categorical set of postulates, and this is just what we might find convenient for an initial system.

Since the well-ordering principle is equivalent to the principle of mathematical induction for the positive integers of J, we gain a new respect for induction. If the logical foundation for J is to be pushed back any further it seems natural to examine induction again. This is exactly what we shall do in a later chapter concerning Peano's axioms.

38.6. Skew-domains and skew-fields

A fundamental postulate for the domain and the field is the assumption of commutative multiplication. We show in this section that there do exist rings which have all the properties of a domain or a field, except that multiplication is not commutative and we call these skew-domains and skew-fields, respectively. The discussion depends in a mild way on the concept of order; hence these examples were not introduced in earlier chapters.

Theorem: If q is a negative square-free number of J, then the subsystem K of $M(J\sqrt{q})$ made up of all matrices of the form

$$Q = \begin{pmatrix} A & B \\ -\bar{B} & \bar{A} \end{pmatrix} = \begin{pmatrix} a_1 I + a_2\sqrt{q} & b_1 I + b_2\sqrt{q} \\ -b_1 I + b_2\sqrt{q} & a_1 I - a_2\sqrt{q} \end{pmatrix}$$

is a skew-domain.

Proof: After checking that $\overline{A + C} = \overline{A} + \overline{C}$ in $J\sqrt{q}$, we have no trouble in showing that K is a commutative group under matric addition. Next we check that K is closed under the matric product, for we recall that $\overline{XY} = \overline{X}\overline{Y}$ in $J\sqrt{q}$, hence

$$\begin{pmatrix} A & B \\ -\overline{B} & \overline{A} \end{pmatrix}\begin{pmatrix} C & D \\ -\overline{D} & \overline{C} \end{pmatrix} = \begin{pmatrix} AC - B\overline{D} & AD + B\overline{C} \\ -\overline{B}C - \overline{A}\overline{D} & \overline{A}\overline{C} - \overline{B}D \end{pmatrix}$$

$$= \begin{pmatrix} AC - B\overline{D} & AD + B\overline{C} \\ -\overline{(AD + B\overline{C})} & \overline{(AC - B\overline{D})} \end{pmatrix}.$$

The well-defined and associative properties and the *two* distributive laws follow from the general discussion of $M(R)$ over a ring R.

We consider $d(Q)$ which is unambiguously defined since $J\sqrt{q}$ is commutative. We find

$$d(Q) = A\overline{A} + B\overline{B} = (a_1{}^2 - qa_2{}^2 + b_1{}^2 - qb_2{}^2)I.$$

Since J is an ordered domain and since $q < 0$, it follows that $d(Q) = Z$ in $J\sqrt{q}$ if and only if $a_1 = a_2 = b_1 = b_2 = 0$, hence if and only if $Q = Z'$ in K. Consequently if Q_1 and Q_2 are in K and if $Q_1Q_2 = Z'$ in K, then $d(Q_1)d(Q_2) = Z$ in $J\sqrt{q}$. If $Q_1 \neq Z'$, then $d(Q_1) \neq Z$; hence $d(Q_2) = Z$ and $Q_2 = Z'$. In other words, K has no proper divisors of zero.

K does contain an identity E, for in Q we may take $A = I$, $B = Z$. But K is noncommutative for we may check that

$$\begin{pmatrix} Z & I \\ -I & Z \end{pmatrix}\begin{pmatrix} \sqrt{q} & Z \\ Z & -\sqrt{q} \end{pmatrix} = \begin{pmatrix} Z & -\sqrt{q} \\ -\sqrt{q} & Z \end{pmatrix}$$

$$\neq \begin{pmatrix} Z & \sqrt{q} \\ \sqrt{q} & Z \end{pmatrix} = \begin{pmatrix} \sqrt{q} & Z \\ Z & -\sqrt{q} \end{pmatrix}\begin{pmatrix} Z & I \\ -I & Z \end{pmatrix}.$$

Corollary: In the preceding theorem, if J is replaced by Ra, the resulting system K is a skew-field.

Proof: Since Ra is an ordered field, all the details in the proof of the theorem can be repeated with J replaced by Ra. Furthermore, it is possible to show that every nonzero matrix in K has an inverse in K. Hence K constitutes what is called a *division ring*, because division by a nonzero element is always possible; or what is called a *skew-field*, as we explained above, because all the properties of a field are satisfied except the commutative property.

To produce the inverse of $Q \neq Z'$ in $M(Ra\sqrt{q})$ we may set $\Delta = a_1{}^2 - qa_2{}^2 + b_1{}^2 - qb_2{}^2$, so that $d(Q) = \Delta I$, and use

$$Q^{-1} = \begin{pmatrix} \bar{A} & -\bar{B} \\ B & A \end{pmatrix} \begin{pmatrix} (1/\Delta)I & Z \\ Z & (1/\Delta)I \end{pmatrix}.$$

This is properly defined since $Q \neq Z'$ implies $\Delta \neq 0$ in Ra, and we check readily that $QQ^{-1} = Q^{-1}Q = E$.

To verify that Q^{-1} is in K we have only to check that $\bar{\bar{A}} = A$ in $Ra\sqrt{q}$ and then use the closure of K under the matric product.

In the exercises we observe that although Q is presented here as a 2-by-2 matrix whose elements in $Ra\sqrt{q}$ are themselves 2-by-2 matrices with elements in Ra, it is easy to write Q in detail as a 4-by-4 matrix whose elements are in Ra, as follows:

$$Q = \begin{pmatrix} a_1 & a_2 & b_1 & b_2 \\ qa_2 & a_1 & qb_2 & b_1 \\ -b_1 & b_2 & a_1 & -a_2 \\ qb_2 & -b_1 & -qa_2 & a_1 \end{pmatrix}.$$

In the particular case that $q = -1$ the system K of the corollary is known as the *rational quaternions*. In the exercises we suggest the connection with the quaternion group of **33.4**.

EXERCISES

38.1. Establish A.4 for the case $a \leqslant b \leqslant z$.

38.2. Establish A.4 for the case $a < z < b$ and $|a| < |b|$.

38.3. In an ordered ring if $a < b$ and $c < d$, show that $a + c < b + d$.

38.4. In an ordered ring if $a < b < z$, show that $z < b^2 < a^2$.

38.5. Consider the domain $J\sqrt{3}$. Define $a_1 I + a_2 \sqrt{3}$ to be "positive" if and only if (in terms of the order in J) (a) $a_1 > 0$, $a_2 \geqslant 0$; or (b) $a_1 > 0$, $a_2 < 0$, and $a_1{}^2 > 3a_2{}^2$; or (c) $a_1 \leqslant 0$, $a_2 > 0$, and $3a_2{}^2 > a_1{}^2$. Under this definition show that $J\sqrt{3}$ is an ordered domain.

38.6. Under the definition proposed in EX. **38.5**, show that $J\sqrt{3}$ is not a well-ordered domain. (Hint: For a direct proof, consider $\bar{A} = 2I - \sqrt{3}$ and its powers, $\bar{A}^2$, $\bar{A}^3$, ... For an indirect proof apply the theorem in **38.5**.)

38.7. Show that $J\sqrt{3}$ does not contain any unit U such that $I < U < 2I + \sqrt{3} = A$. (Hint: Show $-I < \bar{U} < I$ and apply EX. **38.3**.)

38.8. Apply EX. **38.7** and show that $J\sqrt{3}$ does not contain any unit V such that $A^k < V < A^{k+1}$. Show that all units of $J\sqrt{3}$ are given by $\pm A^k$ and $\pm \bar{A}^k$ for $k = 0, 1, 2, \ldots$.

38.9. For the quaternions described in **38.6**, taking $q = -1$, each is determined by giving its first row, say $Q \sim (a_1, a_2, a_3, a_4)$. In particular, let $I \sim (1, 0, 0, 0)$, $i \sim (0, 1, 0, 0)$, $j \sim (0, 0, 1, 0)$, $k \sim (0, 0, 0, 1)$. Show that the eight quaternions $\pm I$, $\pm i$, $\pm j$, $\pm k$ form a noncommutative group of order 8 with $i^2 = j^2 = k^2 = -I$, $ij = k = -ji$, $jk = i = -kj$, $ki = j = -ik$. This group is isomorphic to the group used in **33.4**.

CHAPTER 39

Polynomial rings

39.1. Formal series over a ring

We may use the natural ordering of the set S of all nonnegative integers
i of J to order by subscripts a "formal series" of elements a_i which belong
to a ring R. We use at pleasure either an abbreviated or extended notation
for a formal series:

$$(a_i) = (a_0, a_1, \ldots, a_i, \ldots).$$

We speak of a_i as being the general term of the series.

Let us define an *equality* of series:

(39.1) $(a_i) = (b_i)$ if and only if $a_i = b_i$ for every i in S.

Let us define an *addition* of series:

(39.2) $(a_i) + (b_i) = (c_i)$ where $c_i = a_i + b_i$ for every i in S.

Let us define a *multiplication* of series:

(39.3) $(a_i)(b_i) = (c_i)$ where for every i in S we have $c_i = \sum a_j b_k$
summed over the $i + 1$ cases for which j and k are in S and $j + k = i$.

310

For example, in (39.3) we have $4 + 1 = 5$ terms in finding

$$c_4 = a_0b_4 + a_1b_3 + a_2b_2 + a_3b_1 + a_4b_0.$$

Theorem 1:   The set $R(x)$ of all formal series (a_i) over a ring R is a ring.

Proof: The equality (39.1) is an equivalence relation for $R(x)$, since each required property for $(a_i) = (b_i)$ in $R(x)$ follows from the corresponding property of $a_i = b_i$ in the ring R.

Under (39.2) the system $R(x)$ is a commutative group. Most of the properties for $(a_i) + (b_i)$ in $R(x)$ follows at once, component by component, from the known properties of $a_i + b_i$ in R. In particular, the series $(z, z, z, \ldots)$ serves as zero; and the series $(-a_i)$ is the negative of (a_i).

The operation (39.3) is closed and well defined in $R(x)$, since $c_i = \sum a_jb_k$ with $j + k = i$ is closed and well defined in R and for a fixed i involves a finite number of multiplications and additions. The associative property of (39.3) in $R(x)$ follows from (39.3) and (39.1) and properties of R which imply that

$$\sum_{i+m=n} \left(\sum_{j+k=i} a_jb_k \right) c_m = \sum_{j+s=n} a_j \left(\sum_{k+m=s} b_kc_m \right);$$

for each of these is equal to

$$d_n = \sum a_jb_kc_m$$

summed over all cases where j, k, m are in S and

$$(j + k) + m = j + (k + m) = n.$$

For example,

$$\begin{aligned}
d_3 = {} & a_0b_0c_3 + a_0b_1c_2 + a_0b_2c_1 + a_0b_3c_0 \\
& + a_1b_0c_2 + a_1b_1c_1 + a_1b_2c_0 \\
& + a_2b_0c_1 + a_2b_1c_0 \\
& + a_3b_0c_0.
\end{aligned}$$

Because of associative multiplication in R and properties of addition in R, these terms may be grouped, either by columns or by rows, to obtain the corresponding term of $((a_i)(b_i))(c_i)$ or $(a_i)((b_i)(c_i))$, respectively:

$$\begin{aligned}
(a_0b_0)c_3 + {} & (a_0b_1 + a_1b_0)c_2 + (a_0b_2 + a_1b_1 + a_2b_0)c_1 \\
& + (a_0b_3 + a_1b_2 + a_2b_1 + a_3b_0)c_0 \\
= {} & a_0(b_0c_3 + b_1c_2 + b_2c_1 + b_3c_0) \\
& + a_1(b_0c_2 + b_1c_1 + b_2c_0) + a_2(b_0c_1 + b_1c_0) + a_3(b_0c_0).
\end{aligned}$$

The right-distributive law in $R(x)$, $((a_i) + (b_i))(c_i) = (a_i)(c_i) + (b_i)(c_i)$, will follow from (39.1), (39.2), and (39.3) since

$$\sum (a_j + b_j)c_k = \sum a_j c_k + \sum b_j c_k, \qquad \text{with } j + k = i,$$

which is valid because of the right-distributive law and additive properties in R. Similarly, the left-distributive law holds in $R(x)$.

This completes the proof that $R(x)$ is a ring.

Corollary 1.1:   The set R' of all series of the form

$$(a, z, z, \ldots) \text{ where } a_0 = a \text{ and } a_i = z \text{ when } i > 0$$

is a subsystem of $R(x)$ isomorphic to R.

Proof: Consider the correspondence $aT = (a, z, z, \ldots)$. From (39.1) it is easy to check that T is one-to-one between R and R'. From (39.2) we find

$$(a + b)T = (a + b, z, z, \ldots) = (a, z, z, \ldots) + (b, z, z, \ldots) = aT + bT.$$

From (39.3) we find

$$(ab)T = (ab, z, z, \ldots) = (a, z, z, \ldots)(b, z, z, \ldots) = (aT)(bT).$$

Thus T is operation-preserving.

Because of this isomorphism we may henceforth use the notation

$$a = (a, z, z, \ldots).$$

Corollary 1.2: $R(x)$ is commutative if and only if R is commutative.

Proof: We leave the proof as an exercise.

Perhaps we should mention that the definitions of (a_i) and (39.1) are such that $R(x)$ is an infinite ring, even if R is finite. For example, if R is the simplest Galois field of *two* residue classes of J mod 2, represented by 0 and 1, nevertheless the corresponding ring $R(x)$ is *infinite*, with a distinct formal series (a_i) for every distinct infinite sequence of 0's and 1's.

Theorem 2:   If R contains an identity e, then $e = (e, z, z, \ldots)$ is the identity of $R(x)$. The series $x = (x_{1i}) = (z, e, z, z, \ldots)$, in which $x_{11} = e$ and $x_{1i} = z$ if i is in S and $i \neq 1$, has the property for $n \geqslant 1$ that

(39.4) $x^n = (x_{ni})$ with $x_{nn} = e$ and $x_{ni} = z$ if i is in S and $i \neq n$.

Proof: It is easy to apply (39.3) to show $e(a_i) = (a_i)$ for every series (a_i) in $R(x)$. The property (39.4) will be shown by induction on the positive integers n in S.

(I) When $n = 1$, the property (39.4) holds by the definition of x.

(II) We assume (39.4) for the case n and consider $(x_{n+1, i}) = x^{n+1} = x^n x = (x_{ni})(x_{1i})$. According to (39.3) we have $x_{n+1, i} = \sum x_{nj} x_{1k}$ summed over all cases in which $j + k = i$. Since by the induction hypothesis there is only one nonzero term in (x_{ni}) and by definition, only one nonzero term in (x_{1i}), and since z is an annihilator for R, we find that $x_{n+1, i} = z$ except when $j = n$ and $k = 1$. In that special case $i = j + k = n + 1$, and $x_{n+1, n+1} = x_{nn} x_{11} = ee = e$.

By induction the proof of (39.4) is complete.

Corollary 2.1: If R contains an identity e, then any formal series (a_n) of $R(x)$ may be written in the form

$$(a_n) = a_0 + a_1 x + a_2 x^2 + \cdots + a_n x^n + \cdots$$

where $a_n = (a_n, z, z, \ldots)$ is defined in Corollary 1.1, where x is defined in Theorem 2, and the operations and relations are (39.1), (39.2), (39.3).

Proof: On the one hand by (39.1) and (39.2) we have

$$(a_n) = (A_{0i}) + (A_{1i}) + (A_{2i}) + \cdots + (A_{ni}) + \cdots$$

where (A_{ni}) has $A_{nn} = a_n$ and $A_{ni} = z$ when $i \neq n$.

On the other hand, $a_n = (a_{ni})$ with $a_{n0} = a_n$ and $a_{ni} = z$ when $i \neq 0$. Thus $a_0 = (A_{0i})$. When $n \geqslant 1$, we may use (39.3) and (39.4) to determine $a_n x^n = (a_{ni})(x_{ni}) = (B_{ni})$. Since $B_{ni} = \sum a_{nj} x_{nk}$ with $j + k = i$, we find $B_{ni} = z$, except possibly when $j = 0$ and $k = n$, in which case we have $B_{nn} = a_{n0} x_{nn} = a_n e = a_n$. By (39.1) we have $(B_{ni}) = (A_{ni})$.

Comparison of these results establishes Corollary 2.1.

In the light of Corollary 2.1 it is natural to introduce the notation $(a_n) = \sum a_n x^n$, $n = 0, 1, 2, \ldots$, where it is understood that $x^0 = e$. Then the description of (a_n) as being a *series* will be in agreement with language already known to a student of calculus and he will be used to calling the a_n, the *coefficients* of the series. However, in the discussion here, there are no questions of convergence and no mystery about x being a *variable* or *indeterminate quantity*. Instead x is itself a perfectly definite series, namely, $x = (z, e, z, z, \ldots)$, within the system of all series. Corollary 2.1 also gives a good motivation for the notation $R(x)$ for the ring of formal power series—with R to suggest the source of the a_n and with x to suggest a useful way of representing each series. However, it should be noted that the last remark is applicable only when R contains an identity e.

Illustrating Corollary 2.1 in a noncommutative case we may take R to be $M(J)$ with the matrix I as the identity. Letting $X = (Z, I, Z, Z, \ldots)$ we may represent the general formal power series of $R(X)$ in the form:

$$A_0 + A_1 X + A_2 X^2 + \cdots$$

where each A_i is a matrix in $M(J)$ and the rules (39.1), (39.2), (39.3) are to be used to manipulate these series. For example,

$$(A_0 + A_1 X)(B_0 + B_1 X) = A_0 B_0 + (A_1 B_0 + A_0 B_1)X + A_1 B_1 X^2$$

where the notation shows that all other terms of the factors and the product are understood to have the coefficient Z.

Corollary 2.2: The units of $R(x)$ include the units of R.

Proof: We understand as in Corollary 1.1 that elements of R may be considered to be present in $R(x)$ in their isomorphic disguise as members of R'. Then the desired result is an immediate consequence of the multiplication-preserving property of the isomorphism T in Corollary 1.1.

The converse of Corollary 2.2 is not always correct. For example, if R is the ring of residue classes of J mod 4, then

$$(1, 2, 0, 0, \ldots)^2 = (1 \cdot 1, 1 \cdot 2 + 2 \cdot 1, 2 \cdot 2, 0, 0, \ldots) = (1, 0, 0, \ldots).$$

Hence $(1, 2, 0, 0, \ldots)$ is a unit of $R(x)$ which is not in R'.

39.2. Polynomials over a ring

We define a series (a_i) of $R(x)$ to be a *polynomial over R* if and only if there exists an integer k such that $a_i = z$ when $i \geqslant k$. For example, $z = (z, z, \ldots)$ is a polynomial, for in this instance we may take $k = 0$. In all other cases, if a series is a polynomial, there is a maximal value of n for which $a_n \neq z$, and $a_i = z$ when $i \geqslant n + 1$. We describe n as the *degree* of the polynomial, and we note that the smallest suitable value for k is $n + 1$. All polynomials, except the zero polynomial z, have a degree. In particular, the series belonging to R' are all polynomials which, except for z, have degree 0.

For example, if R is the Galois field $J(2)$, we may list all polynomials of degrees 0, 1, 2 as follows:

degree 0: $1 = (1, 0, 0, \ldots)$;
degree 1: $x = (0, 1, 0, \ldots)$, $1 + x = (1, 1, 0, \ldots)$;
degree 2: $x^2 = (0, 0, 1, 0, \ldots)$, $1 + x^2 = (1, 0, 1, 0, \ldots)$,
$\qquad x + x^2 = (0, 1, 1, 0, \ldots)$, $1 + x + x^2 = (1, 1, 1, 0, \ldots)$.

Theorem 3: The set $PR(x)$ of all polynomials in $R(x)$ is a ring under (39.1), (39.2), (39.3).

Proof: Assume that (a_i) and (b_i) are in $PR(x)$. Because of Theorem 1 it is only necessary to show that $-(a_i)$, $(a_i) + (b_i)$, and $(a_i)(b_i)$ are in $PR(x)$.

If $(a_i) = z$, or if $(b_i) = z$, the desired results are obvious, since $-z = z$, $z + (b_i) = (b_i)$, and $z(b_i) = (a_i)z = z$.

If $(a_i) \neq z$, then $-(a_i) = (-a_i)$ is a polynomial of the same degree n as the degree of (a_i), for $a_n \neq z$ implies $-a_n \neq z$; and $a_i = z$, when $i > n$, implies $-a_i = z$, when $i > n$.

If (a_i) is of degree n and (b_i) is of degree m, and if k is the larger of n and m, then $(a_i) + (b_i) = (a_i + b_i)$ is either z or is a polynomial of degree $\leq k$ inasmuch as $a_i + b_i = z$ when $i > k$.

Under the same conditions $(a_i)(b_i) = (c_i)$ is either z or is a polynomial of degree $\leq n + m$, since $c_i = \sum a_j b_k$ with $j + k = i$ has $c_i = z$ when $i > n + m$. This last remark follows since if $j \leq n$ and $j + k = i > n + m$, then $k > m$, so that $b_k = z$; and if $n < j$, then $a_j = z$.

This completes the proof of Theorem 3.

We cannot in general improve the statement about the degree of $(a_i)(b_i)$, for the ring R may have proper divisors of zero. But the following corollary shows a case in which we can guarantee that the degree of the product is exactly $n + m$.

Corollary 3.1: If D is a domain, then the set $PD(x)$ of all polynomials in $D(x)$ is a domain.

Proof: The identity e of D supplies an identity polynomial e of degree 0 for $PD(x)$. Since D is commutative, so are $D(x)$ and $PD(x)$ by Corollary 1.2. If $(a_i) \neq z$ and $(b_i) \neq z$ are polynomials in $D(x)$ of degrees n and m, respectively, then $(a_i)(b_i) = (c_i) \neq z$, for we can show that the product (c_i) is of degree $n + m$. We noted in the previous proof that $c_i = z$ when $i > n + m$. Since $a_n \neq z$ and $b_m \neq z$, we find that $c_{n+m} = a_n b_m \neq z$, for D is a domain. Thus $PD(x)$ has no proper divisors of zero. All the other properties needed to show that $PD(x)$ is a domain follow from Theorem 3.

39.3. Polynomials over a field

Since a field F is a domain, we know from Corollary 3.1 that the set $PF(x)$ of all polynomials with coefficients in F is a domain. We shall use the notation $a(x) = \sum a_i x^i$.

Theorem 4: Division algorithm theorem: If $a(x)$ and $b(x)$ are in $PF(x)$ and $b(x)$ has degree m, then there exist unique polynomials $q(x)$ and $r(x)$ in $PF(x)$ such that

$$(1) \quad a(x) = q(x)b(x) + r(x),$$
either $\quad (2) \quad r(x) = z$
or $\quad (3) \quad r(x)$ is of degree $< m$.

Proof: (A) If $a(x) = z$, we may take $q(x) = z$ and $r(x) = z$. If $a(x) \neq z$, suppose $a(x)$ is of degree $n \geq 0$ with $a_n \neq z$. If $n < m$, we may take $q(x) = z$ and $r(x) = a(x)$. If $n \geq m$, we shall make an induction argument on the nonnegative integer $k = n - m$.

(I) When $k = 0$, we use properties of the field F to solve $a_m = q_0 b_m$. Since $b_m \neq z$, $q_0 = a_m b_m^{-1}$. We take $q(x) = q_0$ and $r(x) = a(x) - q_0 b(x)$. Since $r(x)$ has $r_m = a_m - q_0 b_m = z$, we are sure that $r(x)$ has either property (2) or property (3).

(II) When $k \geq 1$, we assume solutions of the algorithm are known for every polynomial $a'(x)$ of degree n' for which $n' < n$. We use properties of the field F to solve $a_n = q_k b_m$ for $q_k = a_n b_m^{-1}$. We take $Q(x) = q_k x^k$ and $a'(x) = a(x) - Q(x)b(x)$. Since $a'(x)$ has $a_n' = a_n - q_k b_m = z$, we are sure that either $a'(x) = z$, or that $a'(x)$ has a degree $n' < n$.

In the first instance, we take $q(x) = Q(x)$ and $r(x) = z$ to satisfy properties (1) and (2).

In the second case, since $n' < n$, the induction hypothesis applies and $a'(x) = q'(x)b(x) + r'(x)$ with either $r'(x) = z$ or $r'(x)$ is of degree $< m$. Then we can satisfy (1) and (2), or (1) and (3), by taking $q(x) = Q(x) + q'(x)$ and $r(x) = r'(x)$.

From (I), (II), and induction on k the existence proof is complete for those cases where $n \geq m$.

(B) The uniqueness proof depends on remarks in the proofs of Theorem 3 and Corollary 3.1. For if

$$a(x) = q(x)b(x) + r(x) = q_1(x)b(x) + r_1(x)$$

where each of $r(x)$ and $r_1(x)$ is either z or of degree $< m$, then

$$(q(x) - q_1(x))b(x) = r_1(x) - r(x).$$

The polynomial on the right side is either z or of degree at most $m - 1$. On the left the polynomial is either z or of degree at least m. The only noncontradictory situation is that both sides are z. Then $r_1(x) = r(x)$ and because $b(x) \neq z$ and $PF(x)$ has no proper divisors of zero, we also have $q(x) = q_1(x)$. This completes the proof of Theorem 4.

For example, let F be the field of residue classes of J mod 7, $a(x) = 2x^5 + 4x^2 + 3x + 1$ and $b(x) = 3x^2 + 2x + 2$. After we have noticed that 5 is the inverse of 3 mod 7, we can easily find the various $q_k = a_n b_m^{-1}$

$= 5a_n$ needed in carrying out the division algorithm. Using a natural scheme for the powers of x, we may show the work schematically as follows:

$$
\begin{array}{r|rrrrr}
 & 3 & 5 & 4 & & \\
3 \quad 2 \quad 2 & 2 & 0 & 0 & 4 & 3 & 1 \\
\hline
 & 2 & 6 & 6 & & \\
\hline
 & & 1 & 1 & 4 & 3 & 1 \\
 & & 1 & 3 & 3 & \\
\hline
 & & & 5 & 1 & 3 & 1 \\
 & & & 5 & 1 & 1 \\
\hline
 & & & & 2 & 1 \\
\end{array}
$$

$q(x) = 3x^3 + 5x^2 + 4x,$

$r(x) = 2x + 1.$

For the polynomial domain $PF(x)$ we may define units, prime (or irreducible) polynomials, and composite (or reducible) polynomials in the usual manner.

We may show that the units of $PF(x)$ are precisely the polynomials of degree 0. These correspond, of course, to the nonzero elements of F. On the one hand from Corollary 2.2 we know that the polynomials of degree 0 are units. On the other hand the condition $u(x)v(x) = e$ requires both $u(x)$ and $v(x)$ to be of degree 0 (see the proof of Corollary 3.1). Then $u_0v_0 = e$ implies u_0 and v_0 are units of F.

In $PF(x)$ there always exist some prime polynomials $p(x)$, which are not themselves units, but are such that $p(x) = a(x)b(x)$ requires either $a(x)$ or $b(x)$ to be a unit. For it is easily shown that all polynomials of degree 1 are prime polynomials. This follows from the fact that the degree of the product of nonzero polynomials in $PF(x)$ is the sum of the degrees of the factors. Then $1 = n + m$ and $0 \leqslant n, 0 \leqslant m$ imply that one or the other of n and m must be 0.

The discussion of the existence or nonexistence of prime polynomials of degree > 1 in $PF(x)$ has to be conducted in various ways for various fields F. For the moment we content ourselves with one simple illustration.

If F is the Galois field of order 2, then in $PF(x)$ the only unit is 1, both x and $1 + x$ are primes, obviously x^2, $x + x^2 = x(1 + x)$, and $1 + x^2 = (1 + x)^2$ are composite, and since this exhausts the possible ways of forming products of degree 2 from polynomials of degree 1, it follows that $1 + x + x^2$ is a prime polynomial of degree 2. By the same device of first listing all the composite polynomials of degree 3 and comparing this list with all polynomials of degree 3, we can discover for this field some prime polynomials of degree 3. And indeed, for this particular field, the method can be pursued to produce some prime polynomials of degree n for any $n \geqslant 1$.

Since Theorem 4 establishes a division algorithm based on decreasing degrees, it is easy to devise a Euclid algorithm for polynomials in $PF(x)$ over any field F, so that for any two polynomials $a(x)$ and $b(x)$, not both zero, there can be found polynomials $d(x)$, $s(x)$, $t(x)$, all in $PF(x)$, such that $d(x) = a(x)s(x) + b(x)t(x)$ is a common divisor of $a(x)$ and $b(x)$ divisible by every common divisor of $a(x)$ and $b(x)$.

We illustrate by continuing the previous example over the Galois field of seven elements. With the first step already completed—$a(x) = q(x)b(x) + r(x)$—we consider $b(x) = q_1(x)r(x) + r_1(x)$. A brief computation shows $q_1(x) = 5x + 2$ and $r_1(x) = 0$. Thus $d(x) = r(x) = 2x + 1$, and for this example we may take $s(x) = 1$ and $t(x) = -q(x)$. The greatest common divisor $d(x)$ is unique only up to a unit factor, so over this field there are five other forms for $d(x)$ of which $d'(x) = 4d(x) = x + 4$ may be preferred, since it is monic, that is, it has 1 as its leading coefficient.

Step by step, as in dealing with the domains J and $J\sqrt{3}$, we can show that in $PF(x)$ each nonunit and nonzero polynomial has a representation in the form

$$up_1(x)p_2(x)\cdots p_k(x)$$

where u is a unit and each $p_i(x)$ is a prime polynomial, with the representation being unique except for the order of the factors and the replacement of $p_i(x)$ by an associated polynomial, say $u_ip_i(x)$, where u_i is a unit, with a corresponding replacement of u by $u_i^{-1}u$. To summarize these ideas, whose proof has just been outlined, we state the following theorem.

Theorem 5: For every field F the polynomial domain $PF(x)$ has factorization into prime polynomials which is essentially unique.

39.4. Rational functions over a field

Referring to U.1 in **37.1** we see that the system $Q(PF(x))$ of all quotients $a(x)/b(x)$, where $a(x)$ and $b(x)$ are polynomials of the domain $PF(x)$ and $b(x) \neq z$, is a field. The quotients $a(x)/b(x)$ are called *rational functions* over the field F.

When we pause to consider this method of constructing a field $Q(PF(x))$ from the original field F, we see that a key step is the introduction of the particular polynomial x, for in the notation $\sum a_ix^i / \sum b_ix^i$ we can represent the rational function in terms of x and numbers of F.

On the one hand, we may think of $Q(PF(x))$ as an extension of F, for we can show (*1*) $Q(PF(x))$ contains a subset F' of rational functions of the form a/e isomorphic to F; and (*2*) $Q(PF(x))$ is not isomorphic to F. Property (*1*) follows from Corollary 1.1 in **39.1** and **U.1.1** in **37.1**. Property

(2) follows from (*39.1*) which shows that $\sum a_i x^i = z$ in $Q(PF(x))$ if and only if every $a_i = z$; whereas for every a in F there is a relation $a - ea^1 = z$ in which $a_0 = a$ and $a_1 = -e \neq z$. Thus the polynomial x in $Q(PF(x))$ has a property with respect to addition and multiplication which is not possessed by any element of F, and this precludes isomorphism.

On the other hand, a different way of viewing the property $\sum a_i x^i = z$ if and only if every $a_i = z$, is to say that x is not the solution of a polynomial type equation with nonzero coefficients in F. In other words, the polynomial x is introduced in such a way as to go beyond or transcend algebraic manipulations in F.

Combining these observations we describe $Q(PF(x))$ as a *transcendental extension of the field F*. Transcendental is to remind us of the properties of x, and extension is to remind us that $Q(PF(x))$ contains a subfield isomorphic to F.

There is nothing to prevent us from making a double transcendental extension of the field F. First we can form a domain of polynomials $\sum a_i(x) y^i$ whose coefficients are in $PF(x)$, and then we can take these in pairs, with nonzero denominators, to form a field of rational functions in the two special polynomials x and y over the field F.

EXERCISES

39.1. Prove Corollary 1.2.

39.2. As another example showing that the converse of Corollary 2.2 is not valid, find the product of the matric polynomials $A_0 + A_1 X$ and $B_0 + B_1 X$ when

$$A_0 = \begin{pmatrix} 0 & 1 \\ 1 & 2 \end{pmatrix}, \quad A_1 = \begin{pmatrix} 1 & 1 \\ 1 & 1 \end{pmatrix}, \quad B_0 = \begin{pmatrix} -2 & 1 \\ 1 & 0 \end{pmatrix}, \quad B_1 = \begin{pmatrix} -1 & 1 \\ 1 & -1 \end{pmatrix}.$$

39.3. If F is the Galois field $J(11)$, illustrate the division algorithm in the domain $PF(x)$ by finding the quotient and remainder when $a(x) = 2x^5 + 4x^2 + 3x + 7$ is divided by $b(x) = 3x^2 + 2x + 2$.

39.4. In the domain $PF(x)$ when $F = J(11)$ find $d(x)$, $s(x)$, $t(x)$ so that $d(x) = (a(x), b(x)) = s(x)a(x) + t(x)b(x)$ when

$a(x) = x^4 + 2x^3 + 5x + 2$ and $b(x) = 3x^4 + 6x^3 + 8x^2 + 9x + 8.$

39.5. For $n = 3, 4, 5$ pursue the method suggested in **39.3** for enumerating the prime polynomials of degree n in $PF(x)$ when $F = J(2)$.

39.6. Show there are $(p^2 - p)/2$ and $(p^3 - p)/3$ irreducible monic polynomials of degrees 2 and 3, respectively, in $PF(x)$ when $F = J(p)$ where p is a prime in J.

39.7. In $PF(x)$ when $F = J(5)$ find the standard form for $2x^5 + 2x^4 + 2x^3 + 3x + 1$. (Suggestions: Remove a constant factor so that the remaining factor is monic; then seek linear monic factors, if any; then seek irreducible quadratic monic factors, if any.)

39.8. Show that if a polynomial $a(x)$ of degree s in $PF(x)$ has no factors of degree m in $PF(x)$, where $1 \leqslant m \leqslant [s/2]$, then $a(x)$ is a prime polynomial.

CHAPTER 40

Modular fields

40.1. Residue classes in a ring

Since the elements of a ring R form a commutative group under addition,
we may apply immediately the theorems in Chapter 33.

Thus if H is a subset of R and we define $a \equiv b$ mod H if and only if
$a - b$ is in H, then we know from Theorem 7 in **33.2** that this relation is an
equivalence relation if and only if H is a subgroup of the additive group of
R. Such an equivalence relation divides R exhaustively into mutually
exclusive classes of elements which we shall call *residue classes* of R modulo
H. If we let (a-class) represent the class to which a belongs modulo H,
then we obtain the criterion

(40.1) (a-class) = (b-class)   if and only if $a \equiv b$ mod H.

If H is an additive subgroup of R, then the residue classes of R modulo
H will form a group under addition of residue classes:

(40.2) (a-class) + (b-class) = (($a + b$)-class).

For we know from Theorems 9 and 10 in **33.4** that the additional restriction
on H which is necessary and sufficient to effect this result is that H is an
invariant subgroup of the additive group of R, but this condition is
automatically fulfilled since addition in R is commutative.

321

We turn our attention to the natural definition of multiplication of residue classes of R modulo H—namely,

$$(40.3) \qquad (a\text{-class})(b\text{-class}) = (ab\text{-class}).$$

Since this proposed multiplication is obviously closed, we ask what additional conditions, if any, must be imposed on H to guarantee that this new multiplication is well defined. That is, if $A \equiv a \bmod H$ and $B \equiv b \bmod H$, we seek necessary and sufficient conditions that $AB \equiv ab \bmod H$. In other words, if we know $A = a + h_1$ and $B = b + h_2$, where h_1 and h_2 are any elements of H, what conditions are necessary and sufficient to guarantee that $AB - ab$ is in H? Since

$$AB - ab = (a + h_1)(b + h_2) - ab = h_1 b + a h_2 + h_1 h_2$$

must be in H for every h_1 and h_2 in H and every a and b in R, we can first set $h_1 = z$ (since H must contain z) and later set $h_2 = z$ to obtain these two necessary conditions:

(1) ah must be in H for every h in H and every a in R;
(2) hb must be in H for every h in H and every b in R.

Of course, if the product in R is commutative, we may combine these two conditions into the single condition (1).

As we examine the expression $c = h_1 b + a h_2 + h_1 h_2$, we see that the conditions (1) and (2) are sufficient to make c be in H. For H, being an additive subgroup of R, is closed under addition, and $h_1 b$ is in H by (2), $a h_2$ is in H by (1), and $h_1 h_2$ is in H by (1), or by (2), since h_2 (being in H) is, of course, an element of R.

An additive subgroup H of R having the property (1) is called a *left-ideal* of R. An additive subgroup H of R having the property (2) is called a *right-ideal* of R. An additive subgroup H of R having both properties (1) and (2) is called a *two-sided ideal* of R.

The discussion presented above proves the following theorem.

Theorem 1: Multiplication of residue classes of R modulo an additive subgroup H, defined by (40.3), is well defined if and only if H is a two-sided ideal of R.

For the domain J with residue classes modulo a fixed integer m we have shown directly that Theorem 1 is true. But let us check this result from the new viewpoint. The additive subgroup H which is involved is the set of all integers km which are multiples of m. To show that H is a two-sided ideal we need to check only (1) because multiplication in J is commutative. But checking (1) is trivial, for if a is any integer in J and km is any integer in H, we find that $a(km) = (ak)m$ is in H.

If H is an ideal of R, distinct from R itself, then H will be called a *proper ideal* of R.

Theorem 2: If H is a proper two-sided ideal of R, then under (40.1), (40.2), and (40.3), the residue classes of R modulo H form a ring, designated as R/H and called a *modular ring*.

Proof: Since H is a proper subset of R, there are at least two residue classes in R/H. Because H is additive subgroup of R we know that (40.1) is an equivalence relation and that the residue classes form a commutative group under (40.2). Since H is a two-sided ideal, we know from Theorem 1 that the product (40.3) is closed and well defined. Since multiplication in R is associative and distributive over addition, it follows readily from (40.1), (40.2), and (40.3) that the same properties hold in R/H.

40.2. Modular fields

The product (40.3) is such that if R is commutative, then R/H is also commutative; and if R has an identity e, then the (e-class) serves as the identity for R/H. In this section we determine what further conditions on H will guarantee that R/H is a field.

If H is a proper ideal of R such that the only ideals of R containing H are H and R, then H is called a *maximal ideal* of R.

Theorem 3: If R is a commutative ring with an identity and if H is a proper ideal of R, then a necessary and sufficient condition that R/H is a field is that H is a maximal ideal of R.

Proof: Since R is commutative, an ideal H is of course two-sided, and since H is proper, Theorem 2 guarantees R/H is defined and is at least a ring. Since R has an identity e, the (e-class) serves as the identity for R/H. The (z-class) is made up of the elements of H. For every element a in R, but not in H, so that (a-class) $\neq$ (z-class), we shall show that a necessary and sufficient condition for the existence of an inverse (b-class) such that (a-class)(b-class) $=$ (e-class) is that H is a maximal ideal of R. The test condition is that b and h_0 exist, with h_0 in H, such that $ab + h_0 = e$. This leads us to consider the set H': ($ax + h$) of all elements in R of the form $ax + h$ where x runs over R and h runs over H. We shall show that H' is an ideal of R.

First, to see that H' is an additive subgroup of R we apply the test in Theorem 6 of **33.1**. We find that the combination

$$(ax_1 + h_1) - (ax_2 + h_2) = a(x_1 - x_2) + (h_1 - h_2)$$

is again in H', for $x_1 - x_2$ is in R, since R is an additive group, and $h_1 - h_2$ is in H, since H is an additive subgroup.

Second, we check that H' is closed under right (and left) multiplication by any element r in R. For by the distributive and associative properties in R we have $(ax + h)r = a(xr) + hr$; then xr is in R, since R is closed under multiplication, and hr is in H, because H is an ideal.

Hence H' is an ideal.

Furthermore, by taking $x = z$, we see that H' contains every element in H. By taking $x = e$ and $h = z$, we see that H' contains a, which is not in H. Therefore H' contains H properly.

(A) If we suppose H to be a maximal proper ideal, then H' must be R itself. Hence every element in R can be written in the form $ax + h$. In particular, $x = b$ and $h = h_0$ must exist so that $ab + h_0 = e$. This implies $(a\text{-class})(b\text{-class}) = (e\text{-class})$. Since this is possible for every $(a\text{-class}) \neq (z\text{-class})$, we conclude that R/H is a field.

(B) Conversely, suppose R/H is a field. Since H is a proper ideal of R, there exist elements in R which are not in H. Suppose that H'' is any ideal containing H properly, and let a be in H'', but not in H. Then $(a\text{-class}) \neq (z\text{-class})$ and since R/H is a field, there exists b in R so that $(a\text{-class})(b\text{-class}) = (e\text{-class})$ which means there exists h_0 in H so that $ab + h_0 = e$. Since the ideal H'' is closed under addition and closed under multiplication by any element (such as b) in R, it follows that H'' contains $ab + h_0 = e$. But if H'' contains e, then H'' also contains $er = r$ for every r in R. In other words, $H'' = R$ and H is a maximal ideal.

This completes the proof of Theorem 3.

40.3.   Examples of modular fields

Let us consider several examples to illustrate Theorem 3.

When we considered the domain J modulo m when m is composite, we found $J(m)$ to be not a field, in fact, not even a domain, because of the presence of proper divisors of zero. But if p is a prime, we found $J(p)$ to be a field. Theorem 3 gives us a new explanation of this phenomenon. For the ideal H we have the subset of J made up of all integers km which are multiples of the fixed integer m. If m is composite, say $m = ab$, $1 < a < m$, $1 < b < m$, then the ideal $H = (km)$ is not maximal, being contained in the proper ideal $H_1 = (ka)$ made up of all multiples of a. But if p is a prime, we can show that the ideal $H = (kp)$ is maximal; for if r is not in H, then $(r, p) = 1$ and there exist integers u and v such that $ur + vp = 1$; consequently, if H' is an ideal which contains H and r, then H' contains 1, and hence H' contains every integer in J; in other words, $H = (kp)$ is a maximal ideal of J. By Theorem 3 it follows that $J(p) = J/H$ is a field, the Galois field of p elements, already obtained directly in earlier chapters.

As a second example we can follow exactly the reasoning in the paragraph above to start from the polynomial domain $PF(x)$ over a field F and consider a fixed polynomial $m(x)$. The set $(k(x)m(x))$ of all multiples of $m(x)$ is an ideal H of $PF(x)$; but, by exactly the same reasoning as given above for J and m, the ideal H is proper and maximal if and only if we use for $m(x)$ a polynomial $p(x)$ which is irreducible in $PF(x)$. Hence by Theorem 3 the ring $PF(x)/H$ of residue classes of polynomials of $PF(x)$ reduced modulo $H = (k(x)p(x))$ is a field if and only if $p(x)$ is irreducible in $PF(x)$.

Let us examine in more detail the case where $m(x)$ is neither zero nor a unit, and hence $m(x)$ is of degree $\geqslant 1$. In analogy with **G.1** of **13.1** we can show that each residue class, say the $(a(x)$-class$)$, of $PF(x)$ modulo $H = (k(x)m(x))$ contains one and only one polynomial $r(x)$ which is either the zero polynomial or is of degree less than the degree of $m(x)$. On the one hand, the division algorithm $a(x) = q(x)m(x) + r(x)$ implies $a(x) \equiv r(x)$ mod H, so there is at least one $r(x)$ with the desired properties. On the other hand, $r(x) \equiv r_1(x)$ mod H implies $r(x) - r_1(x) = k(x)m(x)$; but if $k(x) \neq z$, then the degree on the right is at least equal to the degree of $m(x)$; so if the degrees of $r(x)$ and $r_1(x)$ are both less than the degree of $m(x)$ or if either of them is z, then a contradiction has been reached which can only be resolved by having $k(x) = z$ and $r(x) = r_1(x)$.

Of course, every polynomial $r(x)$, either zero or of degree less than the degree of $m(x)$, is in some residue class mod H by the reflexive property of congruence mod H. So a representative residue system for $PF(x)/H$ consists of all polynomials in $PF(x)$ which are either zero or of degree less than the degree of $m(x)$.

We showed that $PF(x)$ always contains irreducible polynomials of degree 1, say $p(x) = x - r$, but these are of little interest as far as Theorem 3 is concerned, for in this case we can show that $PF(x)/H$ is isomorphic to F itself. This follows from the preceding paragraph, for here the representative residue system, modulo $x - r$, consists of all the constant polynomials, that is, zero and the polynomials of degree 0.

But if $PF(x)$ contains irreducible polynomials of degree greater than 1, the application of Theorem 3 is more exciting.

For example, if F is the Galois field $J(2)$, we showed that $p(x) = x^2 + x + 1$ is an irreducible polynomial of degree 2. The representative residue system of $PF(x)/H$, where $H = (k(x)p(x))$, is 0, 1, x, $x + 1$; so

Theorem 3 allows us to produce a field consisting of four classes of polynomials. We show the additive and multiplicative group tables for this field:

$(+)$

0	1	x	$x + 1$
1	0	$x + 1$	x
x	$x + 1$	0	1
$x + 1$	x	1	0

,

$(\cdot)$

1	x	$x + 1$
x	$x + 1$	1
$x + 1$	1	x

.

For example, operating in $PF(x)$ mod H, we have $x(x + 1) = x^2 + x \equiv -1 \equiv 1$, since we can replace $x^2 + x$ by -1, mod $p(x)$, and we can replace -1 by 1, mod 2.

As another example let us consider $p(x) = x^3 - 3$ as a polynomial in $PRa(x)$ where Ra is the rational field. There are several ways to see that $p(x)$ is irreducible in this domain $PRa(x)$. For instance, since the degree of $p(x)$ is 3, if there are no linear factors, then there are no factors of degree 2. But the existence in $PRa(x)$ of a linear factor $x - r$ implies $x^3 - 3 = (x - r)(x^2 + ax + b)$ with r, a, and b rational. But this in turn implies that $r^3 - 3 = 0$ where $r = u/v$ where u and v are integers in J with $v \neq 0$. This is equivalent to $u^3 = 3v^3$, a Diophantine problem. Knowing $v \neq 0$ we consider the exponent of the prime 3 on both sides of the equation and arrive at a contradiction of the fundamental theorem of arithmetic in the domain J. To resolve the contradiction we must conclude that $p(x) = x^3 - 3$ is irreducible in $PRa(x)$.

By Theorem 3, if we take H to be the set of all multiples of $p(x) = x^3 - 3$, then $PRa(x)/H$ is a field. This field has infinitely many classes for which a representative residue system is given by $ax^2 + bx + c$ where a, b, c are any numbers in Ra. Addition mod H is as follows:

$$(ax^2 + bx + c) + (a_1x^2 + b_1x + c_1)$$
$$\equiv (a + a_1)x^2 + (b + b_1)x + (c + c_1).$$

Multiplication mod H is accomplished by replacing x^3 by 3, hence

$$(ax^2 + bx + c)(a_1x^2 + b_1x + c_1)$$
$$\equiv (ac_1 + bb_1 + ca_1)x^2 + (3aa_1 + bc_1 + cb_1)x + (3ab_1 + 3ba_1 + cc_1).$$

As an example of operating within this field, let us find the inverse of $A(x) = 2x^2 + x + 1$.

One method is to use the Euclid algorithm, for if we express $1 = (A(x), p(x)) = u(x)A(x) + v(x)p(x)$, then $u(x)$, reduced modulo $p(x)$

if desired, will be in the inverse class. To facilitate the division process we may use $4p(x)$, instead of $p(x)$:

$$
\begin{array}{r}
2x - 1 \\
\hline
2x^2 + x + 1 \,\big)\, 4x^3 \qquad\qquad\quad - 12 \\
4x^3 + 2x^2 + 2x \\
\hline
-2x^2 - 2x - 12 \\
-2x^2 - x - 1 \\
\hline
-x - 11
\end{array}
$$

$$
\begin{array}{r}
-2x + 21 \\
\hline
2x^2 + x + 1 \,\big)\, 2x^2 + x + 1 \\
2x^2 + 22x \\
\hline
-21x + 1 \\
-21x - 231 \\
\hline
232.
\end{array}
$$

From

$$
\begin{aligned}
232 &= A(x) - (x + 11)(2x - 21) \\
&= A(x) + (2x - 21)(4p(x) - (2x - 1)A(x)) \\
&= (-4x^2 + 44x - 20)A(x) + (8x - 84)p(x)
\end{aligned}
$$

we find $u(x) = (-x^2 + 11x - 5)/58$, and this answer does check.

Another method is to rely on Theorem 3, for knowing that $u(x) = ax^2 + bx + c$ must exist so that $A(x)u(x) \equiv 1 \bmod H$, we find

$$
2ax^4 + (2b + a)x^3 + (a + b + 2c)x^2 + (b + c)x + c
$$
$$
\equiv (a + b + 2c)x^2 + (6a + b + c)x + (3a + 6b + c) \equiv 1
$$

which yields the system of equations

$$
a + b + 2c = 0, \quad 6a + b + c = 0, \quad 3a + 6b + c = 1
$$

for determining a, b, c. These equations are the result, of course, of the uniqueness of the representative residue system.

It may be instructive to consider an alternate development of the last example. Let us examine the system F of all ordered triples (a, b, c) of rational numbers a, b, c subject to the following rules:

$(a, b, c) = (a_1, b_1, c_1)$ if and only if $a = a_1$, $b = b_1$, $c = c_1$;
$(a, b, c) + (a_1, b_1, c_1) = (a + a_1, b + b_1, c + c_1)$;
$(a, b, c)(a_1, b_1, c_1)$
$\quad = (ac_1 + bb_1 + ca_1, 3aa_1 + bc_1 + cb_1, 3ab_1 + 3ba_1 + cc_1)$.

By direct check we can verify that these definitions of equality, addition, and multiplication result in F being a field. If only this one example is to be studied, this is an economical way to proceed, but the properties obtained seem fortuitous, particularly those resulting from the unusual rule of multiplication. From our vantage point of passing from Ra to

$PRa(x)$ to $PRa(x)/H$, where H is the ideal generated by the irreducible polynomial $p(x) = x^3 - 3$, we find no mystery in the rule of multiplication. Furthermore, we are in possession of a method of generating new fields which is of great generality.

40.4.   Algebraic versus transcendental extensions

In the preceding examples of modular fields where the ideal H consists of all multiples of a polynomial $p(x)$ of degree > 1 which is irreducible in $PF(x)$, we describe the field $F_1 = PF(x)/H$ as being an "algebraic extension of the field F." We justify this terminology in the following way.

On the one hand, F_1 contains a subsystem isomorphic to F, for the set F' of all constant polynomials (that is, the zero polynomial and all polynomials of degree 0) represents residue classes mod H with the desired property under the natural correspondence $aT = a$.

On the other hand, F_1 is not isomorphic to F. For if F_1 were isomorphic to F, then the polynomial domains $PF_1(y)$ and $PF(x)$ would be isomorphic. In particular, the correspondence between F' and F already mentioned would imply that $p(y)$ with coefficients in F' should correspond to $p(x)$ with coefficients in F. But in $PF_1(y)$, if $p(x)$ is of degree > 1, we can show that $p(y)$ is reducible, whereas in $PF(x)$ we know that $p(x)$ is irreducible.

For in $PF_1(y)$ we may apply the division algorithm with $p(y)$ as dividend and $y - x$ as divisor. Then $p(y) = (y - x)q(y) + r(x)$ where the remainder is a polynomial not involving y. Replacing y by x we obtain $r(x) = p(x) \equiv z$ mod H. Thus if $p(y)$ is of degree > 1, we can conclude that $p(y) = (y - x)q(y)$ is reducible in $PF_1(y)$.

Finally, this same argument justifies our use of the adjective "algebraic," for we see that the polynomial x used in constructing $PF(x)$ has become in $PF_1(y)$ the solution of a nontrivial polynomial type equation $p(y) = z$ whose coefficients are in F', the isomorphic counterpart of F.

For example, $p(x) = x^3 - 3$ is irreducible in $PRa(x)$. But if $F_1 = PRa(x)/H$, where H is the ideal generated by $p(x)$, then in $PF_1(y)$ we find that $p(y) = y^3 - 3$ is reducible. For we have $x^3 \equiv 3$ mod H, hence we find $y^3 - 3 \equiv y^3 - x^3 = (y - x)(y^2 + xy + x^2)$.

Similarly, $p(x) = x^2 + x + 1$ is irreducible in $PF(x)$, where $F = J(2)$. But if $F_1 = PF(x)/H$, where H is the ideal generated by $p(x)$, then in $PF_1(y)$ we find that $p(y)$ is reducible, for $x^2 + x \equiv 1$ mod H, and hence

$$y^2 + y + 1 \equiv y^2 - x^2 + y - x = (y - x)(y + x + 1).$$

If a polynomial domain $PF(x)$ has only linear irreducible polynomials, then it is impossible to obtain an algebraic extension which contains F properly, so we say that F is algebraically closed. None of the fields which we have thus far studied is algebraically closed. In fact for every Galois field $J(p)$ and for the rational field Ra, we state (without proof) the following result: for every integer $m \geqslant 1$, there exists in the corresponding polynomial domain at least one irreducible polynomial of degree m. So all these fields have algebraic extensions of any desired degree m.

However, there do exist algebraically closed fields. One example with which the reader may already be familiar is the complex field C. One way to obtain C is to start from the real field Re (see Chapter 41), to note that $p(x) = x^2 + 1$ is irreducible in $PRe(x)$, and then to construct the modular field $C = PRe(x)/H$, where H is the ideal generated by $p(x)$. Thus the elements of C are residue classes of polynomials represented by $a + bx$, where a and b are in Re, and in multiplication we have $x^2 \equiv -1 \bmod H$. If we give to x the special abbreviation i, the resulting complex numbers $a + bi$ should look familiar.

In closing we contrast the algebraic extension $F_1 = PF(x)/H$, where H is the ideal generated by an irreducible polynomial $p(x)$, with the transcendental extension $F_2 = Q(PF(x))$ explained in **39.4**. In the first case, x is the solution of a nontrivial polynomial equation $p(y) = z$ with coefficients in F. In the second case, x is not the solution of any polynomial equation with coefficients in F, except the trivial case where every coefficient is zero.

We find the following parallel outline helpful in remembering and contrasting these methods of extension.

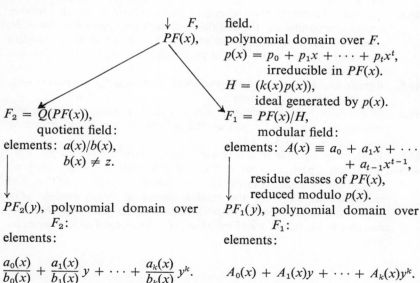

$$\downarrow \quad F, \quad \text{field.}$$
$$PF(x), \quad \text{polynomial domain over } F.$$
$$p(x) = p_0 + p_1 x + \cdots + p_t x^t,$$
$$\text{irreducible in } PF(x).$$
$$H = (k(x)p(x)),$$
$$\text{ideal generated by } p(x).$$

$F_2 = Q(PF(x)),$
    quotient field:
elements: $a(x)/b(x),$
        $b(x) \neq z.$

$F_1 = PF(x)/H,$
    modular field:
elements: $A(x) \equiv a_0 + a_1 x + \cdots$
        $+ a_{t-1} x^{t-1},$
    residue classes of $PF(x),$
    reduced modulo $p(x).$

$PF_2(y)$, polynomial domain over
    $F_2:$
elements:

$PF_1(y)$, polynomial domain over
    $F_1:$
elements:

$$\frac{a_0(x)}{b_0(x)} + \frac{a_1(x)}{b_1(x)} y + \cdots + \frac{a_k(x)}{b_k(x)} y^k.$$

$$A_0(x) + A_1(x)y + \cdots + A_k(x)y^k.$$

Since F_2 contains a subsystem of quotients a/e isomorphic to F, we find $PF_2(y)$ contains a subsystem of polynomials isomorphic to those in $PF(x)$.

But if

$$s(y) = a_0 + a_1 y + \cdots + a_k y^k$$

is any one of these, we find $s(x) = z$ if and only if every $a_i = z$, so we say F_2 is a *transcendental* extension of F.

Since F_1 contains a subsystem of residue classes a_0 isomorphic to F, we find $PF_1(y)$ contains a subsystem of polynomials isomorphic to those in $PF(x)$.

In particular, $PF_1(y)$ contains

$$p(y) = p_0 + p_1 y + \cdots + p_t y^t.$$

Since $p(x) \equiv z$ in $PF_1(y)$ we say that F_1 is an *algebraic* extension of F.

EXERCISES

40.1. If a is in R, the set H of all elements in R of the form xa, where x is in R, is a left-ideal of R. (Check first that H is an additive subgroup of R; check next that H is closed under left-multiplication by every element in R.)

40.2. If a and b are in R, show that the set of all elements in R of the form $xa + yb$, where x and y are in R, is a left-ideal of R.

40.3. Note that if R does not have an identity, then the ideals in EXS. **40.1** and **40.2** may not contain a (or b). For example, consider $R = J_3$, the ring of all multiples of 3, and the ideal H generated by $a = 3$ and $b = 6$.

40.4. Illustrate Theorem 2 by choosing representatives for the residue classes and writing out the addition and multiplication tables for R/H, when R is the ring of polynomials over $F = J(3)$ and H is the ideal generated by $m(x) = x^2 - 1$. In particular, note that R/H has proper divisors of zero.

40.5. Repeat EX. **40.4**, when H is the ideal generated by $p(x) = x^2 - 2$, and thus illustrate Theorem 3.

40.6. In the cubic field of residue classes of $PRa(x)$ modulo the irreducible polynomial $p(x) = x^3 - 4$ find the inverse of the class containing $a(x) = x^2 + 2x + 3$.

40.7. Produce an example of a field with eight elements.

40.8. If q is not a perfect square in the field F, so that $p(x) = x^2 - q$ is an irreducible polynomial in $PF(x)$, write out the equality, addition, and multiplication rules for the residue classes of $PF(x)$ modulo $p(x)$. If H is the ideal generated by $p(x)$, show that the field $PF(x)/H$ is isomorphic to the field $F\sqrt{q}$ of matrices (as in Theorem 9 of **35.4**, or as in **37.3**).

CHAPTER 41

The real field and decimal representation of rational numbers

41.1. Decimal fractions

In this chapter we pursue the matter of constructing a new field from a known field. Although the method used is only one instance of a general method of extension by means of a *valuation*, we shall confine our attention to the case where the base field is the rational field *Ra*, the valuation used is the familiar absolute value of *Ra* (see **38.3**), and the resulting new field is the real field *Re*. We shall approach the subject from the standpoint of decimal fractions and decimal representation of rational numbers.

If the base for representing rational integers is the usual base 10, then it is of particular interest to study decimal fractions a/b, where we limit the denominator b to be of the form $b = 10^k$ with the exponent k a nonnegative integer, interpreting $10^0 = 1$. For such decimal fractions there is a convenient positional notation which we shall now describe in detail.

Since we may express $a > 0$ in the form

$$a = a_m 10^m + \cdots + a_1 10 + a_0; \quad 0 < a_m < 10;$$
$$0 \leqslant a_i < 10, \; 0 \leqslant i < m;$$

331

it follows that when $a > 0$ we may write

$$a/10^k = a_m 10^m/10^k + \cdots + a_1 10/10^k + a_0/10^k.$$

If $m \geqslant k$, we have

$$a/10^k = a_m 10^{m-k} + \cdots + a_{k+1}10 + a_k + a_{k-1}/10 + \cdots \\ + a_1/10^{k-1} + a_0/10^k;$$

and if we define $b_{i-k} = a_i$, for $i = 0, 1, \ldots, m$, then we may write $a/10^k$ in "decimal notation" as follows:

$$a/10^k = b_{m-k}\ldots b_1 b_0.b_{-1}b_{-2}\ldots b_{-k}.$$

In this notation, if $j \geqslant 0$, we are to interpret b_j by its $j + 1$ position to the *left* of the period or "decimal point" to represent $b_j 10^j$; but if $j > 0$, we are to interpret b_{-j} by its jth position to the *right* of the decimal point to represent the decimal fraction $b_{-j}/10^j$; then if the whole symbol is understood to represent the sum of these components, it correctly represents $a/10^k$.

If $m < k$, we again set $b_{i-k} = a_i$, and find

$$a/10^k = a_m/10^{k-m} + \cdots + a_1/10^{k-1} + a_0/10^k \\ = b_{-(k-m)}/10^{k-m} + \cdots + b_{-(k-1)}/10^{k-1} + b_{-k}/10^k.$$

But in this case to effect a suitable positional notation, if $k - m > 1$ we must define $b_{-1} = b_{-2} = \cdots = b_{-(k-m-1)} = 0$, so that in the symbol

$$a/10^k = .00\ldots 0b_{-(k-m)}\ldots b_{-k}$$

we will have b_{-j} occurring in the jth position to the *right* of the decimal point.

Thus, for examples, we have

$$30.302 = 30 + 3/10 + 2/1000 = 31302/1000; \\ .0071 = 7/1000 + 1/10000 = 71/10000.$$

In particular we want to observe that when $j \geqslant i + 1$,

(41.1) $\qquad\qquad .00\ldots 0b_{-(i+1)}\ldots b_{-j} < 1/10^i.$

For the inequality to be checked is equivalent, by the definitions above, to the following inequality:

$$(b_{-(i+1)}10^{j-(i+1)} + \cdots + b_{-j})/10^j < 1/10^i,$$

which reduces to the following inequality in *integers*

$$b_{-(i+1)}10^{j-(i+1)} + \cdots + b_{-j} < 10^{j-i}.$$

But this last inequality is known to be valid because of the restriction $0 \leqslant b_k < 10$ on all of the b's.

If $a < 0$ we may employ the above notation for $(-a)/10^k$ and write $a/10^k = - \{(-a)/10^k\}$, prefixing the negative sign to the decimal representation.

The set D of *all decimal fractions* is a domain, but *not* a field; for D is closed under addition and multiplication, contains $0/1$ and $1/1$, and has all the other properties for a domain because D is a subset of Ra; however, D is *not* a field because the inverse of a nonzero fraction $a/10^k$ of D is in D if and only if a is of the form $2^s 5^t$, $s \geqslant 0$, $t \geqslant 0$. For example, although $7/2 = 35/10$ is in D, the inverse rational number $2/7$ is not in D.

However, we can introduce a larger number system which contains numbers isomorphic to the rational numbers in such a way that we shall be able to represent *any rational number* (or, more precisely, its isomorphic image) using only decimal fractions. This enlarged number system is known as the *real number system* or (since it does have the required properties) as the *real field*.

The device which we use in making this extension is already known to the reader, for he is accustomed to "approximating" a fraction such as $2/7$ by an appropriately chosen decimal fraction, such as .285714285714. Here it will be worth while to examine the method of finding an appropriate decimal fraction, the exact meaning of the approximation, and the periodic character of the representation, for these matters are closely related to the division algorithm, to the properties of inequalities and absolute value, and to the theory of congruences, and these seem proper subjects for a lesson in the theory of numbers.

41.2.   Regular sequences

We shall be interested in this section in infinite sequences of rational numbers. Each such sequence may be indicated by $a_1, a_2, \ldots, a_n, \ldots$ or more briefly by $\{a_i\}$.

A *regular* sequence $\{a_i\}$ is an infinite sequence of rational numbers, such that for any assigned positive rational number ϵ, however small, it is possible to find a corresponding rational integer $N = N(\epsilon)$ so that

$$|a_N - a_i| < \epsilon \quad \text{for all } i > N(\epsilon).$$

The order and the absolute value used in this definition are those described in **38.2** and **38.3** for the particular case of the rational field Ra.

It is important to observe about this definition of a regular sequence, that it is *not* necessary to find one N which will serve for *all* choices of ϵ; rather, all that is required is that each time an ϵ is selected, that it shall be possible to find the corresponding $N(\epsilon)$—purposely written this way to emphasize that N depends upon ϵ. When a sequence is regular what will ordinarily happen is that as ϵ is chosen smaller and smaller, $N(\epsilon)$ must be selected larger and larger. On the other hand, it is *not* sufficient to guarantee that a sequence is regular to produce an $N(\epsilon)$ suitable for *one* assigned ϵ; we must be able to find an $N(\epsilon)$ for *any* assigned ϵ.

The sequence $\{a_i\}$ where $a_i = 2^i$ is *not* a regular sequence, for even with $\epsilon = 1$ it is impossible to make $|a_i - a_j| < \epsilon$ whenever $i \neq j$.

The sequence $\{a_i\}$ where $a_i = 1/3$ for every value of i is a trivial example of a regular sequence, for no matter how small the positive rational number ϵ is chosen, we may take $N(\epsilon) = 1$ and guarantee $|a_1 - a_i| < \epsilon$ for $i > 1$, inasmuch as $a_i - a_j = 0$ for all i and j.

A less trivial example is provided by the sequence $\{a_i\}$ where $a_n = 1 - 1/2^n$. Here $a_j - a_i = 1/2^i - 1/2^j$, hence by **A.4** of **38.3** we may write $|a_j - a_i| < 1/2^i + 1/2^j$. But when $j < i$, we have $2^j < 2^i$ and $1/2^j > 1/2^i$; hence by **W.3**, **W.4** of **38.2** we have $|a_j - a_i| < 2/2^j$ when $i > j$. Given $\epsilon = a/b$, positive, however small, we can make $2/2^j < a/b = \epsilon$ or $2^j a > 2b$, by choosing j sufficiently large; for if, in the binary system, $2b = b_m 2^m + \cdots + b_1 2$, then $j = m + 1$ will suffice. Using the transitive property **W.3**, we may take $N(\epsilon) = m + 1$ and have

$$|a_N - a_i| < \epsilon \quad \text{when } i > N.$$

(For example, if $\epsilon = 1/5000$, then $2b = 10^4 = (10011100010000)_2$, $m = 13$, $N(\epsilon) = 14$, and $|a_{14} - a_i| < 1/5000$ for $i > 14$.) Thus $\{a_i\}$ is a regular sequence.

A fundamental example involving decimal fractions may be described as follows. Let $b_m, b_{m-1}, \ldots, b_0, b_{-1}, \ldots, b_{-i}, \ldots$ be any infinite sequence of integers b_i satisfying $0 \leqslant b_i < 10$; define a corresponding sequence $\{a_i\}$ of decimal fractions as follows: $a_i = b_m \ldots b_0.b_{-1} \ldots b_{-i}$. A sequence of this type will be called an *infinite decimal*, designated by

$$\{a_i\} = b_m \ldots b_0.b_{-1} \ldots b_{-i} \ldots.$$

Theorem: An infinite decimal is a regular sequence.

Proof: If $i > j$, then we may apply (41.1) to see that

$$a_i - a_j = .00 \ldots 0 b_{-(j+1)} \ldots b_{-i} < 1/10^j.$$

Hence if we are given $\epsilon = a/b > 0$ with $b = q_t 10^t + \cdots + q_1 10 + q_0$ and $0 \leqslant q_i < 10$, we may make $1/10^j < \epsilon$ if we can make $10^j a > b$; but this is easily arranged by taking $j = t + 1$. So we select $N(\epsilon) = t + 1$ and by **W.3** we have

$$|a_N - a_i| < \epsilon \quad \text{when } i > N.$$

Thus we have shown $\{a_i\} = b_m \ldots b_0.b_{-1} \ldots b_{-i} \ldots$ to be a regular sequence.

41.3. The real number system

The concepts of the preceding sections may be used to define the real number system.

(1) *Real numbers:*   A real number is a regular sequence $\{a_i\}$ of rational numbers; and every regular sequence of rational numbers defines a real number.

(2) *Equality:*   Two real numbers $\{a_i\}$ and $\{b_i\}$ are said to be equal, written $\{a_i\} = \{b_i\}$, if and only if for any given positive rational number ϵ, there exists an integer $N(\epsilon)$ such that $|a_i - b_i| < \epsilon$ when $i > N$.

(3) *Addition:*   The sum of two real numbers $\{a_i\}$ and $\{b_i\}$ is defined to be the sequence $\{c_i\}$ in which $c_i = a_i + b_i$.

(4) *Multiplication:*   The product of two real numbers $\{a_i\}$ and $\{b_i\}$ is defined to be the sequence $\{c_i\}$ in which $c_i = a_i b_i$.

Logically we should now proceed to prove the theorem: "The set *Re* of all real numbers forms a field, known as the real field." But all the details would take us too far away from our present purpose of exploring some of the number theory concerned with the decimal representation of rational numbers; so we content ourselves with suggesting at the end of this lesson some exercises pertinent to proving the above mentioned theorem.

It is of particular interest that among the real numbers *Re* there is a subset isomorphic to *Ra*. The subset in question contains all sequences of the type $\{a_i\}$ where $a_i = a$ for all i; these sequences may be designated $\{a\}$ and are of a type where it is trivial to show that they are regular and hence represent real numbers. The suitable correspondence *T* to establish the isomorphism is defined by $aT = \{a\}$.

Knowing that every rational number a is represented, isomorphically speaking, by a certain real number $\{a\}$, we question whether $\{a\}$ can be written as an infinite decimal. If this proves possible, it will remedy in a sense the difficulties encountered in **41.1** in studying the domain D of finite decimal fractions. For example, it is seen that $1/3$ is not in D; but now we ask whether $\{1/3\}$ may be written as an infinite decimal, i.e., is there a real number of the type $\{a_i\} = b_m \ldots b_0.b_{-1} \ldots b_{-i} \ldots$ which is "equal" to $\{1/3\}$.

The reader is already familiar with the answer, although the question may never have been put to him in such a hard (precise) way. For we can show

$$\{1/3\} = 0.333\ldots \quad \text{with } b_i = 0 \text{ for } i \geqslant 0 \text{ and } b_{-i} = 3 \text{ for } i > 0.$$

For if we set $\{c_i\} = \{1/3\}$, with $c_i = 1/3$ for all i; and if we set $\{a_i\} = 0.333\ldots$, then we have

$$a_i = (3/10)\{1 + 1/10 + (1/10)^2 + \cdots + (1/10)^{i-1}\}$$

and by applying EX. **2.4**, we find

$$a_i = (3/10)\{1 - (1/10)^i\}/(1 - 1/10) = (1/3)\{1 - (1/10)^i\}.$$

Hence $|c_i - a_i| = (1/3)(1/10)^i$ which can be made less than any given positive rational number ϵ by taking i sufficiently large. Therefore by definition (2) it follows that $\{c_i\} = \{a_i\}$ or that $\{1/3\} = 0.333\ldots$.

To answer the same question in the general case will lead us to a situation that is more obviously part of the theory of numbers. By these preliminary sections we hope to have placed the problem on a sound logical basis.

41.4.   Periodic infinite decimals

An infinite decimal

$$b_m\ldots b_0.b_{-1}\ldots b_{-i}\ldots$$

will be said to be *periodic* or *repeating* if there exist two integers $s \geqslant 0$ and $k > 0$ such that

$$b_{-t} = b_{-t'} \quad \text{whenever } t > s,\ t' > s,\ t \equiv t' \bmod k.$$

For example, it was shown above that $\{1/3\}$ is represented by $0.333\ldots$ which is a periodic infinite decimal having $s = 0$ and $k = 1$.

For a periodic infinite decimal we shall use the notation

$$\{a_i\} = b_m\ldots b_0.b_{-1}\ldots b_{-s}\dot{b}_{-(s+1)}\ldots\dot{b}_{-(s+k)}$$

with a dot above the number $b_{-(s+1)}$ and another dot above $b_{-(s+k)}$; if $k = 1$, only one dot will be required.

We shall call $Q = b_m\ldots b_0$ the *whole number part* of $\{a_i\}$; $S = .b_{-1}\ldots b_{-s}$, the *nonrepeating part*; and $P = b_{-(s+1)}\ldots b_{-(s+k)}$, the *repeating part*.

In this terminology, the example given above would appear as $0.\dot{3}$, indicating that $Q = 0$, $S = 0$, $P = 3$, $s = 0$, $k = 1$. In $31.04\dot{1}2\dot{3}$, we have $Q = 31$, $S = .04$, $P = 123$, $s = 2$, $k = 3$. In $3027.\dot{0}2\dot{7}$, we have $Q = 3027$, $S = 0$, $P = 27$, $s = 0$, $k = 3$. In 5.0125, a *finite* decimal fraction, we may interpret the notation to indicate that $Q = 5$, $S = .0125$, $P = 0$, $s = 4$, $k = 1$; sometimes we shall refer to this case as that of a *terminating* decimal; most of the time we shall prefer, for uniformity, to think of this case as a periodic infinite decimal with $P = 0$, $k = 1$.

Theorem: Every periodic infinite decimal represents a *rational* real number.

Proof: Using the terminology introduced above, if

$$\{a_i\} = b_m \ldots b_0 . b_{-1} \ldots b_{-s} \dot{b}_{-(s+1)} \ldots \dot{b}_{-(s+k)},$$

then for $q \geqslant 0$ we have, again using EX. **2.4,**

$$
\begin{aligned}
a_{s+qk} &= Q + S + (P/10^{s+k})\{1 + (1/10^k) + \cdots + (1/10^k)^{q-1}\} \\
&= Q + S + (P/10^{s+k})\{1 - (1/10^k)^q\}/(1 - 1/10^k) \\
&= Q + S + \{P/10^s(10^k - 1)\}\{1 - (1/10^k)^q\}.
\end{aligned}
$$

For any $i \geqslant s$, we may set $i - s = (q-1)k + r$, $0 \leqslant r < k$, $q \geqslant 1$, and have $a_{s+(q-1)k} \leqslant a_i < a_{s+qk}$. Then if we set

(41.2) $\qquad\qquad X = Q + S + P/10^s(10^k - 1)$

we have $a_i - X < a_{s+qk} - X = -P/10^{s+qk}(10^k - 1)$.
    Since $P \leqslant 10^k - 1$ and $i < s + qk$, it follows that

$$|a_i - X| < 1/10^{s+qk} < 1/10^i, \qquad i \geqslant s.$$

Since we may make $1/10^i < \epsilon$, for any assigned positive rational number ϵ by choosing i sufficiently large, it follows that $\{a_i\} = \{X\}$. Hence we conclude that the given periodic infinite decimal represents the rational number X of (41.2) in its "real disguise" of $\{X\}$.
    For example, using this theorem we may show that:

$$31.04\dot{1}2\dot{3} = 31 + 4/100 + 123/99900 = 31 + 1373/33300;$$
$$3027.\dot{0}2\dot{7} = 3027 + 27/999 = 3037 + 1/37;$$
$$5.0125 = 5 + 125/10000 = 5 + 1/80 = 401/80;$$
$$5.0124\dot{9} = 5 + 124/10000 + 9/90000 = 401/80.$$

Converse theorem: Any positive rational real number $\{a/b\}$ may be represented by a periodic infinite decimal.

Proof: With $a > 0$, $b > 0$, we may use the division algorithm to write

(41.3) $\qquad\qquad a = Qb + r_0, \qquad 0 \leqslant r_0 < b, \qquad Q \geqslant 0.$

Then as in Chapter 5 we may represent Q in the base 10 as $Q = b_m \ldots b_0$. We may use the division algorithm to find

$$10r_0 = q_1 b + r_1, \qquad 0 \leqslant r_1 < b.$$

Since $0 \leqslant r_0 < b$, it follows on the one hand that $0 \leqslant 10r_0$, so that $-b < -r_1 \leqslant q_1 b$, hence $0 \leqslant q_1$; on the other hand, $10r_0 < 10b$, so that

$q_1 b \leqslant q_1 b + r_1 < 10b$, hence $0 \leqslant q_1 < 10$. We continue the algorithm in this same manner with

(41.4) $10r_{i-1} = q_i b + r_i,$ $0 \leqslant r_i < b,$ $0 \leqslant q_i < 10,$ $i \geqslant 1,$

until for minimal values of s and k we arrive at $r_{s+k} = r_s$, whereupon we conclude the algorithm. The conclusion will certainly be reached in at most b steps, for from the restriction $0 \leqslant r_i < b$ there are only b different possible remainders. We now define

$$S = .q_1 \ldots q_s \quad \text{and} \quad P = q_{s+1} \ldots q_{s+k}$$

and assert that

$$\{a/b\} = b_m \ldots b_0 . q_1 \ldots q_s \dot{q}_{s+1} \ldots \dot{q}_{s+k}.$$

One way to establish this equality is to use the direct theorem above which asserts that the periodic infinite decimal which we have constructed is equal to $\{X\}$, where

$$X = Q + S + P/10^s(10^k - 1).$$

For from the relations (41.3) and (41.4) we have $a/b = Q + r_0/b$, $0 = q_1/10 - r_0/b + r_1/10b, \ldots, 0 = q_s/10^s - r_{s-1}/10^{s-1}b + r_s/10^s b$, and upon adding these equations and noting the telescoping cancellations, we find

$$a/b = Q + S + r_s/10^s b.$$

Again using (41.4) we may write

$$r_s/10^s b = q_{s+1}/10^{s+1} + r_{s+1}/10^{s+1}b,$$
$$0 = q_{s+2}/10^{s+2} - r_{s+1}/10^{s+1}b + r_{s+2}/10^{s+2}b, \ldots,$$
$$0 = q_{s+k}/10^{s+k} - r_{s+k-1}/10^{s+k-1}b + r_{s+k}/10^{s+k}b.$$

Upon adding these equations we find

$$r_s/10^s b = P/10^{s+k} + r_{s+k}/10^{s+k}b.$$

Recalling that $r_{s+k} = r_s$, we may solve this last equation to show

$$r_s/10^s b = P/10^s(10^k - 1).$$

Combining these results we see that $X = a/b$ which completes the proof.

The reader will recall from elementary arithmetic that the division process represented by (41.4) may be carried out very handily by mentally shifting the decimal point one place to the right at each step, corresponding to the multiplication of the preceding remainder by 10. For example, to find the periodic infinite decimal representing $\{2/7\}$ we may arrange our work as follows:

$$.285714$$

$$7 \,|\, \overline{2.000000} \qquad r_0 = 2, \quad Q = 0,$$

$$\underline{1\ 4}$$

$$60 \qquad\qquad r_1 = 6, \quad q_1 = 2,$$

$$\underline{56}$$

$$40 \qquad\qquad r_2 = 4, \quad q_2 = 8,$$

$$\underline{35}$$

$$50 \qquad\qquad r_3 = 5, \quad q_3 = 5,$$

$$\underline{49}$$

$$10 \qquad\qquad r_4 = 1, \quad q_4 = 7,$$

$$\underline{7}$$

$$30 \qquad\qquad r_5 = 3, \quad q_5 = 1,$$

$$\underline{28}$$

$$2 \qquad\qquad r_6 = 2, \quad q_6 = 4.$$

Since $r_6 = r_0$ we have $s = 0, k = 6$, and $\{2/7\} = 0.\dot{2}8571\dot{4}$.

From the standpoint of number theory it is of interest that we can predict the minimal values of s and k in the above theorem without carrying through the complete division algorithm.

Theorem: If $b = 2^x 5^y A$ where $(A, 10) = 1$ and if $(a, b) = 1$, then in the division algorithm for finding the periodic infinite decimal representing $\{a/b\}$ the minimal values of s and k for which $r_{s+k} = r_s$ are given as follows: s is the *maximum* of x and y and k is the *exponent to which* 10 *belongs modulo A.*

Proof: Equations *(41.3)* and *(41.4)* may be written as congruences mod b as follows:

$$a \equiv r_0, \qquad 10 r_{i-1} \equiv r_i \bmod b, \qquad i \geqslant 1.$$

Since $10 \equiv 10 \bmod b$, these congruences are equivalent to

$$10^i a \equiv r_i \bmod b, \qquad i \geqslant 0.$$

Then to have $r_{s+k} = r_s$, we must have

$$10^{s+k} a \equiv 10^s a \bmod b;$$

and since $(a, b) = 1$, we must have

$$10^{s+k} \equiv 10^s \bmod b$$

for minimal values of s and k. The last congruence requires the existence of an integer t such that

$$10^s(10^k - 1) = tb = t2^x 5^y A.$$

Since 2^x and 5^y are relatively prime to $10^k - 1$, it follows that they must divide 2^s and 5^s, respectively; hence s must be at least as large as the *maximum* of x and y. If we suppose s so chosen, we are able to find a suitable value of k, for the condition above reduces to

$$2^{s-x}5^{s-y}(10^k - 1) = tA.$$

Since $(A, 10) = 1$, this implies that A must divide $10^k - 1$, or in terms of congruences that $10^k \equiv 1 \bmod A$. Since $(A, 10) = 1$, we may use the language of **19.1** to assert that a positive integer k with this property exists and that the *minimal* value of k which we seek is the exponent to which 10 belongs modulo A. This completes the proof except for the comment that the choice made above guarantees that $q_s \neq q_{s+k}$, for if $q_s = q_{s+k}$, we would have from $r_s = r_{s+k}$ and (41.4) that $r_{s-1} = r_{s-1+k}$, which would contradict the argument given above; hence the first digit of the repeating part is definitely q_{s+1} where s is the maximum of x and y.

Thus in considering $\{17/520\}$, when we have found $520 = 2^3 5^1 13$ and $10^6 \equiv 1 \bmod 13$, we see that $s = 3$ and $k = 6$; hence we may predict $\{17/520\} = 0.q_1 q_2 q_3 \dot{q}_4 q_5 q_6 q_7 q_8 \dot{q}_9$. In fact, by actual computation we find $\{17/520\} = 0.03\dot{2}69230\dot{7}$. If $(a, 520) = 1$, then the last theorem shows $\{a/520\}$ will also have $s = 3$ and $k = 6$.

A few of the numerous corollaries to the above theorem are given in the exercises which follow this lesson. For example, the division algorithm leads to a terminating decimal representation $(k = 1, P = 0)$ for $\{a/b\}$ if and only if b has the form $b = 2^x 5^y$, see EX. **41.10**.

From the preceding theorems we may be tempted to draw the conclusion that rational real numbers and periodic infinite decimals are in one-to-one correspondence. But this is not quite correct, the missing step in the argument being that we have not investigated the uniqueness of representation by means of infinite decimals. The example $5.0125\dot{0} = 5.0124\dot{9}$, given earlier, provides a partial clue.

If we define two infinite decimals

$$b_m \ldots b_0.b_{-1} \ldots b_{-i} \ldots \quad \text{and} \quad b'_m \ldots b'_0.b'_{-1} \ldots b'_{-i} \ldots$$

to be distinct if there exists an integer t such that $b_t \neq b_t'$, then the correct situation is as follows: two distinct infinite decimals represent distinct real numbers, except in the case of terminating infinite decimals $(k = 1, P = 0)$ when two representations are possible, see EX. **41.11**.

It now follows that an infinite decimal represents a rational real number if and only if the infinite decimal is periodic. For our first theorem states that every periodic infinite decimal represents a rational real number. Our second theorem shows that every rational real number may be represented by at least one periodic infinite decimal. The theorem of the preceding paragraph shows that a rational real number may, in general, be represented by only one infinite decimal; even in the exceptional case there are only two corresponding infinite decimals, and these are both periodic.

Inasmuch as we can write infinite decimals that are not periodic, but which are regular sequences and hence real numbers, it follows that there exist real numbers other than rational real numbers and these are called *irrational* real numbers. It is correct to identify irrational real numbers with nonperiodic infinite decimals, since it is possible to show that every real number may be represented by an infinite decimal (see EX. **41.13**), and an irrational real number, by only one infinite decimal, in view of the uniqueness theorem above.

A simple example of an irrational real number is $\sqrt{2}$. For in EX. **25.3** we have seen that there is no rational number x/y satisfying $(x/y)^2 = 2$. But by seeking integers X_i such that $X_i^2 < 2(10)^{2i} < (X_i + 1)^2$ we find a real number $\{X_i/10^i\}$ such that $\{X_i/10^i\}^2 = \{2\}$. It follows readily that $10X_i \leqslant X_{i+1} < X_{i+1} + 1 \leqslant 10X_i + 10$; hence the digits of X_{i+1} differ at most in the units place from those in $10X_i$; thus the digits may be found recursively and $\{X_i/10^i\}$ appears as an infinite decimal, albeit a nonperiodic one, obtainable to any desired number of decimal places. In fact setting $X_{i+1} = 10X_i + q$, $0 \leqslant q < 9$, we see that the algorithm proposed above is one of finding the maximum value of q such that $2(10)^{2(i+1)} > X_{i+1}^2 = 10^2X_i^2 + 20X_iq + q^2$ or such that

$$2(10)^{2(i+1)} - 10^2X_i^2 > (20X_i + q)q.$$

This algorithm may be conveniently condensed in the following manner which will be recognized as the "square-root process" given in many elementary arithmetics, usually without proof.

$$
\begin{array}{l}

\begin{array}{r|rrrl}
& 1 & 4 & 1 & 4 \\
\hline
& 2.\ 00 & 00 & 00 & = m, \qquad\qquad X_0 = 1 \\
& 1 & & & \\
\end{array}\\
20X_0 + q_1 = 24,\quad
\begin{array}{r|rrrl}
1 & 00 & & & = 10^2m - (10X_0)^2,\ q_1 = 4,\ X_1 = 14 \\
& 96 & & & \\
\end{array}\\
20X_1 + q_2 = 281,\quad
\begin{array}{r|rrrl}
4 & 00 & & = 10^4m - (10X_1)^2,\ q_2 = 1,\ X_2 = 141 \\
2 & 81 & & \\
\end{array}\\
20X_2 + q_3 = 2824,\quad
\begin{array}{r|rrrl}
1 & 19 & 00 & = 10^6m - (10X_2)^2,\ q_3 = 4,\ X_3 = 1414 \\
1 & 12 & 96 & \\
& 6 & 04 & = 10^8m - (10X_3)^2.
\end{array}
\end{array}
$$

In this manner we find $\sqrt{2} = 1.41421\ldots$.

In the lesson which follows we shall be particularly interested in such quadratic irrationalities for we shall discover a sense in which these are the most regular of irrational real numbers.

41.5.   Basimal fractions

It is reasonably clear that the discussion of the preceding sections might well have been made more general by taking any desired fixed integer $B > 1$, not necessarily $B = 10$, as the base number in the representation.

Beginning as in Chapter 5, we know that a given positive integer a may be represented in the form

$$a = a_m B^m + \cdots + a_1 B + a_0, \quad 0 < a_m < B; \quad 0 \leqslant a_i < B, \quad 0 \leqslant i < m.$$

We take the liberty of calling a/B^k a *basimal fraction*, inasmuch as the adjective "decimal" is by its Latin original meaning suitable only when $B = 10$; then paralleling **41.1**, we use a positional notation with a "basimal point" to write

$$a/B^k = b_{m-k} \ldots b_0.b_{-1} \ldots b_{-k} \quad \text{or} \quad a/B^k = 0.0 \ldots 0 b_{-(k-m)} \ldots b_{-k}$$

according as $k \leqslant m$ or $k > m$, with $b_{i-k} = a_i$. Where the context does not indicate the value of B, parentheses and a subscript may be used. For example,

$$(3.1052)_6 = 3 + 1/6 + 5/6^3 + 2/6^4.$$

If $b_m, b_{m-1}, \ldots, b_0, b_{-1}, \ldots, b_{-i}, \ldots$ is a given sequence of integers b_i satisfying $0 \leqslant b_i < B$, we may define a corresponding sequence $\{a_i\}$ of rational numbers a_i as follows:

$$a_i = (b_m \ldots b_0.b_{-1} \ldots b_{-i})_B.$$

A sequence of this type will be called an *infinite basimal*, designated by $\{a_i\} = (b_m \ldots b_0.b_{-1} \ldots b_{-i} \ldots)_B$. An infinite basimal is a regular sequence (see EX. **41.15**).

An infinite basimal will be said to be *periodic* if there exist two integers $s \geqslant 0$ and $k > 0$ such that $b_{-t} = b_{-t}'$ whenever $t > s$, $t' > s$, and $t \equiv t'$ mod k. A periodic infinite basimal will be denoted by

$$\{a_i\} = (b_m \ldots b_0.b_{-1} \ldots b_{-s} \overset{.}{b}_{-(s+1)} \ldots \overset{.}{b}_{-(s+k)})_B.$$

Every periodic infinite basimal represents a *rational* real number $\{X\}$ (see EX. **41.16**). Conversely, every positive rational real number may be represented by a periodic infinite basimal (see EX. **41.17**).

If in standard form $B = p_1{}^{s_1} p_2{}^{s_2} \ldots p_k{}^{s_k}$, $s_i > 0$, $p_i < p_{i+1}$, if $b = p_1{}^{x_1} p_2{}^{x_2} \ldots p_k{}^{x_k} A$, where $(A, B) = 1$, and if $(a, b) = 1$, then in the periodic infinite basimal representing $\{a/b\}$ to the base B the minimal value for s is the smallest *integer* greater than or equal to the maximum of $x_1/s_1, x_2/s_2, \ldots, x_k/s_k$ and the minimal value for k is the exponent to which B belong modulo A (see EX. **41.18**).

For example, if $B = 2^2 3$, we may use $x = 9 + 1, L = x + 1, B = L + 1$ and may consider finding the infinite basimal to represent $\{15/260\}_B$. Since $(260)_B = (360)_{10} = 2^3 3^2 5$, we have $x_1/s_1 = 3/2$, $x_2/s_2 = 2$ so that $s = 2$. Since $B \equiv 2 \bmod 5$, we find that B belongs to $4 \bmod 5$ so that $k = 4$. By the theorem we may predict that $\{15/260\}_B = (0.q_1 q_2 \dot{q}_3 q_4 q_5 \dot{q}_6)_B$. The division algorithm in the base B appears as follows:

$$
\begin{array}{r}
.069724 \\
260 \overline{)\,15.00} \\
13\,00 \\ \hline
2\,000 \\
1\,x60 \\ \hline
1600 \\
1560 \\ \hline
600 \\
500 \\ \hline
1000 \\
x00 \\ \hline
200
\end{array}
$$

base $B = 2^2 3$

$x = 9 + 1$

$L = x + 1$

$B = L + 1$

Hence $\{15/260\}_B = (0.0\dot{6}972\dot{4})_B$, as predicted.

It is of some interest to see that the same rational number expanded in various bases may have different periodic character. Thus for the example just given $(15/260)_B = (17/360)_{10}$. Since $10 = 2^1 5^1$ we find $s = 3$; since $10 \equiv 1 \bmod 9$ we have $k = 1$; in fact $(17/360)_{10} = (0.047\dot{2})_{10}$.

A periodic infinite basimal is said to be terminating if $k = 1$, $P = 0$. A rational real number $\{a/b\}$ has a terminating basimal representation to the base $B = p_1^{s_1} p_2^{s_2} \ldots p_k^{s_k}$ only if $b = p_1^{x_1} p_2^{x_2} \ldots p_k^{x_k}$, $x_i \geqslant 0$.

Two infinite basimals are said to be distinct if for some integer t, $b_t \neq b_t'$. Distinct infinite basimals represent unequal real numbers, except in the case of terminating infinite basimals for which two representations are possible, one with $k = 1$, $P = 0$, the other with $k = 1$, $P = B - 1$.

Finally, every real number may be represented by an infinite basimal: rational real numbers if and only if the infinite basimal is periodic; irrational real numbers if and only if the infinite basimal is nonperiodic.

EXERCISES

41.1. Prove that equality of real numbers is *transitive*.
41.2. Prove that the *sum* of two regular sequences is a *regular* sequence, so that *addition* of real numbers is *closed*.
41.3. Prove that *addition* of real numbers is *well defined*.
41.4. Prove that *multiplication* of real numbers is *closed*.

41.5.   Find in lowest terms the rational real numbers represented by the following *infinite decimals*:

(a) $0.03\dot{0}027\dot{1}$; (b) $1.\dot{0}12\dot{1}$; (c) $0.\dot{1}76470588235294\dot{1}$.

41.6.   *Predict* the *form* of the periodic infinite decimals representing the following rational real numbers:

(a) $\{3/410\}$; (b) $\{25/11\}$; (c) $\{16/27\}$, (d) $\{355/4004\}$.

41.7.   If $PP' = 10^k - 1$, discuss the repeating parts of the periodic infinite decimals representing $\{1/P\}$ and $\{1/P'\}$.

41.8.   If $b = 2^x5^yA$ with $(A, 10) = 1$, if $(a, b) = 1$, if $(a', b) = 1$, and if $a \equiv a'$ mod A, show that $\{a/b\}$ and $\{a'/b\}$ have the same repeating part P, in their infinite decimals.

41.9.   If $\{a/b\}$ has remainders r_i and a repeating part $P = q_{s+1}\ldots q_{s+k}$, if $(a', b) = 1$ and if $10^sa' \equiv r_{s+t}$ mod b, show that the infinite decimal representing $\{a'/b\}$ has a repeating part P' obtained from P by a cyclic advancement of digits.

41.10.   Show that the division algorithm leads to a terminating decimal representation for $\{a/b\}$ if and only if b has the form $b = 2^x5^y$.

41.11.   Show that distinct infinite decimals represent unequal real numbers, except in the case of terminating decimals when two representations are possible. (Hint: Consider four cases, each with t maximal such that $b_t \neq b_t'$: (1) $b_t > b_t' + 1$; (2) $b_t = b_t' + 1$, $b_u > 0$ for a maximal $u < t$; (3) $b_t = b_t' + 1$, $b_u = 0$ for $u < t$, $b_v' < 9$ for a maximal $v < t$; (4) $b_t = b_t' + 1$, $b_u = 0$ for $u < t$, $b_v' = 9$ for $v < t$.)

41.12.   If $\{a_i\}$ and $\{b_i\}$ are regular sequences, define $\{a_i\} > \{b_i\}$ if and only if there exists a rational number $\epsilon > 0$ and an integer N such that $a_i - b_i > \epsilon$ for $i > N$. Prove that this order relation for real numbers is *trichotomous*.

41.13.   Show that any subsequence of a regular sequence is regular.

41.14.   If $\{a_i\}$ is a regular sequence of rational numbers, produce an equal sequence $\{b_i\}$ of decimal fractions by using the bracket function to define $b_i = [10^ia_i]/10^i$.

41.15.   Use the preceding exercises to show that any real number is equal to an infinite decimal.

41.16.   Show that the algorithm represented by finding integers X_i such that $X_i^3 < 2(10)^{3i} < (X_i + 1)^3$ constructs an infinite decimal $\{X_i/10^i\}$ which is a real irrational cube root of 2. Explain why this algorithm cannot be so conveniently condensed as the one for square roots.

41.17.   Establish the analog of *(41.1)* and show that an infinite basimal is a regular sequence.

41.18.   Show that a periodic infinite basimal represents a rational real number $\{X\}$, $X = Q + S + P/B^s(B^k - 1)$, analogous to *(41.2)*.

41.19.   Using the analogues of *(41.3)* and *(41.4)* show that every positive rational number may be represented by a periodic infinite basimal.

41.20.   For a periodic infinite *basimal* representing $\{a/b\}_B$ establish the theorem given in the text for the minimal values of s and k.

41.21.   In regard to periodic basimals show that k must divide $\lambda(A)$ and $\phi(A)$. (Recall **G.15.1** and EX. **17.8.**)

41.22. If $b = (11)_{10}$, investigate $(1/b)_B$ for $B = 2, 3, 4, 5, 6, 7, 8, 9, 10, 12$; compare with **G.17**.

41.23. If $b = (13)_{10}$, investigate $(a/b)_5$ for $a = 1, 2, \ldots, b - 1$; compare with EX. **41.9**.

41.24. Show that (a) $(1/(B - 1))_B = 0.\dot{1}$; (b) $(1/(B + 1))_B = 0.\dot{0}(B \dot{-} 1)$; (c) $(1/(B - 1)^2)_B = 0.\dot{0}123\ldots(B - 3)(B \dot{-} 1)$.

41.25. Establish a graphic picture of the periodic character of $\{a/b\}_B$ by using $F(x) = x - [x]$ and $L(x) = x/B$ for $0 \leqslant x < B$, starting with $F(r_0/b)$ on F and proceeding alternately, horizontally to L and vertically to F. Thus the tailpiece to this chapter illustrates $\{1/12\}_3 = (0.0\dot{1}2\dot{1})_3$.

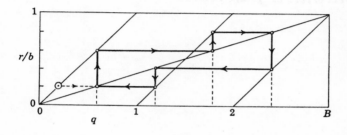

CHAPTER 42

Continued fractions

42.1.   Finite continued fractions

Given the nonnegative integer b_0 and the positive integers $b_1, b_2, \ldots, b_n$
we may define, recursively, the following integers p_i and q_i:

(42.1) $p_{-1} = 1,\ p_0 = b_0,\ p_i = b_i p_{i-1} + p_{i-2},\ 1 \leqslant i \leqslant n;$
$q_{-1} = 0,\ q_0 = 1,\quad q_i = b_i q_{i-1} + q_{i-2},\ 1 \leqslant i \leqslant n.$

We shall call $a_n = p_n/q_n$ a *finite continued fraction* and denote its dependence
upon $b_0, b_1, \ldots, b_n$ by the following symbol:

$$a_n = \{b_0, b_1, \ldots, b_n\}.$$

We shall call $a_i = p_i/q_i$, for $0 \leqslant i \leqslant n$, the ith *convergent* of the continued
fraction. Evidently the notation is so chosen that each convergent is itself
a continued fraction, i.e.,

$$a_i = \{b_0, b_1, \ldots, b_i\}, \qquad 0 \leqslant i \leqslant n.$$

The name, continued fraction, can best be explained by reviewing the
notion of a *complex* fraction. We have seen that when $c \neq 0$, then
$(c/d)(x/y) = (a/b)$ has the solution $x/y = ad/bc$. However, by analogy
with the situation when $b \neq 0$ and $(b/1)(x/y) = (a/1)$ has the solution
346

$x/y = a/b$, it is natural to write the solution to the first given equation in the form $(a/b)/(c/d)$ or $\dfrac{a/b}{c/d}$, with appropriate parentheses or a longer fraction bar or vinculum to explain the order of operation which is intended. Such a "fraction" with other fractions in its "numerator" or "denominator" is called a *complex fraction*. By repeated use of the rules for ordinary fractions and of the definitions above in which

$$(a/b)/(c/d) = ad/bc$$

we may reduce a complex fraction to an ordinary or *simple* fraction.

A continued fraction makes a good exercise in this reduction technique and the exercise reveals why the name *continued* fraction is relevant. For we soon discover that from

$$a_{i-1} = \frac{p_{i-1}}{q_{i-1}} = \frac{b_{i-1}p_{i-2} + p_{i-3}}{b_{i-1}q_{i-2} + q_{i-3}}, \qquad i \geqslant 2$$

we can obtain $a_i = p_i/q_i$ by replacing b_{i-1} by $b_{i-1} + 1/b_i$. Thus

$$\frac{\left(b_{i-1} + \dfrac{1}{b_i}\right)p_{i-2} + p_{i-3}}{\left(b_{i-1} + \dfrac{1}{b_i}\right)q_{i-2} + q_{i-3}} = \frac{b_i(b_{i-1}p_{i-2} + p_{i-3}) + p_{i-2}}{b_i(b_{i-1}q_{i-2} + q_{i-3}) + q_{i-2}}$$

$$= \frac{b_i p_{i-1} + p_{i-2}}{b_i q_{i-1} + q_{i-2}} = \frac{p_i}{q_i}.$$

Hence, for example, starting with $p_0/q_0 = b_0/1 = b_0$ we find

$$\frac{p_1}{q_1} = b_0 + \frac{1}{b_1}, \quad \frac{p_2}{q_2} = b_0 + \cfrac{1}{b_1 + \cfrac{1}{b_2}}, \quad \frac{p_3}{q_3} = b_0 + \cfrac{1}{b_1 + \cfrac{1}{b_2 + \cfrac{1}{b_3}}}.$$

Thus p_n/q_n is really an "n-storied" complex fraction, meaning that fraction bars of n different lengths could be used to indicate its structure. It is readily appreciated that the notation $a_n = \{b_0, b_1, \ldots, b_n\}$ and the recursive relations (42.1) afford a much less cumbersome symbolism.

In the same manner if we set $R_{i,k} = \{b_i, \ldots, b_k\}$, $1 \leqslant i \leqslant k \leqslant n$, and replace b_i by $R_{i,k}$ in the expressions for p_i and q_i, we find that

$$(42.2) \qquad \frac{p_k}{q_k} = \frac{R_{i,k}p_{i-1} + p_{i-2}}{R_{i,k}q_{i-1} + q_{i-2}}.$$

If the integers b_i are small, the successive computations required by (42.1) may be done mentally and entered in the following chart, working from left to right:

b		b_0	b_1	b_2	b_3	b_4	$\ldots$	b_n
p	1	b_0	p_1	p_2	p_3	p_4	$\ldots$	p_n
q	0	1	q_1	q_2	q_3	q_4	$\ldots$	q_n

Comparison with (7.2) and the example in **7.2** will be interesting and suggestive.

For theoretical purposes it is worth while to note that the relations (42.1) may be written in matric form:

$$\begin{pmatrix} p_0 & q_0 \\ p_{-1} & q_{-1} \end{pmatrix} = \begin{pmatrix} b_0 & 1 \\ 1 & 0 \end{pmatrix}, \quad \begin{pmatrix} p_i & q_i \\ p_{i-1} & q_{i-1} \end{pmatrix} = \begin{pmatrix} b_i & 1 \\ 1 & 0 \end{pmatrix}\begin{pmatrix} p_{i-1} & q_{i-1} \\ p_{i-2} & q_{i-2} \end{pmatrix}, \quad i \geq 1$$

Then by an easy induction it follows that

$$\begin{pmatrix} p_i & q_i \\ p_{i-1} & q_{i-1} \end{pmatrix} = \begin{pmatrix} b_i & 1 \\ 1 & 0 \end{pmatrix}\begin{pmatrix} b_{i-1} & 1 \\ 1 & 0 \end{pmatrix}\cdots\begin{pmatrix} b_0 & 1 \\ 1 & 0 \end{pmatrix}, \quad i \geq 0.$$

Recalling **M.7** in **31.1** concerning determinants, we have the following useful result:

$$(42.3) \qquad p_i q_{i-1} - p_{i-1} q_i = (-1)^{i+1}, \qquad i \geq 0.$$

It follows at once that the numerator and denominator of any convergent are relatively prime, i.e., $(p_i, q_i) = 1$, so the convergents are automatically in lowest terms.

C.1: A finite continued fraction represents a positive rational number; conversely, a positive rational number may be represented as a finite continued fraction.

Proof: The direct proposition is obvious from the definition of a finite continued fraction. For the converse if the given *positive* rational number is x/y we consider the Euclid algorithm for finding $d = (x, y)$ and rewrite the equations of the algorithm in the following manner:

$x = b_0 y + r_0, \ 0 < r_0 < y,$ $x/y = b_0 + r_0/y = b_0 + 1/(y/r_0);$

$y = b_1 r_0 + r_1, \ 0 < r_1 < r_0,$ $y/r_0 = b_1 + r_1/r_0 = b_1 + 1/(r_0/r_1);$

$\ldots$ $\ldots$ $\ldots$

$r_{k-2} = b_k r_{k-1} + r_k, \ 0 < r_k < r_{k-1},$ $r_{k-2}/r_{k-1} = b_k + r_k/r_{k-1};$

$r_{k-1} = b_{k+1} r_k, \qquad 0 = r_{k+1},$ $r_k/r_{k-1} = 1/b_{k+1}.$

If $x \geq y$, then $b_0 > 0$; if $x < y$, then $b_0 = 0$. In the other equations we have $b_i > 0$, $i = 1, \ldots, k + 1$. Hence the finite continued fraction $\{b_0, b_1, \ldots, b_{k+1}\}$ exists and by the equations above we see that this continued fraction, considered as a $k + 1$-storied complex fraction, is equal to x/y.

Corollary: If $(x, y) = d$, to find integers s and t such that $xs - ty = \pm d$ it suffices to expand x/y as a finite continued fraction, say $x/y = \{b_0, b_1, \ldots, b_n\}$ and take $t = p_{n-1}, s = q_{n-1}$.

Proof: By the theorem a finite continued fraction representing x/y exists. Since $(p_n, q_n) = 1$ and $x/y = p_n/q_n$, it follows that $x = p_n d, y = q_n d$. Since (42.3) holds, we may multiply (42.3) by d and obtain $xq_{n-1} - p_{n-1}y = (-1)^{n+1}d$. Thus with $s = q_{n-1}$ and $t = p_{n-1}$ we have $xs - ty = \pm d$.

For example, since $39/15 = 2 + 9/15$, $15/9 = 1 + 6/9$, and $9/6 = 1 + 1/2$, we have $39/15 = \{2, 1, 1, 2\}$. From the table of convergents:

b		2	1	1	2
p	1	2	3	5	13
q	0	1	1	2	5

we check that $(39)(2) - (15)(5) = 3$ which illustrates the corollary with $x = 39, y = 15, s = 2, t = 5, d = 3$.

Using (42.2) and (42.3) for $1 \leqslant i < k \leqslant n$ we find

$$(42.4) \quad a_k - a_i = \frac{R_{i+1,k}p_i + p_{i-1}}{R_{i+1,k}q_i + q_{i-1}} - \frac{p_i}{q_i} = \frac{(-1)^i}{q_i(R_{i+1,k}q_i + q_{i-1})}.$$

In particular, when $k = i + 1$, we find $R_{i+1,i+1} = b_{i+1}$ so that

$$(42.5) \quad a_{i+1} - a_i = (-1)^i/q_i q_{i+1}, \quad 1 \leqslant i < n.$$

Again, when $k = i + 2$, we find $R_{i+1,i+2} = b_{i+1} + 1/b_{i+2}$ so that

$$(42.6) \quad a_{i+2} - a_i = (-1)^i b_{i+2}/q_i q_{i+2}, \quad 1 \leqslant i < n - 1.$$

C.2: For a finite continued fraction the successive convergents always have the following order: those of even subscript occur in increasing order; those of odd subscript occur in decreasing order; and every convergent of odd subscript is greater than every one of even subscript.

Proof: Since $b_i \geqslant 1$ for $i \geqslant 1$, it follows that $q_i \geqslant 1$ for $i \geqslant 1$ and that $R_{i,k} \geqslant 1$ for $k \geqslant i \geqslant 1$. Hence when i is *even*, (42.6) shows $a_{i+2} > a_i$; but when i is *odd*, (42.6) shows $a_{i+2} < a_i$; and these inequalities prove the first two parts of **C.2**. Let i be any *even* integer; then for any odd integer k with $k > i$ we may use (42.4) to see that $a_k > a_i$; since we have previously shown for *odd K* and k that $a_K > a_k$ when $K < k$, it follows that for *any* odd k and any even i we have $a_k > a_i$, which completes the proof.

For example, with $a_6 = \{2, 1, 4, 2, 1, 12, 3\}$ we find

b		2	1	4	2	1	12	3
p	1	2	3	14	31	45	571	1758
q	0	1	1	5	11	16	203	625

Here

$$a_0 = 2 < a_2 = 14/5 < a_4 = 45/16 < a_6 = 1758/625$$

and

$$a_6 = 1758/625 < a_5 = 571/203 < a_3 = 31/11 < a_1 = 3.$$

An important property of a convergent to a finite continued fraction is that it is a closer approximation to the value of the continued fraction than any rational number of smaller denominator. It is this property which has given the study of continued fractions many practical applications.

C.3: If $a_n = \{b_0, b_1, \ldots, b_n\}$ and if $a_i = p_i/q_i = \{b_0, b_1, \ldots, b_i\}$ with $1 \leqslant i < n$ and if q is an integer with $0 < q < q_i$, then

$$|a_n - a_i| < |a_n - p/q|$$

for all integers p.

Proof: The proof is by contradiction. If we set $T_{i+1} = R_{i+1, n}q_i + q_{i-1}$, then (42.4) shows $a_n - a_i = (-1)^i/q_i T_{i+1}$. Hence if we suppose p/q closer to a_n than a_i we must have

$$-1/q_i T_{i+1} < (-1)^{i+1}(a_n - p/q) < 1/q_i T_{i+1}$$

where the sign $(-1)^{i+1}$ has been introduced to use in what follows. Adding $1/q_i T_{i+1}$ to these inequalities, we find

$$0 < (-1)^{i+1}(a_n - (-1)^i/q_i T_{i+1} - p/q) = (-1)^{i+1}(a_i - p/q) < 2/q_i T_{i+1}.$$

Noting that $R_{i+1, n} \geqslant b_{i+1}$ we have $T_{i+1} \geqslant q_{i+1}$ and may write

$$0 < (-1)^{i+1}(p_i/q_i - p/q) < 2/q_i q_{i+1}.$$

Multiplying these inequalities by the *positive* integer qq_i we find

$$0 < (-1)^{i+1}(p_i q - pq_i) < 2q/q_{i+1}.$$

Since $q_1 = b_1 \geqslant 1$, it follows from (42.1) that $q_i < q_{i+1}$ for $i \geqslant 1$. Since $q < q_i < q_{i+1}$, we have $2q/q_{i+1} < 2$, so the inequalities last displayed require the central *integer* to have the value $+1$; hence $p_i q - pq_i = (-1)^{i+1}$. But this is a Diophantine equation which by the theory in **15.1** can have *at most one* solution with $0 < q < q_i$. By *(42.3)* there *is* such a solution: namely, $p = p_{i-1}$, $q = q_{i-1}$. However with $q = q_{i-1}$ the inequality $1 < 2q/q_{i+1}$ or $q_{i+1} < 2q_{i-1}$ cannot hold; for since $q_{i+1} = b_{i+1}q_i + q_{i-1}$, it follows that $q_{i+1} \geqslant 2q_{i-1}$ for $i \geqslant 1$. This contradiction establishes the theorem.

For illustration we may take the previous example and assert that $45/16$ is a better approximation to $1758/625$ than any rational number p/q with $0 < q < 16$, such as $27/10$ or $39/14$.

42.2.   Infinite continued fractions

Given any sequence of rational integers $b_0, b_1, \ldots, b_i, \ldots$ with $b_0 \geqslant 0$ and $b_i \geqslant 1$ for $i \geqslant 1$, we may define a corresponding sequence $\{a_i\}$ of rational numbers by setting $a_i = \{b_0, b_1, \ldots, b_i\}$. Such a sequence $\{a_i\}$ is called an *infinite continued fraction* and may be designated by

$$\{a_i\} = \{b_0, b_1, \ldots, b_i, \ldots\}.$$

C.4:   An infinite continued fraction is a regular sequence.

Proof: Since *(42.4)* is valid here for $1 \leqslant i < k$ and since $R_{i+1, k} \geqslant b_{i+1}$ so that $R_{i+1, k}q_i + q_{i-1} \geqslant q_{i+1}$, we have

$$(42.7) \qquad |a_k - a_i| < 1/q_i q_{i+1}, \qquad 1 \leqslant i < k.$$

Since the q_i form an increasing sequence of rational integers with $q_{i+1} > q_i > i$ for $i > 3$ (see EX. **42.5**), we may apply *(42.7)* with $i = N$ to see that

$$|a_N - a_k| < 1/q_N q_{N+1} < 1/N^2 \qquad \text{for } 3 < N < k.$$

Since for any assigned rational number $\epsilon > 0$, we may find a positive integer $N > 3$ such that $N^2 > 1/\epsilon$ and thus $1/N^2 < \epsilon$, it follows that we can guarantee that $|a_N - a_k| < \epsilon$ for $k > N$. Therefore by the definition in **41.2** the sequence $\{a_i\}$ is regular.

To continue this development we need to use the notions of order, absolute value, and the bracket function for real numbers; the intuitive descriptions of Chapters 1 and 12 will suffice; a rigorous development can be made starting from the ideas in EX. **41.12**.

C.5:   Any positive irrational real number x may be represented by an infinite continued fraction.

Proof: The following process is, in general, not complete in a finite number of steps, so it cannot properly be called an algorithm; rather it is a recursive process that can be carried out to any desired number of steps:

$$b_0 = [x], \quad r_0 = x - b_0;$$
$$b_i = [1/r_{i-1}], \quad r_i = 1/r_{i-1} - b_i, \quad i \geqslant 1.$$

By definition of the bracket function we would naturally have $0 \leqslant r_i < 1$, $i \geqslant 0$; but since x is irrational, each r_i must be irrational, so the 0 value is excluded, and we have $0 < r_i < 1$, $i \geqslant 0$. Then $1/r_i$ is defined and $1/r_i > 1$, $i \geqslant 0$, so that $b_i \geqslant 1$, $i \geqslant 1$. Since $x > 0$, we have $b_0 \geqslant 0$. Thus the b_i are proper elements for an infinite continued fraction and we claim that $x = \{a_i\} = \{b_0, b_1, \ldots, b_i, \ldots\}$.

By induction we may see that the construction above makes

$$(42.8) \qquad x = \frac{(b_{i+1} + r_{i+1})p_i + p_{i-1}}{(b_{i+1} + r_{i+1})q_i + q_{i-1}}, \quad i \geqslant 0.$$

(I) When $i = 0$ we have, using (42.1),

$$x = b_0 + r_0 = b_0 + 1/(b_1 + r_1) = \frac{(b_1 + r_1)b_0 + 1}{(b_1 + r_1)1 + 0} = \frac{(b_1 + r_1)p_0 + p_{-1}}{(b_1 + r_1)q_0 + q_{-1}}.$$

(II) If we assume (42.8) correct for i, we have only to use (42.1) and $r_{i+1} = 1/(b_{i+2} + r_{i+2})$ to be able to write

$$x = \frac{p_{i+1} + r_{i+1}p_i}{q_{i+1} + r_{i+1}q_i} = \frac{(b_{i+2} + r_{i+2})p_{i+1} + p_i}{(b_{i+2} + r_{i+2})q_{i+1} + q_i},$$

which is the form that (42.8) should take for the case $i + 1$.

From (42.8) and (42.3) it follows that

$$(42.9) \qquad x - a_i = (-1)^i/q_i(q_{i+1} + r_{i+1}\mathring{q}_i), \quad i \geqslant 0.$$

Since $0 < r_{i+1}$ and $i < q_i < q_{i+1}$ when $i > 3$, it follows that $|x - a_i| < 1/q_iq_{i+1} < 1/i^2$ for $i > 3$. Hence by taking i sufficiently large, say $i > N$ where $N^2 > 1/\epsilon$, and where ϵ is any assigned positive real number, we may make $|x - a_i| < \epsilon$, for $i > N$, which proves that $x = \{a_i\}$.

It is worth while to note that if x is a *rational* number the process described above becomes exactly the Euclid algorithm, but since the process will now terminate in a finite number of steps, the continued fraction that is obtained to represent x is finite, instead of infinite.

C.6: If $x = \{a_i\} = \{b_0, b_1, \ldots, b_i, \ldots\}$ is an infinite continued fraction, then the successive convergents always have the following order: those of even subscript occur in increasing order and all are less than x;

those of odd subscript occur in decreasing order and all are greater than x. If q is an integer such that $0 < q < q_i$, then

$$|x - a_i| < |x - p/q|$$

for all integers p.

Proof: Concerning the order of the convergents the proofs are the same as in **C.2**. We may use (42.9) to see the order relation between x and a_i, according as i is even or odd. The result concerning closeness of approximation is proved exactly as in **C.3** *except* for replacing a_n by x and $R_{i+1, n}$ by $R_{i+1} = \{b_{i+1}, b_{i+2}, \ldots\} = b_{i+1} + r_{i+1}$ and using (42.9) instead of (42.4).

To illustrate these theorems we may study x, where $x^2 = 21$, and carry forward the recursive process of **C.5** as follows: $x = 4 + r_0$,

$$1/r_0 = 1/(x - 4) = (x + 4)/5 = 1 + r_1,$$
$$1/r_1 = 5/(x - 1) = (x + 1)/4 = 1 + r_2,$$
$$1/r_2 = 4/(x - 3) = (x + 3)/3 = 2 + r_3,$$
$$1/r_3 = 3/(x - 3) = (x + 3)/4 = 1 + r_4,$$
$$1/r_4 = 4/(x - 1) = (x + 1)/5 = 1 + r_5,$$
$$1/r_5 = 5/(x - 4) = (x + 4)/1 = 8 + r_6;$$

but at this point we find $r_6 = r_0$, so the process now repeats itself. For an adequate notation for this phenomenon let us digress from the illustration to make certain definitions.

An infinite continued fraction $x = \{b_0, b_1, \ldots, b_i, \ldots\}$ will be said to be *periodic* if there exist integers $s \geqslant 0$ and $k > 0$ such that whenever $t > s$, $t' > s$, and $t \equiv t' \bmod k$, then $b_t = b_{t'}$. We may use the same convention as with periodic infinite decimals to write a periodic infinite continued fraction as follows:

$$x = \{b_0, \ldots, b_s, \dot{b}_{s+1}, \ldots, \dot{b}_{s+k}\}.$$

With this agreement the example worked above becomes $x = \{4, \dot{1}, 1, 2, 1, 1, \dot{8}\}$ with $s = 0$ and $k = 6$. The first few convergents for x appear in the following table:

b		4	1	1	2	1	1	8	1
p	1	4	5	9	23	32	55	472	527
q	0	1	1	2	5	7	12	103	115

In illustration of part of **C.6** we find the convergents are arranged as follows:

$$4 < 9/2 < 32/7 < 472/103 < x < 527/115 < 55/12 < 23/5 < 5.$$

By (42.9) we know 472/103 is an approximation to x correct to within

$1/(103)(115) = 1/11845$ and by **C.6** that it is a better approximation than any other rational number of denominator less than 103.

A real number of the type $(A + \sqrt{M})/C$ where A, C, M are rational integers with $C \neq 0$, $M > 0$, and M *not* a perfect square is called a *real quadratic surd*. Such real numbers take on a peculiar interest from the standpoint of continued fractions because of the following theorem (and its converse).

C.7: A periodic infinite continued fraction represents a real quadratic surd.

Proof: Given $x = \{b_0, \ldots, b_s, \dot{b}_{s+1}, \ldots, \dot{b}_{s+k}\}$ from (*42.8*) we may write

$$x = \frac{R_{s+1}p_s + p_{s-1}}{R_{s+1}q_s + q_{s-1}}$$

and make the proof depend upon evaluating $R_{s+1} = \{\dot{b}_{s+1}, \ldots, \dot{b}_{s+k}\}$. This latter continued fraction by its periodic character has the property $R_{k+1}' = \{b_{s+k+1}, b_{s+k+2}, \ldots\} = R_{s+1}$. If we denote the convergents of R_{s+1} by $p_i'/q_i' = \{b_{s+1}, \ldots, b_{s+i+1}\}$, then by (*42.8*) we have

$$R_{s+1} = \frac{R_{k+1}'p_k' + p_{k-1}'}{R_{k+1}'q_k' + q_{k-1}'} = \frac{R_{s+1}p_k' + p_{k-1}'}{R_{s+1}q_k' + q_{k-1}'}.$$

Hence R_{s+1} is a solution of the equation

$$q_k'R_{s+1}{}^2 + (q_{k-1}' - p_k')R_{s+1} - p_{k-1}' = 0.$$

Since this equation has rational integers as coefficients, its solutions, obtained by the quadratic formula, are of the form $(A + \sqrt{M})/C$ with $C = 2q_k' \neq 0$. Since the discriminant $M = (q_{k-1}' - p_k')^2 + 4q_k'p_{k-1}'$ > 0, the roots are real; furthermore, only one root is positive, so R_{s+1} is uniquely determined as this positive root. Finally, M is not a perfect square and R_{s+1} is irrational, for if R_{s+1} were rational, its representation as a continued fraction would be finite (see EX. **42.7**). If we substitute the value of R_{s+1} in x and rationalize the denominator, we find that x is also a quadratic surd.

For example if $x = \{2, \dot{1}, \dot{3}\}$, we set $R = \{\dot{1}, \dot{3}\} = 1 + 1/(3 + 1/R)$ and find $3R^2 - 3R - 1 = 0$, whence $R = (3 + \sqrt{21})/6$. Then $x = 2 + 1/R = 2 + 6/(3 + \sqrt{21}) = 2 + (\sqrt{21} - 3)/2 = (1 + \sqrt{21})/2$.

It is more difficult to prove that every real quadratic surd may be represented by a periodic infinite continued fraction. In particular, surds of the type $\sqrt{M}$ always have $s = 0$ and repeating parts that are rather symmetric

$$\sqrt{M} = \{\dot{b}_0, b_1, b_2, \ldots, b_2, b_1, 2\dot{b}_0\}.$$

These results show in a fascinating way, from the standpoint of continued fractions, that the quadratic are better behaved than the other irrationalities.

EXERCISES

42.1. Expand the decimal fraction 3.1415926535 as a continued fraction and show that $a_3 = 355/113$ is a correct approximation to within $1/(113)(33102)$.

42.2. Expand the decimal fraction 2.71828 as a continued fraction.

42.3. Use a continued fraction to help solve $53s - 17t = 1$.

42.4. Establish formula (*42.2*) by induction on k.

42.5. Prove that $q_i > i$ for $i > 3$.

42.6. Show that $\{1, 3, 4\} = \{1, 3, 3, 1\}$.

42.7. Show that representation by a continued fraction is unique except for finite continued fractions where exactly two representations are possible (both finite). See EX. **42.6**.

42.8. Prove that $\{a, 2\dot{a}\} = \sqrt{a^2 + 1}$ and that $\{2a, \dot{a}, 4\dot{a}\} = 2\sqrt{a^2 + 1}$.

42.9. Prove that $\{a, \dot{a}, 2\dot{a}\} = \sqrt{a^2 + 2}$, and that $\{a, \dot{1}, 2\dot{a}\} = \sqrt{a^2 + 2a}$.

42.10. Show that $\sqrt{7}$ has $k = 4$, $\sqrt{19}$ has $k = 6$, and $\sqrt{9a^2 + 3} = \{3a, 2\dot{a}, 6\dot{a}\}$.

42.11. Show that $\sqrt{(2k + 1)^2 + 4} = \{2k + 1, k, 1, 1, k, \overline{4k + 2}\}$.

42.12. Show that $\sqrt{41}$ has $k = 3$ and $\sqrt{13}$ has $k = 5$.

42.13. Use (*42.9*) and (*42.5*) to show that $|x - a_{i+1}| < |x - a_i|$ and that $1/2q_i q_{i+1} < |x - a_i| < 1/q_i q_{i+1}$.

42.14. Investigate Fibonacci numbers, which are the p_i (or q_i) in $x = \{\dot{1}\}$, independently or in reference books.

42.15. Investigate Pell's Diophantine equation $x^2 - Ay^2 = N$, independently or in reference books.

42.16. Investigate in reference books the use of continued fractions in the design of gears.

42.17. On the usual coordinate system where *points* are designated by $P = (x, y)$ and $O = (0, 0)$, plot the lattice points $P_i = (q_i, p_i)$. Use $a_i = p_i/q_i = $ slope OP_i to illustrate graphically *every* part of theorem **C.6** (F. Klein).

42.18. Establish a graphic picture of the periodic character of the continued fraction representing $\sqrt{M}$ by using $F(x) = x - [x]$ for $x \geqslant 0$ and $H(x) = 1/x$ for $x > 1$, starting with $F(\sqrt{M})$ on F and proceeding alternately, horizontally to H and vertically to F. Thus the tailpiece to this chapter illustrates $\sqrt{7} = \{2, \dot{1}, 1, 1, \dot{4}\}$.

42.19. Illustrate EX. **42.18** by drawing the graphic picture of $\sqrt{M}$ for each of the cases: $M = 3, 2, 8, 6, 5, 13$. (Note how the figure degenerates in the cases $M = 2, 5$.)

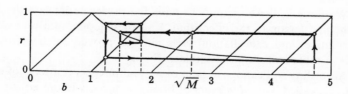

Abstract methods have given
mathematics a new and vital principle and
a powerful instrument for exhibiting the
essential unity of all its branches.

—J. W. YOUNG

CHAPTER 43

Peano's axioms for the natural integers

43.1. Peano's axioms

In Chapter 38 we learned that a description of the domain J of integers, unique in the sense of isomorphism, is the characterization of J as the only well-ordered domain. It should be remembered, however, that in discussing the existence of a system satisfying all the axioms of a well-ordered domain, we appealed to our intuitive knowledge of J. In this chapter and the next we shall see that the study of J can be pushed back one step further and made to depend upon an abstract description of the natural integers, that is, the positive integers or counting numbers. The following description which is due essentially to G. Peano (1858–1932) seems natural for us to pursue, for an essential part of Peano's axioms is the very postulate of mathematical induction with which we have been concerned in previous chapters.

We hope in these sections to have the reader appreciate the remarks of the first lesson to the effect that ". . . these [commutative, associative, distributive, and cancellation] laws may be proved as theorems on the basis of other still simpler postulates."

According to Peano, a system of natural integers is a set S of elements $a, b, \ldots$, called *natural integers* or briefly *integers*, with an equals relation written $a = b$ or $a \neq b$ (to be read "a equals b" or "a is not equal to b," respectively), and a "sequels" operation, indicated by a' and read "a' is the *sequel* of a" or "a is the *antecedent* of a'," subject to the following postulates:

S.1: There exists an integer called "one," written 1.

S.2: Every integer a has a unique sequel a'.

S.3: The integer 1 has no antecedent.

S.4: If $a' = b'$, then $a = b$.

S.5: If M is a set of integers such that:
    (I) M contains 1;
    (II) if M contains a, then M contains a';
    then M contains all the integers of S.

By way of preliminary comment on the various axioms we note that **S.1** guarantees that the set S is not empty; **S.2** implies that if $a = b$, then $a' = b'$; **S.3** implies $a' \neq 1$; **S.4** says that antecedents are unique; and **S.5** is one form of the principle of mathematical induction, described as **L.2** in Chapter 2.

In the proofs of the following theorems we shall write under each equality sign the name of the definition, postulate, hypothesis, or previously proved theorem which justifies the equality. To avoid some tediousness we shall use various properties of the equivalence relation, especially the transitive property, without explicit mention.

43.2.   The operation of addition

In terms of Peano's axioms it is possible to define for the integers of S an ordered binary operation, called addition and written $a + b$, having many familiar properties to justify this terminology. The *definition of addition* may be made as follows:

D.I: We define $1 + b = b'$ for every b in S.

D.II: For every a in S for which
    A.I: $a + 1 = a'$, and
    A.II: $a + b' = (a + b)'$ for every b in S,
    we define $a' + b = (a + b)'$ for every b in S.

Theorem: The operation of addition is closed and well defined.

Proof: Before beginning the proof we should mention that the above definition is due to Grandjot, Landau, and Kalmar who first pointed out in Landau's *Foundations of Analysis* that the definition of Peano which employed only **A.I** and **A.II** is actually incomplete, defined only for a *fixed a*, not for *all a*. Attempts to prove well-definedness, for example, using **A.I** and **A.II** only, are unsuccessful.

(A) Let M be the set of all integers a for which the operations of addition defined by **D.I** and **D.II** has properties **A.I** and **A.II**.

(I) M contains 1: for

$$1 + 1 = 1'$$
$$\text{D.I}$$

which is **A.I** when $a = 1$; and then

$$1 + b' = (b')' = (1 + b)'$$
$$\text{D.I} \quad \text{D.I, S.2}$$

which is **A.II** when $a = 1$.

(II) If by hypothesis **H**: M contains a, then M contains a': for

$$a' + 1 = (a + 1)' = (a')'$$
$$\text{D.II} \qquad \text{H, A.I}$$

which is **A.I** for a'; and then

$$a' + b' = (a + b')' = ((a + b)')' = (a' + b)'$$
$$\text{D.II} \qquad \text{H, A.II} \qquad \text{D.II, S.2}$$

which is **A.II** for a'.

By (I), (II), and **S.5** it follows that M contains all integers. But with **A.I** and **A.II** holding for *every a*, it follows that $a + b$ is a uniquely defined integer of S for every a and b in S, so the operation of addition is closed.

(B) To show that addition is well defined we suppose **G**: $b = B$ and let M be that set of all integers a for which $a + b = a + B$.

(I) M contains 1, for

$$1 + b = b' = B' = 1 + B.$$
$$\text{D.I} \quad \text{G, S.2} \quad \text{D.I}$$

(II) If M contains a, so that **H**: $a + b = a + B$, then M contains a', for

$$a' + b = (a + b)' = (a + B)' = a' + B.$$
$$\text{D.II} \qquad \text{H, S.2} \qquad \text{D.II}$$

By (I), (II), and **S.5** it follows that M contains all integers.

Similarly (except that we use **A.I** and **A.II** instead of **D.I** and **D.II**, respectively), we may show that if $a = A$, then $a + b = A + b$ for every b in S.

When $a = A$ and $b = B$, we combine the above results and have

$$a + b = a + B = A + B$$

so that addition is well defined.

Attention to this last property is by no means trivial, for in the next proof we find that we often need to make replacements, such as $a + 1$ by a'.

T.1:   The *associative* law of addition: $(a + b) + c = a + (b + c)$.

Proof: Let a, b be fixed and let M be the set of all integers c for which **T.1** holds.

(I) M contains 1, for

$$(a + b) + 1 \underset{\text{A.I}}{=} (a + b)' \underset{\text{A.II}}{=} a + b' \underset{\text{A.I}}{=} a + (b + 1).$$

(II) If M contains c, so that **H:** $(a + b) + c = a + (b + c)$, then M contains c', for

$$(a + b) + c' \underset{\text{A.II}}{=} ((a + b) + c)' \underset{\text{H, S.2}}{=} (a + (b + c))'$$

$$\underset{\text{A.II}}{=} a + (b + c)' \underset{\text{A.II}}{=} a + (b + c').$$

By (I), (II), and **S.5**, M contains all integers, hence **T.1** is always valid.

T.2:   The *commutative* law for addition: $a + b = b + a$.

Proof: Let b be fixed and let M be the set of all integers a for which **T.2** holds.

(I) M contains 1. To prove this we use another induction argument, letting N be the set of all integers b for which $1 + b = b + 1$. Clearly, N contains 1, for $1 + 1 = 1 + 1$. Suppose that N contains b, so that **H:** $1 + b = b + 1$. Then N contains b', for

$$1 + b' \underset{\text{A.II}}{=} (1 + b)' \underset{\text{H, S.2}}{=} (b + 1)' \underset{\text{A.I}}{=} (b + 1) + 1 \underset{\text{A.I}}{=} b' + 1.$$

Hence by **S.5**, N contains all integers. Hence M contains 1.

(II) If M contains a, so that **H:** $a + b = b + a$, then M contains a', for

$$a' + b \underset{\text{A.I}}{=} (a + 1) + b \underset{\text{T.1}}{=} a + (1 + b) \underset{\text{(I)}}{=} a + (b + 1)$$

$$\underset{\text{T.1}}{=} (a + b) + 1 \underset{\text{A.I}}{=} (a + b)' \underset{\text{H}}{=} (b + a)' \underset{\text{A.II}}{=} b + a'.$$

By (I), (II), and **S.5**, M contains all integers and **T.2** is always valid.

T.3:   The *cancellation* law for addition: if $a + c = b + c$, then $a = b$.

Proof: Let M be the set of all integers c for which **T.3** holds.

(I) M contains 1, for if $a + 1 = b + 1$, then by **A.I** we have $a' = b'$, whence by **S.4** it follows that $a = b$.

(II) If M contains c, so that **H**: $a + c = b + c$ implies $a = b$, then M contains c', because if $a + c' = b + c'$, then by **A.II** we have $(a + c)' = (b + c)'$, and by **S.4** we have $a + c = b + c$, whence by **H**, $a = b$.

By (I), (II), and **S.5**, M contains all integers, hence **T.3** is always valid.

T.4:   For all a, b in S, the following relation holds: $a \neq a + b$.

Proof: Let b be fixed and let M be the set of all integers a for which **T.4** holds.

(I) M contains 1. For if we assume $1 = 1 + b$, we find by **D.I** that $1 = b'$ which contradicts **S.3**.

(II) If M contains a, so that $a \neq a + b$, then M contains a'. For if we assume $a' = a' + b$, then by **D.II** we find $a' = (a + b)'$; but then **S.4** implies $a = a + b$ which contradicts the induction hypothesis.

By (I), (II), and **S.5**, M contains all integers; hence **T.4** is always valid.

T.5:   If $a \neq 1$, there exists just one integer u such that $a = u'$.

Proof: By **S.3** the exclusion of 1 is explained. By **S.4** there is not more than one integer u with the desired property. Let M be the set consisting of 1 and all integers $a \neq 1$ which satisfy **T.5**.

(I) By definition M contains 1.

(II) If M contains a, so that either $a = 1$, or $a \neq 1$ and $a = u'$, then M contains a'. In the first case: if $a = 1$, then $a' = 1'$ by **S.2**, so for a' we may use $u = 1$. In the second case, if $a = u'$, then $a' = (u')'$ by **S.2**, so for a' we may use u' in the role of u.

By (I), (II), and **S.5**, M includes all integers, so **T.5** is valid.

T.6:   The *trichotomy* law: for every pair of integers a, b in S, one and only one of the following cases must hold:

$$(1) \quad a + u = b; \qquad (2) \quad a = b; \qquad (3) \quad a = b + v.$$

Proof: (A) Hold b fixed and let M be the set of all integers a for which at least one of the cases in **T.6** is valid.

(I) M includes 1: either $b = 1$ and (2) holds; or $b \neq 1$ and we may use **T.5** and **D.I** to show $b = u' = 1 + u$, so that (*1*) holds.

(II) If M includes a, so that (*1*), (2), or (3) holds, then we can show that (*1*), (2), or (3) holds for a', so that M includes a'.

If (1) holds for a, so $a + u = b$; then either $u = 1$ and $a' = a + 1 = b$, so that (2) holds for a'; or $u \neq 1$ and by **T.5** we have $u = x'$ so that $b = a + x' = (a + x)' = a' + x$ by **A.II** and **D.II**; hence (1) holds for a'.

If (2) holds for a, so that $a = b$, then by **S.2** and **A.I** we have $a' = b' = b + 1$, so that (1) holds for a'.

If (3) holds for a, so that $a = b + v$, then by **S.2** and **A.II** we have $a' = (b + v)' = b + v'$, so that (3) holds for a'.

By (I), (II), and **S.5**, M includes all integers a, so that at least one of the cases (1), (2), or (3) is always valid.

(B) From **T.4** it is impossible that two of the cases (1), (2), and (3) can hold. Thus (1) and (2) imply $a = a + u$, contradicting **T.4**; (2) and (3) imply $b = b + v$, contradicting **T.4**; and (3) and (1), together with **T.1**, imply $a = (a + u) + v = a + (u + v)$, contradicting **T.4**.

Definition: We write $a < b$, read "a is less than b," if and only if there exists an integer u such that $a + u = b$; we write $a \leqslant b$, read "a is less than or equal to b," if either $a < b$ or $a = b$.

As an obvious corollary to **T.6**, but very important in future argument, we have the trichotomy of the order relation: for every pair of integers a, b in S one and only one of the following must hold:

$$(1) \quad a < b; \qquad (2) \quad a = b; \qquad (3) \quad b < a.$$

We also need the following lemmas.

Lemma 1: For every a in S, we have $1 \leqslant a$.

Proof: Either $a = 1$; or $a \neq 1$ and by **T.5** we have $a = u' = 1 + u$, so that $1 < a$. We combine the two cases by writing $1 \leqslant a$.

Lemma 2: If $a < b$, then $a + 1 \leqslant b$.

Proof: We are given $a < b$, so $a + u = b$. Either $u = 1$ and $a + 1 = b$; or $u \neq 1$ and by **T.5** we have $u = v' = 1 + v$, so that $b = a + u = a + (1 + v) = (a + 1) + v$ by **T.1**, which shows $a + 1 < b$.

Definition: If in a given set N of integers there is an integer m such that $m \leqslant x$ for all integers x in N, then m is called a *least integer in N*.

T.7: In every nonempty set of integers there is a least integer.

Proof: We already noticed that **S.5** is simply a restatement of **L.2** in **2.4** and now we recognize that **T.7** is a restatement of **L.3** in **2.4**.

Consequently, the proof (A) in **2.4** that **L.2** implies **L.3** may be readily adapted to establish **T.7**. Instead of EXS. **2.8** and **2.9** we may use Lemma 1 and Lemma 2 given above.

T.8: Peano's axioms are categorical.

Proof: We can establish **T.8** by modifying the proof in **38.5**. We need to show that any two systems, say S and $\bar{S}$, which satisfy Peano's axioms are isomorphic with respect to the sequels operations in the two systems. Let S and $\bar{S}$ have basic integers 1 and $\bar{1}$, respectively, as required by **S.1**. Consider the mapping T in which

$$\text{(I)} \quad 1T = \bar{1}, \qquad \text{(II)} \quad a'T = aT + 1T,$$

where the $+$ refers, of course, to the addition defined in $\bar{S}$. From (I), (II), and **S.5** it follows that T is a mapping of all of S into a subsystem S' of $\bar{S}$. Since $a'T = aT + 1T = aT + \bar{1} = (aT)'$, it follows that T is an isomorphism between S and S' with respect to the sequels operations in the two systems. It remains for us to show that S' is actually all of $\bar{S}$.

Suppose that $\bar{S}$ contains a nonempty set S'' of elements not in S'. Then by **T.7**, S'' contains a least element m which is in $\bar{S}$ but not in S'. By Lemma 1 we know $\bar{1} \leqslant m$. But $\bar{1} \neq m$, for by (I) we know $\bar{1}$ is in S'. Since $\bar{1} \neq m$, we know by **T.5** there exists an element u in $\bar{S}$ such that $m = u' = u + \bar{1}$. Hence $u < m$ and by the definition of m it follows that u is in S'. Hence $u = aT$ for some element a in S. But then $m = u + \bar{1} = aT + 1T = a'T$, so that m is in S', a contradiction. The contradiction arises from the assumption that S'' is nonempty. Hence S'' is empty, S' coincides with $\bar{S}$, and therefore $\bar{S}$, like S', is isomorphic to S.

Since all the other usual operations on integers may be defined in terms of the sequels operation, it follows that **T.8** is of considerable logical importance in that although several different schemes of representing the integers may be proposed, they are abstractly the same. There is no theorem provable with one scheme of representation that is not true under all the other schemes. For example, of the various representations suggested in Chapter 5, some one may be more familiar or more convenient for a particular proof, but **T.8** assures us that the results, correctly translated, are true in every representation.

Ordinarily it is rather restricted and uninteresting to study a mathematical system that is categorical. But when we consider how the natural integers are building blocks for so many other systems, it is comforting to know that this basic system is essentially unique.

Perhaps the reader has noted that no attempt has been made to prove that Peano's axioms are consistent—this is another reflection of the basic nature of the system of integers. To avoid circular reasoning there must surely be some basic system whose consistency cannot be demonstrated and the integers seem a natural choice for this basic role.

43.3.   The operation of multiplication

Just as in elementary arithmetic, where multiplication is introduced as a convenient short-hand for certain types of addition problems, so here in the abstract development, it proves convenient to define the operation of multiplication in terms of the previously studied addition. We wish to define for the integers of S an ordered binary operation, called multiplication, written ab. Following Landau, rather than Peano, we proceed as follows:

R.I: We define $1b = b$, for every b in S.

R.II: For every a in S for which

  M.I: $a1 = a$, and

  M.II: $ab' = ab + a$, for every b in S,
  we define $a'b = ab + b$, for every b in S.

The following theorems will be left as exercises, it being understood that they had best be considered in sequence.

Theorem: The operation of multiplication is closed and well defined.

T.9:   The *distributive* law: $(a + b)c = ac + bc$.

T.10:   The *commutative* law for multiplication: $ab = ba$.

T.11:   The *associative* law for multiplication: $(ab)c = a(bc)$.

T.12:   The *cancellation* law for multiplication: if $ac = bc$, then $a = b$.

In terms of the sequels operation and the operation of multiplication it is possible (see Landau) to define for the integers of the system S a binary operation, called *exponentiation*, written a^b, that is closed and well defined and has the following properties:

E.I: $a^1 = a$;   **E.II:** $a^{b'} = a^b a$.

The following theorems then represent exercises in the use of **S.5** and the previous theorems and definitions.

T.13: $a^b a^c = a^{b+c}$.

T.14: $(a^b)^c = a^{bc}$.

T.15: $(ab)^c = a^c b^c$.

EXERCISES

43.1.   Show that for a fixed integer a there is only one way of defining an operation of addition that will possess properties A.I and A.II.

43.2.   Prove that the operation of multiplication defined in **43.3** is closed and well defined.

43.3.   Prove T.9.

43.4.   Prove T.10.

43.5.   Prove T.11.

43.6.   Prove T.12.

43.7.   Define $1' = 2$, $2' = 3$, $3' = 4$, and show by the use of the theorems that $(2)(2) = 4$.

43.8.   Supposing that positive integers written with the base 10 form a system S satisfying Peano's axioms, prove that all positive multiples of 5 form a system $\bar{S}$ satisfying Peano's axioms. Find the isomorphism between S and $\bar{S}$ that illustrates **T.8**.

43.9.   Prove T.13.

43.10.   Prove T.14.

43.11.   Prove T.15.

43.12.   Prove that there exist no integers a and x, such that $a < x < a'$.

Strictly speaking, the theory of numbers
has nothing to do with negative, or
fractional, or irrational quantities, as such.
—G. B. MATHEWS

CHAPTER 44

Integers—positive, negative, and zero

44.1. Integers as pairs of natural integers

We wish to devote one more lesson to the foundations of our subject and to indicate one way in which the complete system of integers, positive, negative, and zero, which we indicated in the first lesson to be the elements of our study, may be developed in a logical manner from the natural integers as described, say, by Peano's axioms. Although all theorems about integers can be written in terms of the natural integers alone, there is a certain tediousness and vexation in doing so. Hence we are going to employ a device that is frequently useful in the study of algebraic systems, namely, the embedding of the system in question (in the sense of an isomorphism) within a larger system wherein it is hoped that the theorems in question may be more easily formulated and more easily proved valid.

In our case most of the difficulties, if we do not use this embedding idea, will be found to arise from the fact that in the system of natural integers the equation $a = b + x$ has no solution when $a = b$ and when $a < b$ as is seen by reference to T.4 in 43.2. Hence we may set ourselves the problem of inventing a number system, retaining as many features as possible of the system of natural integers and, in particular, containing a subset isomorphic to the natural integers, and within which

365

the *type* equation "$a = b + x$" is always solvable. If the elements of the new system are called "integers," we must henceforth be rather strict in calling the elements previously discussed by their full title "natural integers."

Let us define the system of *integers* to be the set N of all ordered pairs (a, b) of natural integers a, b subject to the following definitions:

E: equality: $(a, b) = (c, d)$ if and only if $a + d = b + c$;

A: addition: $(a, b) + (c, d) = (a + c, b + d)$;

M: multiplication: $(a, b)(c, d) = (ac + bd, ad + bc)$.

Note that each of these concepts is defined entirely in terms of elements, relations and operations in the system S of natural integers; hence all the following theorems may be proved by referring back to the previously assumed postulates or the previously established theorems about natural integers.

In the proofs of the next theorems we will use the notation "$\ldots$" $\rightarrow$ "$\ldots$" to indicate that the first statement *implies* the second statement, and we will write under the arrow the name of the definition, postulate or theorem which justifies the implication. Note that if $p \rightarrow q$ and $q \rightarrow r$, then $p \rightarrow r$. Similarly, the notation "$\ldots$" $\longleftrightarrow$ "$\ldots$" will indicate that the first statement is valid *if and only if* the second statement is valid.

Our principal objective is the theorem **N.6** which shows that the system N is a well-ordered domain under the relation **E**, the operations **A** and **M**, and a suitable definition of positive elements. In other words, in the light of **39.5** and in the sense of isomorphism, the system N is the rational domain J which is the object of study in the theory of numbers.

N.1:   The equality **E** of integers of N is an equivalence relation.

Proof: **R.1:** **E** is determinative because the addition of natural integers is closed (see **43.2**) and the equality of natural integers is determinative.

R.2:   **E** is reflexive, for $a + b = b + a \underset{\text{E}}{\rightarrow} (a, b) = (a, b)$.
$$\underset{\text{T.2}}{}$$

R.3:   **E** is symmetric, for

$$(a, b) \underset{\text{H}}{=} (c, d) \underset{\text{E}}{\rightarrow} a + d = b + c \underset{\text{T.2, R.3 in S}}{\rightarrow} c + b = a + d \underset{\text{E}}{\rightarrow} (c, d) = (a, b).$$

R.4:   **E** is transitive, for if we assume

H.1: $(a, b) = (c, d) \underset{\text{E}}{\rightarrow} a + d = b + c$;

H.2: $(c, d) = (e, f) \underset{\text{E}}{\rightarrow} c + f = d + e$; then

$$d + (a + f) \underset{\text{T.1}}{=} (d + a) + f \underset{\text{T.2}}{=} (a + d) + f \underset{\text{H.1}}{=} (b + c) + f$$

$$\underset{\text{T.1}}{=} b + (c + f) \underset{\text{H.2}}{=} b + (d + e) \underset{\text{T.1}}{=} (b + d) + e \underset{\text{T.2}}{=} (d + b) + e$$

$$\underset{\text{T.1}}{=} d + (b + e) \underset{\text{T.3}}{\to} a + f = b + e \underset{\text{E}}{\to} (a, b) = (e, f).$$

N.2: The system N is a commutative group under the relation **E** and the operation **A** of addition.

Proof: Because of **N.1** we need to show only that **A** (*1*) is closed and well defined; (*2*) is associative; (*3*) has a zero; (*4*) has a negative for each element of N; and (*5*) is commutative.

(*1*) By definition **A** and by **A.I** and **A.II** of **43.2**, the sum of two integers is an integer. If by hypothesis **H**:

$$(a, b) = (A, B) \underset{\text{E}}{\to} a + B = b + A, \ (c, d) = (C, D) \underset{\text{E}}{\to} c + D = d + C;$$

then

$$a + c + B + D \underset{\text{H, T.1, T.2}}{=} b + d + A + C \underset{\text{E}}{\to} (a + c, b + d) = (A + C, B + D)$$

$$\underset{\text{A}}{\to} (a, b) + (c, d) = (A, B) + (C, D).$$

(*2*) $\{(a, b) + (c, d)\} + (e, f) \underset{\text{A}}{=} (a + c, b + d) + (e, f)$

$$\underset{\text{A}}{=} \{(a + c) + e, (b + d) + f\} \underset{\text{T.1, E}}{=} \{a + (c + e), b + (d + f)\}$$

$$\underset{\text{A}}{=} (a, b) + (c + e, d + f) \underset{\text{A}}{=} (a, b) + \{(c, d) + (e, f)\}.$$

(*3*) For a zero we may use (a, a) since

$$(a, a) + (c, d) \underset{\text{A}}{=} (a + c, a + d) = (c, d) \underset{\text{E}}{\longleftrightarrow} (a + c) + d \underset{\text{T.1, T.2}}{=} (a + d) + c.$$

(*4*) For a negative of (c, d) we may use (d, c) since

$$(d, c) + (c, d) \underset{\text{A}}{=} (d + c, c + d) = (a, a) \underset{\text{E}}{\longleftrightarrow} (d + c) + a \underset{\text{T.2}}{=} (c + d) + a.$$

(*5*) $(a, b) + (c, d) \underset{\text{A}}{=} (a + c, b + d) \underset{\text{T.2, E}}{=} (c + a, d + b) \underset{\text{A}}{=} (c, d) + (a, b).$

N.3: The system N is a domain under the relation **E** and the operations **A** of addition and **M** of multiplication.

Proof: Because of **N.2** we need to show only that **M** (*1*) is closed and well defined; (*2*) is associative; (*3*) has an identity; (*4*) has no proper divisors of zero; (*5*) is commutative; and (*6*) is distributive over addition.

(*1*) By definition **M** and by **A.I**, **A.II**, **M.I**, and **M.II** of **43.2** and **43.3**, the product of two integers is an integer. If by hypothesis **H**:

$$(a, b) = (A, B) \underset{E}{\to} a + B = b + A, \ (c, d) = (C, D) \underset{E}{\to} c + D = d + C,$$

then

$$(aD + bC + bD + aC) + (ac + bd + AD + BC)$$

$$\underset{\textbf{T.1, T.2, T.9, T.10}}{=} a(c + D) + b(d + C) + (b + A)D + (a + B)C$$

$$\underset{\textbf{H}}{=} a(d + C) + b(c + D) + (a + B)D + (b + A)C$$

$$\underset{\textbf{T.1, T.2, T.9, T.10}}{=} (aD + bC + bD + aC) + (ad + bc + AC + BD)$$

$$\underset{\textbf{T.3}}{\to} ac + bd + AD + BC = ad + bc + AC + BD$$

$$\underset{\textbf{E}}{\to} (ac + bd, ad + bc) = (AC + BD, AD + BC)$$

$$\underset{\textbf{M}}{\to} (a, b)(c, d) = (A, B)(C, D).$$

(*2*) $$\{(a, b)(c, d)\}(e, f) \underset{\textbf{M}}{=} (ac + bd, ad + bc)(e, f)$$

$$\underset{\textbf{M, T.9, T.11, T.1, E}}{=} (ace + bde + adf + bcf, acf + bdf + ade + bce)$$

$$\underset{\textbf{T.1, T.2, E}}{=} (ace + adf + bcf + bde, acf + ade + bce + bdf)$$

$$\underset{\textbf{E, T.1, T.11, T.9, M}}{=} (a, b)(ce + df, cf + de) \underset{\textbf{M}}{=} (a, b)\{(c, d)(e, f)\}.$$

(*3*)   For an identity we may use $(a + 1, a)$ since

$$(a + 1, a)(c, d) \underset{\textbf{M, T.9, T.1}}{=} (ac + c + ad, ad + d + ac) = (c, d)$$

$$\underset{\textbf{E}}{\longleftrightarrow} ac + c + ad + d = ad + d + ac + c. \quad \textbf{T.1, T.2}$$

(*4*)   If **H.1**: $(c, d) \neq (a, a)$ and **H.2**: $(x, y)(c, d) = (a, a)$, we must show that $(x, y) = (a, a)$. However,

$$(c, d) = (a, a) \underset{\textbf{E}}{\longleftrightarrow} c + a = d + a \underset{\textbf{T.3}}{\longleftrightarrow} c = d.$$

Hence **H.1** implies $c \neq d$ and **H.2** implies $xc + yd = xd + yc$. By **T.6** either $c = d + u$ or $d = c + v$. If $c = d + u$, then

$$xc + yd = xd + yc \underset{\textbf{T.9}}{\longleftrightarrow} xd + xu + yd = xd + yd + yu$$

$$\underset{\textbf{T.3}}{\longleftrightarrow} xu = yu \underset{\textbf{T.12}}{\longleftrightarrow} x = y \longleftrightarrow (x, y) = (a, a).$$

Similarly, if $d = c + v$, we find $(x, y) = (a, a)$.

(*5*) $$(a, b)(c, d) \underset{\textbf{M}}{=} (ac + bd, ad + bc)$$

$$\underset{\textbf{T.2, T.10, E}}{=} (ca + db, cb + da) \underset{\textbf{M}}{=} (c, d)(a, b).$$

(6) $(a, b)\{(c, d) + (e, f)\} = (a, b)(c + e, d + f)$
$$\underset{\text{A}}{}$$

$$\underset{\text{M, T.9, E}}{= (ac + ae + bd + bf, ad + af + bc + be)}$$

$$\underset{\text{T.1, T.2, E}}{= (ac + bd + ae + bf, ad + bc + af + be)}$$

$$\underset{\text{T.1, A, E}}{= (ac + bd, ad + bc) + (ae + bf, af + be)}$$

$$\underset{\text{M}}{= (a, b)(c, d) + (a, b)(e, f).}$$

To prepare the way for showing that N is an ordered domain we introduce a classification of the integers of N as positive, negative, or zero. From **T.6** one and only one of the cases $a < b$, $a = b$, $b < a$ must hold, hence there are three and only three types of integers (a, b). This classification may be made even more explicit as follows:

Lemma: $(x, y) = (a + k, a)$ if and only if $x = y + k$;
$(x, y) = (a, a)$ if and only if $x = y$;
$(x, y) = (a, a + k)$ if and only if $y = x + k$.

Proof: $(x, y) = (a + k, a) \underset{\text{E}}{\longleftrightarrow} x + a = y + a + k \underset{\text{T.1, T.2, T.3}}{\longleftrightarrow} x = y + k$;

$(x, y) = (a, a) \underset{\text{E}}{\longleftrightarrow} x + a = y + a \underset{\text{T.2, T.3}}{\longleftrightarrow} x = y$;

$(x, y) = (a, a + k) \underset{\text{E}}{\longleftrightarrow} x + a + k = y + a \underset{\text{T.1, T.2, T.3}}{\longleftrightarrow} y = x + k$.

In the light of this lemma the following more convenient notations may be introduced and the new definitions may be described as *well defined*, because, as the lemma shows, the definitions are independent of the natural integer a which appears in them.

Definitions: $(a + k, a) = k$, called the "positive integer, *plus k*";
(a, a) $= 0$, called the "zero integer";
$(a, a + k) = -k$, called the "negative integer, *minus k*."

N.4:   The system of natural integers is isomorphic to the subsystem of the integers consisting of the positive integers, the correspondence between the two systems being preserved under *both* addition and multiplication.

Proof: It is easy to check that the correspondence F defined by $kF = (a + k, a)$ is a one-to-one mapping of the system S of natural integers onto the subsystem P of N consisting of all the positive integers of N. Properties **F.1** and **F.3** follow from the definitions of F and P. Properties **F.2** and **F.4** will follow if we show that $kF = mF$ if and only if $k = m$; but this is exactly the content of the lemma above, which shows that $(a + k, a) = (x, b)$ if and only if $x = b + k$.

Since the following relations hold:

$$kF + mF = (a + k, a) + (b + m, b) = (a + b + k + m, a + b)$$
$$= (c + k + m, c) = (k + m)F;$$
$$(kF)(mF) = (a + k, a)(b + m, b)$$
$$= (ab + am + kb + km + ab, ab + kb + ab + am)$$
$$= (d + km, d) = (km)F;$$

it follows that F is an isomorphism, being operation-preserving (property **F.5**) both with respect to the operations of addition in the two systems and with respect to the operations of multiplication in the two systems.

N.5: The system N is an ordered domain under the relation **E**, the operations **A** and **M**, and the definition of positive elements given above.

Proof: Because of **N.3** we need to show only that the set P of all positive integers of N, defined above, has properties **V.1**, **V.2**, **V.3**, and **V.4** discussed in **38.1**. Property **V.1** follows from the lemma above which shows that an integer of N which is equal to a positive integer is itself positive. Since $(a + k, a)$ is the negative of $(a, a + k)$ as shown in the proof of **N.2**, the trichotomy established in the lemma shows that property **V.2** holds; that is, if a nonzero integer of N is not in P, then its negative is in P. The properties **V.3** and **V.4** which demand that P be closed under addition and multiplication are simply reinterpretations of **N.4**.

Before we continue it is of interest to examine the order relation which is introduced into N by the definition **(38.1)** and the choice of P. In the system N we have

O: $(a, b) < (c, d)$ if and only if $a + d < b + c$ in the system S.

Proof: By *(38.1)* we have $(a, b) < (c, d)$ if and only if $(c, d) - (a, b)$ is a positive element of N. But by **N.2** we know $(c, d) - (a, b) = (c, d) + (b, a)$ $= (c + b, d + a)$; and by the lemma and **T.2**, this integer is a positive element of N if and only if $a + d < b + c$.

We are now in a position to establish the principal theorem.

N.6: The system N is a well-ordered domain.

Proof: Because of **N.3**, **N.4**, and **N.5** we only have to invoke **T.7** to complete the proof.

The definitions $(a + k, a) = k$, $(a, a) = 0$, and $(a, a + k) = -k$ have already suggested how to reconcile the system N with the familiar system J. Perhaps the following relation will also be revealing: in N it is easy to show that $(c, d) = (a + c, a) + (b, b + d)$, but the expression on the right, in terms of J, is simply $c - d$. By remembering this relation we can easily reconstruct the rules **E**, **A**, **M**, and **O**.

However, we must not let these easy memory aids distract us from the goal achieved in Chapters 43 and 44—namely, to describe the system J of all integers, in its isomorphic disguise N, entirely in terms of the system S of natural integers.

General References for Part I

From the extensive literature available in any large library we select a few references useful for collateral reading and further research.

R. D. Carmichael, *Theory of Numbers*, New York, John Wiley, 1914.

L. E. Dickson, *Introduction to the Theory of Numbers*, Chicago, University of Chicago Press, 1931.

————, *Modern Elementary Theory of Numbers*, Chicago, University of Chicago Press, 1939.

————, *History of the Theory of Numbers*, Carnegie Institution, Vol. I, 1919; Vol. II, 1920; Vol. III, 1923; available in reprint, New York, Chelsea, 1952.

G. H. Hardy and E. M. Wright, *An Introduction to the Theory of Numbers*, 3rd edition, Oxford, Clarendon Press, 1954.

W. J. LeVeque, *Topics in Number Theory*, Reading, Mass., Addison-Wesley, 1956.

I. Niven and H. S. Zuckerman, *An Introduction to the Theory of Numbers*, New York, John Wiley, 1960.

O. Ore, *Number Theory and Its History*, New York, McGraw-Hill, 1949.

J. V. Uspensky and M. H. Heaslet, *Elementary Number Theory*, New York, McGraw-Hill, 1939.

Notes to individual chapters of Part I

Chapter 1. Preliminary considerations. Concerning the position of our subject there is a saying: "Mathematics is the queen of the sciences, but arithmetic is the queen of mathematics." By arithmetic is meant our subject, theory of numbers, and this attitude in regard to the queenship is based on two almost opposite attributes: on one hand, the theory of numbers is the purest of pure mathematics, many of its problems being of interest only in themselves and not for any applications they may have; on the other hand, most of the number systems used in more practical branches of mathematics have the integers as their basic building blocks. So it is perhaps not too surprising that there have been some very remarkable interchanges of ideas, problems, and solutions between the ivory towers of number theory and the laboratories of applied mathematics.

Historically our subject has important roots in the works of Diophantus of the third century in whose honor we term the search for integer solutions of a given equation the solving of a "Diophantine equation." Early in our work we will encounter the names of Pythagoras and Euclid—yes, the Euclid of fame in geometry, the latter an important contributor to our subject as early as 300 B.C. From these earliest men to the present there is hardly a mathematician of note who has not contributed in some way to number theory. As we pursue the subject we find some names such as those of Fermat, Euler, Legendre, Gauss, Eisenstein, and Jacobi occurring often; but other men of lesser fame are remembered too, sometimes for just one particular theorem.

Dickson's monumental *History of the Theory of Numbers* is a mine of historical and factual information that the student will find particularly valuable if he makes some little discovery of his own (and one of the nice features of our subject is how soon the student can explore for himself) and wonders whether it has been published before. Our subject is not a dead one, many famous problems are still being attacked and new ones are being proposed, and the most recent journals carry articles and problems that concern our course directly. At certain places in the development we will suggest some generalizations of the subject, and then, for the interested student, whole new fields of exploration and study will be opened.

Chapter 2. Mathematical induction. The material in 2.4 showing the equivalence of various forms of mathematical induction has been influenced by the treatment of the same topic in S. Borofsky, *Elementary Theory of Equations*, New York, Macmillan, 1950, Appendix I.

Chapter 4. Solitaire. Further references on this topic may be found in B. M. Stewart, "Solitaire on a Checkerboard," *Amer. Math. Monthly*, Vol. 48, No. 4, April, 1941, pp. 228–233.

Chapter 5. Representation. See Ore, *op. cit.*, Chapter I. See D. E. Smith, *History of Mathematics*, Boston, Ginn, 1923, Vol. I, Chap. I; Vol. II, Chap. II.

Chapter 6. The Euclid algorithm. See *Great Books of the Western World*, Chicago, Encyclopaedia Britannica, 1952, Vol. II, pp. 127–129.

Chapter 8. Fundamental theorem. Zermelo's proof in 8.5 is adapted from Hardy and Wright, *op. cit.*, Section 2.11.

Chapter 9. Primes. We call attention again to the references in the text to D. N. Lehmer and Trygve Nagell. See LeVeque, *op cit.*, Vol. I, Chap. 6.

Chapter 11. Number-theoretic functions. In Chapter 16 of the first edition of the text in hand the formula for $\phi(n)$ is developed in another way by combinatorial logic, and the question of solving $\phi(x) = a$ is treated in detail.

Chapter 12. The bracket-function. By an extension of Ex. 12.9 it is possible to construct an everywhere continuous, but nowhere differentiable, real function. See E. Landau, *Differential and Integral Calculus* (English translation), New York, Chelsea, 1951, Theorem 100. In Chapter 10 of the first edition of the text in hand, the question of solving $E(p, x) = m$ is treated in detail.

Chapters 15 and 16. Systems of linear equations and congruences. A modern exposition concerning the most general systems of this type is given in A. T. Butson and B. M. Stewart, "Systems of Linear Congruences," *Canadian J. Math.*, Vol. 7, 1955, pp. 358–368. The form of the solution of the generalized Chinese remainder theorem suggested in Ex. 16.7 is due to B. Fraenkel.

Chapter 26. Four squares. A translation of Euler's solution of the four square problem appears in D. E. Smith, *A Source Book in Mathematics*, New York, McGraw-Hill, 1929, chapter on Euler, pp. 91–94.

Chapter 28. Egyptian fractions. Journal references for exploration in this area are as follows: B. M. Stewart, "Sums of Distinct Divisors," *Amer. J. Math.*, Vol. 76, No. 4, 1954, pp. 779–785. W. Sierpinski, *Mathesis*, Vol. 65, 1956, pp. 16–32. G. Palama, *Boll. Un. Mat. Ital.*, Vol. 13, 1958, pp. 65–72. P. J. van Albada and J. H. van Lint, "Reciprocal Bases for the Integers," *Amer. Math. Monthly*, Vol. 70, No. 2, 1963, pp. 170–173. R. L. Graham, forthcoming papers in the *J. Australian Math. Soc.*

General References for Part II

G. Birkhoff and S. Mac Lane, *A Survey of Modern Algebra*, revised edition, New York, Macmillan, 1953.

M. Hall, *The Theory of Groups*, New York, Macmillan, 1959.

N. Jacobson, *Lectures in Abstract Algebra*, New York, D. Van Nostrand, 1951.

E. Landau, *Foundations of Analysis*, New York, Chelsea, 1951.

C. C. MacDuffee, *Introduction to Abstract Algebra*, New York, John Wiley, 1940.

B. L. van der Waerden, *Modern Algebra* (English translation), Vol. I, New York, Ungar, 1953.

Notes to individual chapters of Part II

Chapter 29. Mathematical systems. The general approach is adapted from lectures by C. B. Allendoerfer. For a specific philosophy about algebraic systems see the prize-winning essay of S. Mac Lane, "Some Recent Advances in Algebra," *Amer. Math. Monthly*, January, 1939; republished and extended in *Studies in Modern Algebra*, Mathematical Association of America, distributed by Prentice-Hall, Englewood Cliffs, N.J., 1963.

Chapter 34. Direct products. For the structure theorems of finite commutative groups see M. Hall, *op. cit.*, Chapter 3, and C. C. MacDuffee, *op. cit.*, Chapter II.

Chapter 36. The fundamental theorem reconsidered. For more details concerning the restoration of unique factorization see MacDuffee, *op. cit.*, Chapter IV. Also see H. M. Pollard, *The Theory of Algebraic Numbers*, Carus Monograph No. 9, New York, John Wiley, 1950.

Chapter 38. Ordered rings. Characterization of the rational domain as the only well-ordered domain is treated in Birkhoff and Mac Lane, *op. cit.*, Chapters I and II.

Chapters 39 and 40. Polynomials and modular fields. Questions of factorization of polynomials over the rational field have fascinating aspects for number-theory enthusiasts. For example, see Gauss's lemma, Eisenstein's theorem, and Kronecker's method, in van der Waerden, *op. cit.*, Sections 22–25.

Chapter 41. The real field. Of great interest in number theory are the p-adic fields obtained from the rational field by use of a p-adic valuation and the corresponding regular sequences. See MacDuffee, *op. cit.*, Chapter VI, and van der Waerden, *op. cit.*, Chapter X.

Chapter 42. Continued fractions. For historical interest see D. E. Smith, *Source Book*, chapter on Bombelli and Cataldi, pp. 80–84. For more details of the theory see Hardy and Wright, *op. cit.*, Chapter X; also see Niven and Zuckerman, *op. cit.*, Chapter 7.

Chapter 43. Peano's axioms. See Landau, *op. cit.*, Chapter I.

INDEX

INDEX